MAN OR MATTER

MAN OR MATTER

Introduction

to a Spiritual Understanding of Nature

on the Basis of Goethe's Method

of Training Observation and Thought

Third Edition, Revised and Enlarged

by

ERNST LEHRS

RUDOLF STEINER PRESS
LONDON

First English edition 1951
Second revised edition published by Faber & Faber 1958
Third edition, revised and enlarged, published by Rudolf Steiner Press 1985

Edited and revised by Nick Thomas and Peter Bortoft

ISBN 0-85440-430-9

Printed in Great Britain by
Whitstable Litho Ltd., Whitstable, Kent

CONTENTS

EDITOR'S NOTE   1

PREFACE TO THE SECOND EDITION   3

PREFACE TO THE FIRST EDITION   5

INTRODUCTORY   7

The author's search for a way of extending the boundaries of scientific understanding. His meeting with Rudolf
Steiner, and with the work arising from his teachings.

Part One

SCIENCE AT THE THRESHOLD

I. WHERE DO WE STAND TODAY?   19

The self-restriction of scientific inquiry to one-eyed
colour-blind observation. Its effect: the lack of a true
conception of 'force'.

II. THE BIRTH OF THE ONLOOKER IN MAN   25

The threefold psycho-physical organisation of Man. Its
evolutionary aspect — explaining the necessity of the rise,
at the beginning of the Modern Age, of man's onlooker-
relationship to the world and of a science based on this.
Galileo — the perfect onlooker.

III. THE ONLOOKER'S PHILOSOPHIC MALADY   38

Thought — the sole reality and yet a pure non-entity for the modern spectator. Descartes and Hume. Robert Hooke's 'proof' of the non-reality of conceptual thinking. The modern principle of Indeterminacy — a sign that science is still dominated by the Humean way of thinking.

IV. THE COUNTRY THAT IS NOT OURS   46

Electricity, man's competitor in modern civilisation. The onlooker in search of the soul of nature. Galvani and Crookes. Paradoxes in the discovery of electricity. 'Something unknown is doing we don't know what.' The tragic element in the present-day situation of science. Man's Knowing and man's Doing outrunning each other. The evolutionary significance of man's First and Second 'Fall'. Ancient and modern witnesses to this.

Part Two

GOETHEANISM — WHENCE AND WHITHER?

V. THE ADVENTURE OF REASON   73

Kant and Goethe. Goethe's study of the plant — a path toward seeing with the eye-of-the-spirit. Nature a script that asks to be read. 'The senses do not deceive, but the judgment deceives'. Goethe's exact sensorial fantasy.

VI. 'ALWAYS STAND BY FORM'   110

Spiritual kinsmen of Goethe in the British sphere of human culture. Ruskin and Howard — two readers in the book of nature. Goethe's meteorological ideas. Goethe and Howard. Goethe's conception of the ur-phenomenon.

VII. EXCEPT WE BECOME . . .   125

Thomas Reid's philosophic discovery. Its significance for
the overcoming of the onlooker-standpoint in science.
The picture of man inherent in Reid's philosophy.
Goethe's testimony for Reid. Man's original gift of
remembering his pre-earthly life. The disappearance of
this memory in the past, and its reappearance in modern
times. Pelagius *versus* Augustine. Wordsworth and
Traherne. Traherne a 'Reidean before Reid was born'.
Goethe as the fulfiller of Reid's demand.

VIII. DYNAMICS *VERSUS* KINETICS   160

The question of the relationship between the mathematical faculties of the human mind and the mathematical
order of nature. 'Geometry and Experience'. Galileo's
discovery of the law of the Free Fall and of the Parallelogram of Forces, recorded as instances of a true seeing
with the eye-of-the-spirit. The physical law viewed as
ur-phenomenon. Reid's conception of this. The proper
approach to the concept 'force'. Goethe — the 'Galileo of
the organic sciences'.

IX. PRO LEVITATE   172

PRELIMINARY REMARK
Shifting of the border between 'auxiliary' concepts and
'existence' (ontological) concepts by overcoming the
boundaries of the onlooker-consciousness.
ALERTNESS CONTRA INERTNESS
Mechanical and non-mechanical causation. Introduction
of the term 'magical' as opposed to mechanical. The
phenomenon of the rising arm. Introduction of the term
'alertness' as opposed to 'inertness' (inertia). Van
Helmont's discovery of the gaseous state of matter. The

four Elements. The original concept of 'Chaos'. *Young* and *old* matter. The natural facts behind the ancient fire rites. The event on Mount Sinai.

LEVITY CONTRA GRAVITY

The *Contra-Levitatem* maxim of the Florentine Academicians. Ruskin's warning against science as an interpreter of its own observations. How man's inner nature and the outer universe interpret one another. The volcanic phenomenon. Goethe's experience of the supra-physical nature of volcanism. The concept of the force-field, extended from the central to the peripheral type of field.

X. SPACE AND COUNTER-SPACE   202

Geometrical considerations required by the recognition of levity. The value in this respect of projective geometrical thinking. The contrast between Einstein's way and the one taken here. Mental exercises as an introduction to anti-Euclidean concepts. The all-embracing plane and the all-relating point. The fluid character of counter-space. Traherne as harbinger of the anti-Euclidean orientation of man's soul before birth and in early childhood. The transition from Euclidean to anti-Euclidean thinking — a fulfilment of Reid's philosophical demand.

XI. PHYSICAL SUBSTANCES AS PART OF
    NATURE'S ALPHABET   218

Changes in the conception of combustion at the close of the Middle Ages. The phlogiston theory. The concept of the chemical element before and after the discovery of radium. The chemical element as 'idea'. Ur-matter. Polarities of the first and second order. Sulphur and phosphorus as representatives of a secondary polarity. Volcanism and snow-formation as manifestations of

functional sulphur and phosphorus respectively. Crystallisation as an ur-phenomenon. Carbon as a mediator
between sulphur and phosphorus. Physical substances are
congealed cosmic functions. Further examples: water,
hydrogen and oxygen; flint and chalk, clay. The three
basic concepts of alchemy in modern application. Line
and sphere as a morphological polarity in the different
kingdoms of nature. The lemniscate as mediator between
the two.

XII. THE FOURTH STATE OF MATTER   247

Nature's two borders. The true foundations of the mechanistic concept of heat. Ruskin's opposition to it. The
laws of conservation, their origin and their validity. Joule
and Mayer. The different conditions of matter seen in the
light of the levity-gravity polarity. Heat, the fourth state
of matter. Homoeopathy, an example of the effect of
dematerialised matter. The process of friction. The primeval way of generating heat and the modern liberation
of atomic energy as counterparts at nature's upper and
nether border. Creation of physical substance — a natural
occurrence. The case of Tillandsia. The functional significance of the trace-elements. The meteorological circuit of
water. The nature of lightning. The necessary transformation of the concept of the atom. Faraday's intuition.
The physicist's atom in relation to the 'qualitative atom'.

XIII. 'RADIANT MATTER'   282

Electricity and Magnetism as manifestations of interacting
levity and gravity in the form of a secondary polarity.
The different modes of generating electricity as letters of
a script revealing its nature. Electromagnetism. The
concepts, electrical current, resistance, etc., examined.
The oscillating circuit. The absolute qualities of the

electric and magnetic poles. Electricity as a criterion of atomism. Radioactivity as a symptom of the earth's ageing. Man's cosmic responsibility in the age of electricity.

XIV. COLOURS AS 'DEEDS AND SUFFERINGS OF LIGHT'   309

Goethe's *Farbenlehre* — the foundation of an optical science based on the colour-seeing faculty of the eye. The modern physicist's view of the Newtonian interpretation of the spectrum. A short history of Goethe's search for a satisfactory conception of Light and Colour. His discovery of Newton's cardinal error. First results of his own studies. The 'negative' spectrum.

XV. SEEING AS 'DEED' — I   324

Goethe's way of studying the totality of the act of seeing. The 'inner light'. Newton's and Goethe's interpretation of the complementary colours. Ideas of Reid and Ruskin concerning the act of seeing. Ruskin's demand for a 'moral theory of light', fulfilled by Goethe.

XVI. SEEING AS 'DEED' —II   338

Extension of Goethe's inquiry to a study of the act of seeing beyond the boundaries of the body. The colour-polarity as a polarity of the second order. Distinction between the pair of primary concepts, Light and Dark, and the pair of secondary concepts, lightness and dark-ness. Comparison with kindred secondary polarities. Right-eyed seeing and left-eyed seeing. The polar organis-ation of the eye. Purkinje's phenomenon.

XVII. OPTICS OF THE DOER   353

Purging optics of its onlooker concepts. The case of the

pin-hole camera. The role of foregone conclusions in the conception of the velocity of light. Discussion of the various experimental observations deemed to confirm a finite velocity of light. The true nature of this velocity. The consequences for Einstein's theory. The coin-in-the-bowl phenomenon. The contraction of optical distance. Snell's law of refraction presented as an ur-phenomenon.

XVIII. THE SPECTRUM AS A SCRIPT OF THE SPIRIT   372

Evaluation of the foregoing studies for a new under-standing of the prismatic phenomenon. The secret of the rainbow. The sun as a centre of negative density. Inti-mation of new possibilities of experimental research guided by the new conception of the spectrum.

Part Three

TOWARDS A NEW COSMOSOPHY

XIX. THE COUNTRY IN WHICH MAN IS NOT
     A STRANGER   389

INTRODUCTORY NOTE
THE FOUR KINDS OF ETHER
Warmth — Light — Sound — Life. The etheric origin of electricity and magnetism. The limits of the validity of the quantum theory. From seeing with the eye-of-the-spirit to Spiritual Imagination.

XX. PRO ANIMA   419

THE WELL-SPRINGS OF NATURE'S DEEDS
AND SUFFERINGS
The sentient (astral) forces of the universe as governors of the various interactions between levity and gravity. The cosmic aspect of the three alchemical functions. The two

polar groups of astral forces, one instigating motion ('deeds'), the other sensation ('sufferings'). The astral aspect of the planetary system. The limits of the validity of the Copernican aspect. The sevenfold organisation of the realm of astral forces. Beginnings of an astral conception of the human organism in modern physiology. Natural phenomena as a script of the workings of the planetary (astral) forces. Rediscovery of the quality of soul in cosmic and earthly nature.

HEARING AS DEED

From the present-day 'deaf' science of acoustics to a truly 'hearing' one. From hearing with the ear-of-the-spirit to Spiritual Inspiration.

KEPLER AND THE MUSIC OF THE SPHERES

Goethe's view of Kepler. Kepler's third law — a revelation of the musical order of the universe.

XXI. KNOW THYSELF   449

PROSPECT:

THE CREATIVE POWERS IN NATURE   457

Appendix I: THOMAS TRAHERNE   479

Appendix II: ARISTOTLE AND GALILEO   489

Appendix III: GOETHE, FARADAY, AND
              MATHEMATICS   495

Appendix IV: NEWTON'S RE-INTERPRETATION OF
             KEPLER'S THIRD LAW   515

NOTES   521

INDEX   533

AUTHOR'S NOTE

The author makes grateful acknowledgement of the help he has gained from other works in the wide field opened up by Rudolf Steiner, and of his debt to the friends who in various ways assisted him in preparing his manuscript.

Quotations have been made from the following books by kind permission of their respective publishers:

The Life of Sir William Crookes by E.E. Fournier d'Albe (Messrs. Ernest Benn Ltd.); *Man the Unknown* by A. Carrel (Messrs. Hamish Hamilton Ltd.); *The Philosophy of Physical Science* and *The Nature of the Physical World* by A. Eddington (University Press, Cambridge); *Science and the Human Temperament* by E. Schrödinger (Messrs. George Allen and Unwin Ltd.); *Centuries of Meditations* and *Poetical Works* by Th. Traherne (Messrs. P.J. and A.E. Dobell).

EDITOR'S NOTE

Modern philosophy has wrestled with the question 'What is science?', which has proved surprisingly difficult to answer. It is a pity the work of Dr. Rudolf Steiner has been overlooked in this respect. Probably the most consistent answer apart from Steiner's is that of Sir Karl Popper. The object appears to be to find a foolproof criterion that distinguishes genuine scientific statements from others. However, science need not be seen as a system but rather as the activity of scientists. Steiner's approach takes into account the process of cognition of the researcher, and in particular allows for the evolution of that process. A rigidly conceived scientific method, fixed for all time, may easily become outmoded.

Dr. Ernst Lehrs was an outstanding pupil of Steiner who penetrated deeply into these questions, and the fruits of his work are presented in this book. Following Steiner he starts from the scientific method of Goethe who was very far seeing in this respect. Goethe's devotion to accurate observation was happily free from the then prevailing paradigm, enabling him to evolve a non-hypothetical scientific method. This requires an even greater self-discipline than conventional science, but has failed to gain widespread support. Lehrs' lucid account shows how Goethe's method needs to be extended, as indicated by Steiner, making even greater demands on the researcher. Popper's method requires an hypothesis to be invented, which is then tested observationally by his falsifiability criterion. In contrast Goethe's method is polar opposite to this, seeking as it does to 'read Nature's script'. Lehrs shows the fruitfulness of such an approach throughout this book.

Although first published in 1950, far from being out of date the book is overdue for reprinting. Books that have appeared in recent years relating physics to Eastern mysticism need to be contrasted with the other way of deepening physics presented here: by reference to Western spiritual life. Any retreat from scientific clarity and sobriety to vague mistiness would be retrogressive, whereas Steiner's insistence on clarity and enhanced consciousness, as expounded by Lehrs, is fully in accord with modern scientific thinking.

Peter Bortoft and I have revised the book to allow for progress made since it was written. This was done in correspondence with Dr. Lehrs before his death, and with his approval. Nevertheless, the responsibility remains ours. We have added two appendices, on Goethe, Faraday and mathematics, and on Newton's reinterpretation of Kepler: these appendices previously appeared only in the German edition, as chapters. Because the German edition was written independently its material is presented in a slightly different sequence, so it was felt advisable to incorporate these chapters as appendices.

Nick Thomas

PREFACE TO THE SECOND EDITION

Since this book was first written and published, the world has changed, and so has my own life, and both changes have had some influence on the shaping of this new edition.

The book was written during and just after the Second World War — a time when it was difficult and partly impossible for me to take stock of current scientific literature, or to keep in touch with other scientists whose efforts were in the same direction as my own. Certain imperfections in what I wrote are due to these circumstances. Both in form and in content, after all, the book was a first attempt in this field.

Since then, conditions have improved in many ways. Not only is free movement between countries possible again, at least in the West, but through extensive lecturing I have been able to revive old connections and make new ones, in Europe and North America. Hence it has been possible, in personal conversations as well as through lecturing on the theme of the book in its various aspects, to clarify some of its ideas and to carry them further. Equally helpful have been the correspondence and personal meetings with readers of the book, whose circle has been considerably enlarged since the appearance in 1953 of a German edition (published as *Mensch und Materie* by Vittorio Klostermann, Frankfurt/Main). In this German edition the fruits of such interchanges proved their value, and now in the preparation of this second English edition they have done so in still greater measure.

In its opening act, at any rate, the fundamental alteration now proceeding in outer world conditions played already into the original edition, for I was in the midst of writing it when the first atom bombs were dropped. This demanded a recasting of several passages. For what up till then had lived in my mind as a concern for the future, and indeed had been one of the considerations prompting me to attempt the book at all, had now become an inescapable concern for the present, for myself as for my fellow men. Since then the progressive releasing of nuclear energies has not only called forth a far-reaching revolution in practical affairs; it has also set up entirely new conditions for human consciousness. It is dawning on people that with the twentieth century an apocalyptic age set in; to be or not to be has in all soberness become the alternative for mankind, and in the shadow of this there are questions now arising which hitherto the majority of people had never even glimpsed.

In this new edition such a situation had to be taken into account as far as possible, and much needed to be said which twelve years ago would have seemed altogether premature. This has called not only for more emphatic statement in some places and in others for more developed exposition, but also for the addition of a new concluding chapter, regarding which — it is well to insert here — the caution given about the book as a whole at the end of the preface to the first edition has a quite special application.

The original first chapter now opens the book as a kind of foreword, while the second chapter has been divided into two parts, making Chapters I and II. In some places the argument has been worked out more extensively; elsewhere there are curtailments and even omissions, which, where necessary, are explained in the text.

Again, by altering the position either of a whole chapter or of parts of chapters, I have sought to straighten out the book's entire line of thought. Apart from this the illustrative material has been reduced by leaving out several plates which came to seem not altogether necessary, and by replacing others with illustrations in the text itself.

Michaelmas 1957   *Ernst Lehrs*

PREFACE TO THE FIRST EDITION

In this book the reader will find expounded a method of investigating nature by means of which scientific understanding can be carried across the boundaries of the physical-material to the supersensible sources of all natural events, and thereby into the realm where is rooted the true being of man.

The beginnings of this method were worked out by Goethe more than 150 years ago. The nineteenth century, however, failed to provide any fertile ground for the development of the seeds thus sown. It was left to Rudolf Steiner, shortly before the end of the century, to recognise the significance of 'Goetheanism' for the future development not only of science but of human culture in general. It is to him, also that we owe the possibility of carrying on Goethe's efforts in the way required by the needs of our own time.

The following pages contain results of the author's work along the path thus opened up by Goethe and Rudolf Steiner — a work begun twenty-seven years ago, soon after he had made the acquaintance of Rudolf Steiner. With the publication of these results he addresses himself to everyone — with or without a specialised scientific training — who is concerned with the fate of man's powers of cognition in the present age.

* * * * *

The reader may welcome a remark as to the way in which this book needs to be read.

It has not been the author's intention to provide an encyclopaedic collection of new conceptions in various fields of natural observation. Rather did he wish, as the sub-title of the book indicates, to offer a new method of training both mind and eye (and other senses as well), by means of which our modern 'on-looking' consciousness can be transformed into a new kind of 'participating' consciousness. Hence it would be of no avail to pick out one chapter or another for first reading, perhaps because of some special interest in its subject-matter. The chapters are stages on a road which has to be *travelled*, and each stage is necessary for reaching the next. It is only through thus accepting the method with which the book has been written that the reader will be able to form a competent judgment of its essential elements.

Easter 1950   *Ernst Lehrs*

INTRODUCTORY

If I introduce this book by relating how I came to encounter Rudolf Steiner and his work, more than twenty-five years ago, and what decided me not only to make his way of knowledge my own, but also to enter professionally into an activity inspired by his teachings, it is because in this way I can most directly give the reader an impression of the kind of spirit out of which I have written. I am sure, too, that although what I have to say in this chapter is personal in content, it is characteristic of many in our time.

When I first made acquaintance with Rudolf Steiner and his work, I was finishing my academic training as an electrical engineer. At the end of the 1914-18 war my first thought had been to take up my studies from where I had let them drop, four years earlier. The war seemed to imply nothing more than a passing interruption of them. This, at any rate, was the opinion of my former teachers; the war had made no difference whatever to their ideas, whether on the subject-matter of their teaching or on its educational purpose. I myself, however, soon began to feel differently. It became obvious to me that my relationship to my subject, and therefore to those teaching it, had completely changed. What I had experienced through the war had awakened in me a question of which I had previously been unaware; now I felt obliged to put it to everything I came across.

As a child of my age I had grown up in the conviction that it was within the scope of man to shape his life according to the laws of reason within him; his progress, in the sense in which I then understood it, seemed assured by his increasing ability to determine his own outer conditions with the help of science. Indeed, it was the wish to take an active part in this progress that had led me to choose my profession. Now, however, the war stood there as a gigantic social deed which I could in no way regard as reasonably justified. How, in an age when the logic of science was supreme, was it possible that a great part of mankind, including just those peoples to whom science had owed its origin and never-ceasing expansion, could act in so completely unscientific a way? Where lay the causes of the contradiction thus revealed between human thinking and human doing?

Pursued by these questions, I decided after a while to give my studies a new turn. The kind of training then provided in Germany at the so-called Technische Hochschulen was designed essentially to give students a close practical acquaintance with all sorts of technical appliances; it included only as much theory as was wanted for understanding the mathematical calculations arising in technical practice. It now seemed to me necessary to pay more attention to theoretical considerations, so as to gain a more exact knowledge of the sources from which science drew its conception of nature. Accordingly I left the Hochschule for a course in mathematics and physics at a university, though without abandoning my original idea of preparing for a career in the field of electrical engineering. It was with this in mind that I later chose for my Ph.D. thesis a piece of experimental research on the uses of high-frequency electric currents.

During my subsequent years of study, however, I found myself no nearer an answer to the problem that haunted me. All that I experienced, in scientific work as in life generally, merely gave it an even sharper edge. Everywhere I saw an abyss widening between human knowing and human action. How often, for instance, was I not bitterly disillusioned by the behaviour, both in private and in public, of men for whose ability to think through the most complicated scientific questions I had the utmost admiration!

On all sides I found this same bewildering gulf between scientific achievement and the way men conducted their own lives and influenced the lives of others. I was forced to the conclusion that human thinking, at any rate in its modern form, was either powerless to govern human actions, or at least unable to direct them towards right ends. In fact, where scientific thinking had done most to change the practical relations of human life, as in the mechanisation of economic production, conditions had arisen which made it more difficult, not less, for men to live in a way worthy of man. At a time when humanity was equipped as never before to investigate the order of the universe, and had achieved triumphs of design in mechanical constructions, human life was falling into ever wilder chaos. Why was this?

The fact that most of my contemporaries were apparently quite unaware of the problem that stirred me so deeply could not weaken my sense of its reality. This slumber of so many souls in face of the vital questions of modern life seemed to me merely a further symptom of the sickness of our age. Nor could I think much better of those who, more sensitive to the contradictions in and around them, sought refuge in art or religion. The catastrophe of the war had shown me that this departmentalising of life, which at one time I had myself considered a sort of ideal, was quite inconsistent with the needs of today. To make use of art or religion as a refuge was a sign of their increasing separation from the rest of human culture. It implied a cleavage between the different spheres of society which ruled out any genuine solution of social problems.

I knew from history that religion and art had once exercised a function which is today reserved for science, for they had given guidance in even the most practical activities of human society. And in so doing they had enhanced the quality of human living, whereas the influence of science has had just the opposite effect. This power of guidance, however, they had long since lost, and in view of this fact I came to the conclusion that salvation must be looked for in the first place from science. Here, in the thinking and knowing of man, was the root of modern troubles; here must come a drastic revision, and here, if possible, a completely new direction must be found.

Such views certainly flew in the face of the universal modern conviction that the present mode of knowledge, with whose help so much insight into the natural world has been won, is the only one possible, given once for all to man in a form never to be changed. But is there any need, I asked myself, to cling to this purely static notion of man's capacity for gaining knowledge? Among the greatest achievements of modern science, does not the conception of evolution take a foremost place? And does not this teach us that the condition of a living organism at any time is the result of the one preceding it, and that the transition implies a corresponding functional enhancement? But if we have once recognised this as an established truth, why should we apply it to organisms at every stage of development except the highest, namely the human, where the organic form reveals and serves the self-conscious spirit?

Putting the question thus, I was led inevitably to a conclusion which science itself had failed to draw from its idea of evolution. Whatever the driving factor in evolution may be, it is clear that in the kingdoms of nature leading up to man this factor has always worked on the evolving organisms from outside. The moment we come to man himself, however, and see how evolution has flowered in his power of conscious thought, we have to reckon with a fundamental change.

Once a being has recognised itself as a product of evolution, it immediately ceases to be that and nothing more. With its very first act of self-knowledge it transcends its previous limits, and must in future rely on its own conscious actions for the carrying on of its development.

For me, accordingly, the concept of evolution, when thought through to the end, began to suggest the possibility of further growth in man's spiritual capacities. But I saw also that this growth could no longer be merely passive, and the question which now beset me was: by what action of his own can man break his way into this new phase of evolution? I saw that this action must not consist merely in giving outer effect to the natural powers of human thinking; that was happening everywhere in the disordered world around me. The necessary action must have inner effects; indeed, it had to be one whereby the will was turned upon the thinking powers themselves, entirely transforming them, and so removing the discrepancy between the thinker and the doer in modern man.

Thus far I could go through my own observation and reflection, but no further. To form a general idea of the deed on which everything else depended was one thing; it was quite another to know how to perform the deed, and above all where to make a start with it. Anyone intending to make a machine must first learn something of mechanics; in the same way, anyone setting out to do something constructive in the sphere of human consciousness — and this, for me, was the essential point — must begin by learning something of the laws holding sway in that sphere. But who could give me this knowledge?

Physiology, psychology and philosophy in their ordinary forms were of no use to me, for they were themselves part and parcel of just that kind of knowing which had to be overcome. In their various accounts of man there was no vantage point from which the deed I had in mind could be accomplished, for none of them looked beyond the ordinary powers of knowledge. It was the same with the accepted theory of evolution; as a product of the current mode of thinking it could be applied to everything except the one essential — this very mode of thinking. Obviously, the laws of the development of human consciousness cannot be discovered from a standpoint within the contemporary form of that consciousness. But how could one find a view-point outside, as it were, this consciousness, from which to discover its laws with the same scientific objectivity which it had itself applied to discovering the laws of physical nature?

It was when this question stood before me in all clarity that destiny led me to Rudolf Steiner and his work. The occasion was a conference held in 1921 in Stuttgart by the anthroposophical movement; it was one of several arranged during the years 1920-2 especially for teachers and students at the Hochschulen and Universities. What chiefly moved me to attend this particular conference was the title of a lecture to be given by one of the pupils and co-workers of Rudolf Steiner — 'The Overcoming of Einstein's Theory of Relativity'.[1]

The reader will readily appreciate what this title meant for me. In the circles where my work lay, an intense controversy was just then raging round Einstein's ideas. I usually took sides with the supporters of Einstein, for it seemed to me that Einstein had carried the existing mode of scientific thinking to its logical conclusions, whereas I missed this consistency among his opponents. At the same time I found that the effect of this theory, when its implications were fully developed, was to make everything seem so 'relative' that no reliable world-outlook was left. This was proof for me that our age was in need of an altogether different form of scientific thinking, equally consistent in itself, but more in tune with man's own being.

What appealed to me in the lecture-title was simply this, that whereas everyone else sought to prove Einstein right or wrong, here was someone who apparently intended, not merely to add another proof for or against his theory — there were plenty of those already — but to take some steps to *overcome* it. From the point of view of orthodox science, of course, it was absurd to speak of 'overcoming' a theory, as though it were an accomplished fact, but to me this title suggested exactly what I was looking for.

Although it was the title of this lecture that drew me to the Stuttgart Conference (circumstances prevented me from hearing just this lecture), it was the course given there by Rudolf Steiner himself which was to prove the decisive experience of my life. It comprised eight lectures, under the title: 'Mathematics, Scientific Experiment and Observation, and Epistemological Results from the Standpoint of Anthroposophy'; what they gave me answered my question beyond all expectation.

In the course of a comprehensive historical survey the lecturer characterised, in a way I found utterly convincing, the present mathematical interpretation of nature as a transitional stage of human consciousness — a kind of knowing which is on the way from a past pre-mathematical to a future post-mathematical form of cognition. The importance of mathematics, whether as a discipline of the human spirit or as an instrument of natural science, was not for a moment undervalued. On the contrary, what Rudolf Steiner said about Projective (Synthetic) Geometry, for instance, its future possibilities and its role as a means of under-standing higher processes of nature than had hitherto been accessible to science, clearly explained the positive feelings I myself had·experienced — without knowing why — when I had studied the subject.

Through his lectures and his part in the discussions — they were held daily by the various speakers and ranged over almost every field of modern knowledge — I gradually realised that Rudolf Steiner was in possession of unique powers. Not only did he show himself fully at home in all these fields; he was able to connect them with each other, and with the nature and being of man, in such a way that an apparent chaos of unrelated details was wrought into a higher synthesis. Moreover, it became clear to me that one who could speak as he did about the stages of human consciousness past, present and future, must have full access to all of them at will, and be able to make each of them an object of exact observation. I saw a thinker who was himself sufficient proof that man can find within the resources of his own spirit the vantage ground for the deed which I had dimly surmised, and by which alone true civilisation could be saved. Through all these things I knew that I had found the teacher I had been seeking.

Thus I was fully confirmed in my hopes of the Conference; but I was also often astonished at what I heard. Not least among my surprises was Rudolf Steiner's presentation of Goethe as the herald of the new form of scientific knowledge which he himself was expounding. I was here introduced to a side of Goethe which was as completely unknown to me as to so many others among my contemporaries, who had not yet come into touch with Rudolf Steiner's teachings. For me, as for them, Goethe had always been the great thinker revealing his thoughts through poetry. Indeed, only shortly before my meeting with Rudolf Steiner, it was in his poetry that Goethe had become newly alive to me as a helper in my search for a fuller human experience of nature and my fellow men. But despite all my Goethe studies I had been quite unaware that more than a century earlier he had achieved something in the field of science, organic and inorganic alike, which could help modern man towards the new kind of knowledge so badly needed today. This was inevitable for me, since I shared the modern conviction that art and science were fields of activity essentially strange to one another. And so it was again left to Rudolf Steiner to open the way for me and others to Goethe as botanist, physicist and the like.

I must mention another aspect of the Stuttgart Conference which belongs to this picture of my first encounter with Anthroposophy, and gave it special weight for anyone in my situation at that period. In Stuttgart there were many different activities concerned with the practical application of Rudolf Steiner's teachings, and so one could become acquainted with teachings and applications at the same time. There was the Waldorf School, founded little more than a year before, with several hundred pupils already. It was the first school to undertake the translation into educational practice of the knowledge of man gained through Spiritual Science; later it was followed by others, in Germany and elsewhere. There was one of the clinics, where qualified doctors were applying the same knowledge to the study of illness and the action of medicaments. In various laboratories efforts were made to develop news methods of experimental research in physics, chemistry, biology and other branches of science. Further, a large business concern had been founded in Stuttgart in an attempt to embody some of Rudolf Steiner's ideas for the reform of social life. Besides all this I could attend performances of the new art of movement, again the creation of Rudolf Steiner and called by him 'Eurythmy', in which the astounded eye could see how noble a speech can be uttered by the human body when its limbs are moved in accordance with its inherent spiritual laws. Thus, in all the many things that were going on besides the lectures, one could find direct proof of the fruitfulness of what one heard in them.[2]

Under the impression of this Conference I soon began to study the writings of Rudolf Steiner. Not quite two years later, I decided to join professionally with those who were putting Spiritual Science into outer practice. Because it appeared to me as the most urgent need of the time to prepare the new generation for the tasks awaiting it through an education shaped on the entire human being. I turned to Rudolf Steiner with the request to be taken into the Stuttgart School as teacher of natural science. On this occasion I told him of my general scientific interests, and how I hoped to follow them up later on. I spoke of my intended educational activity as something which might help me at the same time to prepare myself for this other task. Anyone who learns so to see nature that his ideas can be taken up and understood by the living, lively soul of the growing child will thereby be training himself, I thought, in just that kind of observation and thinking which the new science of nature demands. Rudolf Steiner agreed with this, and it was not long afterwards that I joined the school where I was to work for eleven years as a science master in the senior classes, which activity I have since continued outside Germany in a more or less similar form.

This conversation with Rudolf Steiner took place in a large hall where, while we were talking, over a thousand people were assembling to discuss matters of concern to the anthroposophical movement. This did not prevent him from asking me about the details of my examination work, in which I was still engaged at that time; he always gave himself fully to whatever claimed his attention at the moment. I told him of my experimental researches in electrical high-frequency phenomena, briefly introducing the particular problem withs which I was occupied. I took it for granted that a question from such a specialised branch of physics would not be of much interest to him. Judge of my astonishment when he at once took out of his pocket a notebook and a huge carpenter's pencil, made a sketch and proceeded to speak of the problem as one fully conversant with it, and in such a way that he gave me the starting point for an entirely new conception of electricity. It was instantly borne in on me that if electricity came to be understood in this sense, results would follow which in the end would lead to a quite new technique in the use of it.

From that moment it became one of my life's aims to contribute whatever my circumstances and powers would allow to the development of an understanding of nature of this kind.

PART ONE

SCIENCE AT THE THRESHOLD

Chapter I

WHERE DO WE STAND TODAY?

In the year 1932, when the world celebrated the hundredth anniversary of Goethe's death, Professor W. Heisenberg, one of the foremost thinkers in the field of modern physics and a pioneer in atomic research, delivered a speech before the Saxon Academy of Science which may be regarded as symptomatic of the need in recent science to investigate critically the foundations of its own efforts to know nature.[1] In this speech Heisenberg draws a picture of the progress of science which differs significantly from the one generally held during the nineteenth and in the earlier part of the twentieth century. Instead of giving the usual description of this progress as 'a chain of brilliant and surprising discoveries', he shows it as resting on the fact that, with the aim of continually simplifying and unifying the scientific conception of the world, human thinking, in course of time, has narrowed more and more the scope of its inquiries into outer nature.

'Almost every scientific advance is bought at the cost of renunciation, almost every gain in knowledge sacrifices important standpoints and established modes of thought. As facts and knowledge accumulate, the claim of the scientist to an *understanding* of the world in a certain sense diminishes.' Our justifiable admiration for the success with which the unending multiplicity of natural occurrences on earth and in the stars has been reduced to so simple a scheme of laws — Heisenberg implies — must therefore not make us forget that these attainments are bought at the price 'of renouncing the aim of bringing the phenomena of nature to our thinking in an immediate and living way'.

In the course of his exposition, Heisenberg also speaks of Goethe, in whose scientific endeavours he perceives a noteworthy attempt to set scientific understanding upon a path other than that of progressive self-restriction.

'The renouncing of life and immediacy, which was the premise for the progress of natural science since Newton, formed the real basis for the bitter struggle which Goethe waged against the physical optics of Newton. It would be superficial to dismiss this struggle as unimportant: there is much significance in one of the most outstanding men directing all his efforts to fighting against the development of Newtonian optics.' There is only one thing for which Heisenberg criticises Goethe: 'If one should wish to reproach Goethe, it could only be for not going far enough — that is, for having attacked the *views* of Newton instead of declaring that the whole of Newtonian Physics — Optics, Mechanics and the Law of Gravitation — were from the devil.'

Although the full significance of Heisenberg's remarks on Goethe will become apparent only at a later stage of our discussion, they have been quoted here because they form part of the symptom we wish to characterise. Only this much may be pointed out immediately, that Goethe — if not in the scientific then indeed in the poetical part of his writings — did fulfil what Heisenberg rightly feels to have been his true task.[2]

We mentioned Heisenberg's speech as a symptom of a certain tendency, characteristic of the more recent phase in science, to survey critically its own epistemological foundations. A few years previous to Heisenberg's speech, the need of such a survey found an eloquent advocate in A.N. Whitehead, in his book *Science and the Modern World*, where, in view of the contradictory nature of modern physical theories, he insists that 'if science is not to degenerate into a medley of *ad hoc* hypotheses, it must become philosophical and enter upon a thorough criticism of its own foundations'.

Among the scientists who have felt this need, and who have taken pains to fulfil it, Sir Arthur Eddington holds an eminent place. Among his relevant utterances we will quote here the following, because it contains a concrete statement concerning the field of external observation which forms the basis for the modern scientific world-picture. In his *Philosophy of Physical Science* we find him stating that 'ideally, all our knowledge of the universe could have been reached by visual sensation alone – in fact by the simplest form of visual sensation, colourless and non-stereoscopic'.[3] In other words, in order to obtain scientific cognition of the physical world, man has felt constrained to surrender the use of all his senses except the sense of sight, and to limit even the act of seeing to the use of a single, colour-blind, eye.

Let us listen to yet another voice from the ranks of present-day science, expressing a criticism which is symptomatic of our time. It comes from the physiologist, Professor A. Carrel, who, concerning the effect which scientific research has had on man's life in general, says in his book, *Man the Unknown*: 'The sciences of inert matter have led us into a country that is not ours .... Man is a stranger in the world he has created.'

Of these utterances, Eddington's is at the present point of our discussion of special interest for us; for he outlines in it the precise field of sense-perception into which science has withdrawn in the course of that general retreat towards an ever more restricted questioning of nature which was noted by Heisenberg.

The pertinence of Eddington's statement is shown immediately one considers what a person would know of the world if his only source of experience were the sense of sight, still further limited in the way Eddington describes. Out of everything that the world brings to the totality of our senses, there remains nothing more than mere movements, with certain changes of rate, direction, and so on. The picture of the world received by such an observer is a purely *kinematic* one.[4] And this is, indeed, the character of the world-picture of modern physical science. For in the scientific treatment of natural phenomena all the qualities brought to us by our other senses, such as colour, tone, warmth, density and even electricity and magnetism, are reduced to mere movement-changes.

In the course of our investigations we shall discover the peculiarity in human nature which – during the first phase, now ended, of man's struggle towards scientific awareness – has caused this renunciation of all sense-experiences except those which come to man through the sight of a single colour-blind eye, resulting in a corresponding restriction of his questions to nature. It will then also become clear out of what historic necessity this self-restriction of scientific inquiry arose. The acknowledgment of this necessity, however, must not prevent us from recognising the fact that, as a result, modern scientific research finds itself in a peculiar situation.

In reviewing the conceptual foundation of their own science, modern thinkers — first among them the great Austrian physicist-philosopher Ernst Mach (1838-1916) — have come to realise that within his given frame of consciousness man has no perception of such a thing as 'force', and that the scientist, therefore, is not permitted to rank the concept 'force' — and similarly a number of others — among the concepts of things he really knows of through perceptual observation. To quote Professor Philipp Frank of Harvard University: 'All concepts such as atom, energy, force, and matter are, according to Mach, only auxiliary concepts, allowing one to make statements about sense perceptions in a simpler and more synoptic form than if they were formulated directly as statements about the perceptions. In this way, all questions concerning the nature of force, matter and so on, become meaningless .... '[5] Mach, therefore, is rightly seen by thinkers such as Frank as the first great critic who purges scientific epistemology of its traditional metaphysical ingredients. As the quotation implies, the question concerning the 'real' existence of force, etc, is a metaphysical one and therefore not amenable to scientific inquiry.

This situation of science in respect to the concept 'force' actually came to symptomatic expression already in the early days of physical science — though without being noticed either then or later — namely in the use Newton made of this concept in his *Principia*. Careful scrutiny of the beginnings of science by thinkers of the kind just mentioned has brought to light what follows.

Newton's first law, as given in his *Principia* reads:

'Every body continues in its state of rest, or of uniform

motion in a straight line, unless it is compelled to change that state by a force impressed on it.'

Now, if we want to know what Newton means by 'impressed force', we have to look up his 'Definitions'. There we read, actually a few pages before the above theorem, under Definition IV:

'An impressed force is an action exerted upon a body, in order to change its state, either of rest, or of uniform motion in a straight line.'

Here Newton is saying, in the form of a definition, put the other way round, exactly what he later sets down as a law of nature derived, it seems, from observation. In its first form the statement is one truly appropriate to the consciousness out of which the scientist makes his observations, since 'force' is defined here purely from its kinetically manifest effect. Hence, the later statement, intended to express the law connecting the effect and its cause, can contain nothing beyond the definition itself. Newton's first law, because it describes as the effect of a cause the very thing through which the cause was first defined, has thus rightly been called a tautology. We have brought it forward here as an illuminating instance of how the scientific mind, when trying to deal with force as a reality, is thrown back on itself.

When we survey the concepts mentioned above, which the physicist-thinker has to rank among the 'auxiliary' concepts, we find that they pertain to the very things with which the physicist has managed to produce most decisive realities in the life of modern man. And in this fact lies the root of many of the dangers which beset the present age. As we shall see later, scientific inquiry has at essential moments been guided not by its own concepts, but by the very forces it tries to handle.

He who recognises this, therefore, feels impelled to look for a way which leads beyond a one-eyed, colour-blind conception of the world. It is the aim of this book to show that such a way exists and how it can be followed. Proof will thereby be given that along this way not only is a true understanding achieved of the forces already known to science (though not really understood by it), but also that other forces, just as active in nature as for example

electricity and magnetism, come within reach of scientific observation and understanding. And it will be shown that these forces
are of a kind that requires to be known today if we are to restore
the lost balance to human civilisation.

Chapter II

THE BIRTH OF THE ONLOOKER IN MAN

There is a rule known to physicians that 'a true diagnosis of a case contains in itself the therapy'. No true diagnosis is possible, however, without investigation of the 'history' of the case. Applied to our task, this means that we must try to find an aspect of human development, both individual and historical, which will enable us to recognise in man's own being the cause responsible for the peculiar narrowing of the scope of scientific inquiry, as described by the scientists cited above.

A characteristic of scientific inquiry, distinguishing it from man's earlier ways of solving the riddles of the world, is that it admits as instruments of knowledge exclusively those activities of the human soul over which we have full control because they take place in the full light of consciousness. This also explains why there has been no science, in the true sense of the word, prior to the beginning of the era commonly called 'modern' — that is, before the fifteenth century. For the consciousness on which man's scientific striving is based is itself an outcome of human evolution.

This evolution, therefore, needs to be considered in such a way that we understand the origin of modern man's state of mind, and in particular why in this condition the mind cannot of itself have any other relationship to the world than that of a spectator. For let us be clear that this peculiar relationship by no means belongs only to the scientifically engaged mind. Every adult in our age is, by virtue of his psycho-physical structure, more or less a world-spectator. What distinguishes the state of man's mind when engaged in scientific observation is that it is restricted to a one-eyed colour-blind approach.

Among the most important findings of nineteenth-century science in the field of evolution is the law that every organism repeats at the embryonic level the earlier stages of its evolutionary history. In recent years it has become realised along various paths of investigation that this law is valid equally for the psycho-physical development of the human race and of the single human being, since the child on the way to adulthood passes through former stages of mankind's development. Let us therefore turn our attention to certain basic facts of individual development in order to gain from them a picture of the corresponding facts in historical evolution.

All organic bodies, in their earliest condition, are traversed throughout by life. Only gradually certain parts of the organism become precipitated, as it were, from the general organic structure, and they do so increasingly towards the end of the organism's life-span.

In the human body this separation sets in gently during the later stages of embryonic development and brings about the first degree of independence of bones and nerves from the rest of the organism. The retreat of life continues after birth, reaching a certain climax in the nervous system at about the twenty-first year. In the body of a small child there is not yet much difference between the various organic systems as regards their degree of vitality. There is equally little difference between sleeping and waking conditions in its soul. And the nature of the soul at this stage is volition throughout. Never, in fact, does man's soul so intensively *will* as in the time when it is occupied in bringing the body into an upright position, and never again does it exert its strength with the same unconsciousness of the goal to which it strives.

What, then is the soul's characteristic relationship to the surrounding world at this stage? The following observations will enable us to answer this question.

It is well known that small children often angrily strike an object against which they have stumbled. This has been interpreted as 'animism', by which it is meant that the child, by analogy with his experience of himself as a soul-filled body, imagines the things in his surroundings to be similarly ensouled. Anyone who really observes the child's mode of experience (of which we as adults, indeed, keep something in our will-life) is led to a quite different interpretation of such a phenomenon. For he realises that the child neither experiences himself as soul-entity distinct from his body, nor faces the content of the world in so detached a manner as to be in need of using his imagination to read into it any soul-entities distinct from his own.

In this early period of his life the human being still feels the world as part of himself, and himself as part of the world. Consequently, his relation to the objects around him and to his own body is one and the same. To the example of the child beating the external object he has stumbled against, there belongs the complementary picture of the child who beats himself because he has done something which makes him angry with himself.

In sharp contrast to this state of oneness of the child's soul, in regard both to its own body and to the surrounding world, there stands the separatedness of the adult's intellectual consciousness, severed from both body and world. What happens to this part of the soul during its transition from one condition to the other may be aptly described by using a comparison from another sphere of natural phenomena. (Later descriptions in this book will show that a comparison such as the one used here is more than a mere external analogy.)

Let us think of water in which salt has been dissolved. In this state the salt is one with its solvent; there is no visible distinction between them. The situation changes when part of the salt crystallises. By this process the part of the salt substance concerned loses its connection with the liquid and contracts into individually outlined and spatially defined pieces of solid matter. It thereby becomes optically distinguishable from its environment.

Something similar happens to the soul within the region of the nervous system. What keeps the soul in a state of unconsciousness as long as the body, in childhood, is traversed by life throughout, and what continues to keep it in this condition in the parts which remain alive after the separation of the nerves, is the fact that in these parts — to maintain the analogy   the soul is dissolved in the body. With the growing independence of the nerves, the soul itself gains independence from the body. At the same time it undergoes a process similar to contraction whereby it becomes discernible to itself as an entity distinguished from the surrounding world. In this way the soul is enabled, eventually, to meet the world from outside as a selfconscious onlooker.

By thus bringing the awakening of the soul to full adult consciousness into connection with the severance of parts of the organism from the original life of the body, we refer to something not at all unknown to modern psychology. It was perhaps expressed for the first time by the German philosopher, C. Fortlage (1806-1881), who in his *System of Psychology as Empirical Science* suggested that consciousness is not based on life-processes, but on death-processes in the body. Yet no attention was paid at that time to his solitary voice because of the universally prevailing conviction that thought was an outcome of the body's life and so of its matter-building processes. And when in our century Rudolf Steiner drew attention to the same fact, which he had found along his own lines of investigation, showing thereby the true role of the nervous system in regard to the various activities of the soul, official science still turned a deaf ear to his pronouncement.[1]

Meanwhile, ordinary scientific research has been led towards the same recognition, enabling, for instance, Professor Carrel in his previously mentioned book to say simply that 'death is the price man has to pay for his brain and his personality'.

It is by thus recognising the dependence of consciousness on processes of bodily disintegration that we first come to understand why consciousness, once it has reached a certain degree of brightness, is bound to suffer repeated interruptions. Every night, when we sleep, our nervous system becomes alive (though with gradually decreasing intensity as the years go by), in order that what has been destroyed during the day may be restored. While the system is kept in this condition, no consciousness can obtain in it.

* * * * *

What we have here described as the emergence of an individual's intellectual consciousness from the original, purely volitional condition of the soul is nothing but a replica of a greater
process through which mankind as a whole, or more exactly
Western mankind, has gone in the course of its historical development. Man was not always the 'brain-thinker' he is today. Homer's
men still thought with the diaphragm (*phrenes*). Similarly, the
ancient practice of Yoga, as a means of acquiring knowledge,
shows that at the time when it flourished man's conceptual
activity was felt to be seated elsewhere than in the head. Directly
the separation of the nerve system was completed, and thereby
the full clarity of the brain-bound consciousness achieved, man
began to concern himself with science in the modern sense.

To understand why the newly-awakened intellect, severed
as it was from the life of both body and world, had to restrict
itself to one-eyed, colour-blind observation, we must cast a glance
at the total psycho-physical structure of present-day adult man.

Besides the nervous system and in complete functional
contrast to it, our organism includes the system of metabolic
processes which, by continuously renewing the body's substances,
maintain its life. As the nerves extend into the various sense-organs
by means of which our mind receives communications from the
outer world, so the metabolic processes extend into the muscles
which enable us to act on the outer world. In later parts of this
book we shall take pains to gain a deeper insight into the nature
of both sense-perception and muscular movement as a basis for
transcending the limitations of the one-eyed colour-blind approach
to the phenomenal world. At the present stage it suffices to add
to the description of the relationship between mental life and the
nervous system, a corresponding one concerning volition and
metabolism.

In this respect the — at first sight provocative — statement must be made that the will is based on the body's metabolic processes not less directly than the mind is on nervous processes. Scientific research was blocked against recognising this fact ever since, in the course of the nineteenth century, a certain theory came into being concerning the twofold purpose of the central nervous system. This theory asserts that there are two kinds of cerebro-spinal nerves: the so-called sensory nerves, which provide for the communication of outer sense-impressions; and the so-called motor nerves, which are held to be responsible for the voluntary movements of the body. The sensory nerves are therefore regarded as 'afferent', and the motor nerves as 'efferent'. So much has this view ingrained itself in modern thinking that until lately it was not disturbed even by occasional scientific observations which quite evidently contradicted it. Nor was it affected by Rudolf Steiner's corresponding statement in the aforementioned book. And yet, recognition of the truth in this matter is indispensable for proper human self-knowledge, for the progress so greatly needed in general scientific understanding, and for the development of workable sociological concepts. That is why the problem calls for immediate discussion here.

If we wish to obtain a clear picture of the function of the brain and its attendant nerves, we must concentrate on that part of the soul's life which is free from all emotional and volitional ingredients. This consists in the purely mental happenings which go to make up the mental representations of the various impressions we receive through our sense-organs. If the senses worked alone, we should have transient sensations to which we might react momentarily, a sort of happening we are indeed familiar with. But this belongs to a sphere below our truly waking consciousness. Sensations and reactions of this kind, therefore, can also occur while we are asleep. It is only in the fully waking part of our psyche that conscious mental representations come to pass. In this sphere, and in this alone, man develops the experience of himself as a self.

Recent neurological research has found that the continuous

electrical processes in the brain normally suffer a considerable decrease of their intensity the moment the psyche engages in a truly mental process, such as concentrating on some sense-perception or some content of the mind, whereas emotional happenings do not have this effect. Increase of the electrical activity of the brain, on the other hand, has been observed as accompanying epileptic fits, indeed, of an intensity and character which prompted researchers to speak of an 'electrical thunder-storm' in the brain. All this is entirely in line with what Rudolf Steiner points out in his book[1] where he says that a 'method of exclusion' would have to be developed for recognising the nerve function proper — all else being of the nature of rhythmical or metabolic processes extending into the region of the brain.

To assure ourselves of the truth concerning the interaction of our will with our body, however, we need not wait until an adequate method has been developed by outer scientific research. In the sense of the method pursued in this book we may turn to direct self-observation as a valid means of investigation, even if it is of a rather elementary kind compared with what is customary in orthodox science. In such a case the reader, therefore, is begged not to get annoyed by finding himself now and again exposed to some observation of this kind. Some readiness will be required from him in such instances to take the attitude of the little child in Hans Andersen's fairy story, *The Emperor's New Clothes*. While all the people are loud in praise of the magnificent robes of the Emperor, who is passing through the streets of his town in a festive pageant with actually no clothes on at all, a little child in the arms of his father witnesses to the truth by exclaiming: 'But the Emperor has nothing on!' What then does simple self-observation tell us about the interplay between our will and the motor system of our body?

When we move an arm, a hand, or one or more fingers, and if we do this very quietly and with full attention to our actual experience, we notice unmistakably that we are causing the motion not by sending there any impulse from the region of the brain, but at the very spot of its happening. This becomes all the

more evident the farther away from the brain the part set in
motion is situated. Exact self-observation tells us further that the
volitional process itself goes on quite outside the region of our
consciousness. All we know of is the intention (in its conceptual
form) which rouses the will and gives it direction, and the fact
of the completed deed. We have no consciousness of all the
complex happenings which are set into play within the muscles
themselves in order to carry out the intended movement. And it
is these that are the direct outcome of the activity of our will. We
have as little awareness of all this as we have of our total existence
during sleep. How could it be otherwise, since consciousness is
based on corporeal 'dying', while the processes involved in volitional
action belong to the body's life?

How, then, do we come to know anything of will as part of
our soul's life? This knowledge is obtained by an indirect means
not unlike that which enables us to 'see' a black area in the midst
of a coloured surface although our eye is not affected by that
area. It is the interruption of the sense-impression which appeals
to our consciousness as clearly as the sense-impression itself. In
a similar manner we get to know of the existence of our will
through the 'dark' area in the field of our mental life. Again, it
is the total interruption of our consciousness during sleep to
which we owe our awareness of being a Self during our waking
condition.

There remains the question as to the purpose of the nerves
to which hitherto the causation of movement has been ascribed.
The answer comes from observing that in whatever position we
hold some part of our body, or in whatever way we move it, we
have — unless there is some nervous disturbance — an exact inner
awareness of the position and its changes. In this way we are
able, for instance, to touch with the tip of a finger at will any spot
of our own body without the aid of the eye. Some time ago
scientific research recognised this kind of perception as a sense-
activity no less definite than that of our usually acknowledged
senses, and gave it the name of 'sense of movement' or 'muscular
sense' — still without drawing the obvious conclusion as regards

the true purpose of the so-called motor nerves. For it is they that serve this particular form of perception, just as e.g., the optical nerve serves the sense of sight.

Thus the psycho-physical organism of man presents itself as based on a polarity of functional systems: on the one hand the nervous system with its extension into the senses; on the other the metabolic system with its extension into the limbs. One system forms a kind of 'death-pole' and thereby the pole of consciousness; the other a 'life-pole' and thereby the pole of unconsciousness.

On this polarity of man's being there rests also the polarity of two particular faculties of the soul: *memory* and *fantasy*. In view of their significance for our later investigations, they call for some discussion here.

Both memory and fantasy are activities of the soul which lead to the formation of certain mental images, but these images are of opposite nature and have opposite origins. Memory pictures are generally based on past sense-perceptions; they can also be remembered imaginations or dream experiences. Even then, the original impressions, in order to be remembered, must have been fixed in the mind in a way similar to the fixation of outer perceptions. This is always a process engaging the nervous system. We note as a characteristic of memory that it has the task of reflecting past impressions in an unchanged manner and with the details as distinct as possible. Thus it is typical of memory to have a certain static character.

Fantasy is of a quite different nature. Here the soul is as much occupied with free production as in memory it is with reproduction. Compared with the static nature of memory, fantasy has a dynamic character. In this respect it shows a striking resemblance to the ever-moving, creatively working blood. In other respects, too, a close relationship can be found between the soul's imaginative actions and events within the body's blood-system. Quite in line with their opposite nature, fantasy and memory are distributed in a characteristic way over the span of life: in early years the soul dwells predominantly in imaginations, and in closing years predominantly in recollections.

Our observation of the functional systems of the human organism would be incomplete without taking into regard a third system, again of clearly distinct character, which functions as a mediator between the other two. Here all processes are of a strictly rhythmic nature, as is shown by the process of breathing and the pulsation of the blood. This system, too, provides a direct foundation for a certain type of psychological process, namely feeling. (That feeling is an activity of the soul distinct from both thinking and willing, and that it has its direct counterpart in the rhythmic processes of the body, can be most easily tested through observing oneself when listening to music.)

As one might expect from its median position, the feeling sphere of the soul is characterised by a degree of consciousness half-way between waking and sleeping. Of our feelings we are not more conscious than of our dreams; we are as little detached from them as from our dream experiences while these last; what remains in our memory of past feelings is usually not more than what we remember of past dreams.

In view of the triad of soul-functions, we might ask whether the soul possesses a faculty which mediates between memory and fantasy, as feeling does between thought and will. Such a faculty indeed exists, though not as part of man's original nature, but as an outcome of the soul's conscious effort. We shall meet it when considering Goethe's way of training observation and thought.

* * * * *

This picture of threefold man will enable us to appreciate, as has been our aim, the peculiar situation in which man, striving for an understanding of the sense-world, found himself at the outset of the modern age.

A characteristic of organic formations is that the general structure of the organism is repeated in its various parts. Thus the threefold differentiation of man's total organism is found in each of its several systems, and, again, within the sensory system itself in each single sense-organ. To see this, we need only compare, say, the senses of sight and smell, and notice in what different degree we are conscious of the impressions they convey, and how differently the corresponding elements of conception, feeling and willing are blended in each. We never turn away as instinctively from an objectionable colour arrangement as from an unpleasant smell. How small a part, on the other hand, do the representations of odours play in our recollection of past experiences, compared with those of sight. (This must not be confused with the fact that a smell may evoke other memories by way of association.) The same is valid in descending measure for all other senses. Of all senses, the sense of sight has in greatest measure the qualities of a 'conceptual sense'. The experiences which it brings, and these alone, were suitable as a basis for the new science, and even so a further limitation was necessary. For in spite of the special quality of the sense of sight, it is still not free from certain elements of feeling and will — that is, from elements with the character of dream or sleep. The first plays a part in our perception of colour; the second, in observing the forms and perspective ordering of objects we look at.

Here is repeated in a special way the threefold organisation of man, for the seeing of colour depends on an organic process apart from the nerve processes and similar to that which takes place between heart and lungs, whilst the seeing of forms and spatial vision depend upon certain movements of the eyeball (quick traversing of the outline of the viewed object with the line of sight, alteration of the angle between the two axes of sight according to distance), in which the eye is active as a sort of outer limb of the body, an activity which enters our consciousness as little as does that of our limbs. It now becomes clear that no world-content obtained in such more or less unconscious ways could be made available for the building of a new scientific world-conception. Only as much as man experiences through the sight of a single, colour-blind eye, could be used. For one who endeavours to observe historical facts in the manner here described, it is no mere play of chance that the father of scientific atomism,

John Dalton, was by nature colour blind. In fact colour blindness
was known, for a considerable time during the last century, as
'Daltonism', since it was through the publication of Dalton's
self-observations that for the first time general attention was
drawn to this phenomenon.

* * * * *

In searching for a fitting characterisation of the onlooker-
consciousness, nothing could suit us better than the example of
Galileo, who is rightly deemed to be the founder of natural
science in the modern sense — i.e. of the science based on man's
relationship with the world in his condition of a one-eyed colour-
blind onlooker. Among his fundamental observations, several of
which will occupy us in the course of our further discussion, his
discovery of the law of the pendulum will serve best our present
purpose.

History relates that Galileo found this law through observing
in the cathedral of Pisa a hanging lamp which had probably been
set swinging by a gust of air. The law of the pendulum states that
a swinging pendulum always takes the same amount of time for
moving from one extreme position to the other, irrespective of the
width of the swing (the amplitude). In order to establish this fact,
Galileo had to measure the time which the lamp took for each
swing. No clock or watch was available: the first pendulum clock
was built later using the law Galileo had discovered. An ingenious
inspiration led him to use the beat of his pulse.

Let us picture the concrete situation in which this discovery,
essential for the foundation of the science of mechanics, came
about. Galileo had certainly gone to the Cathedral for the divine
service. Now, a faithful Christian who allows himself to be touched
in his soul, however slightly, by what he believes to occur at the
altar during the Holy Act, cannot but experience some change in
the rhythm of his heart-beat. In order to use this heart as a chronometer, Galileo had to remain entirely unaffected, at best for a
few moments, by the event, holy though it was for his belief.

Thus we may imagine him sitting in the midst of the pious crowd, his gaze fixed on the swinging lamp, the finger of one of his hands on the pulse of his other wrist, while he carefully counts the beats — a picture of the perfect onlooker!

Chapter III

THE ONLOOKER'S PHILOSOPHIC MALADY

In his isolation as world spectator, the modern philosopher was
bound to reach two completely opposite views regarding the
objective value of human thought. One of these was given expression in Descartes' famous words: *Cogito ergo sum* ('I think,
therefore I am'). Descartes (1596-1650), rightly described as the
inaugurator of modern philosophy, thus held the view that only
in his own thought-activity does man find a guarantee of his own
existence.

In coming to this view, Descartes took as his starting-point
his experience that human consciousness contains only the thought
pictures evoked by sense-perception, and yet knows nothing of
the how and why of the things responsible for such impressions.
He thus found himself compelled, in the first place, to doubt
whether any of these things had an objective existence at all.
Hence, there remained over for him only one indubitable item in
the entire content of the universe – his own thinking; for were he
to doubt even this, he could do so only by again making use of it.
From the 'I doubt, therefore I am', he was led in this way to the
'I think, therefore I am'.

The other conception of human thought reached by the
onlooker-consciousness was diametrically opposed to that of
Descartes, and entirely cancelled its conceptual significance. It
was put forward – not long afterwards – by Robert Hooke
(1635-1703), the first scientist to make systematic use of the
newly invented microscope by means of which he made the
fundamental discovery of the cellular structure of plant tissues.
It was, indeed, on the strength of his microscopic studies that he
boldly undertook to determine the relationship of human thought

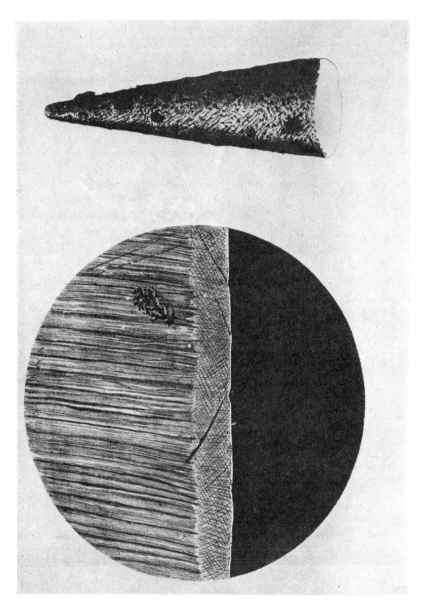

PLATE I

Robert Hookes's 'proof' of the non-reality of human concepts:
a needle ('point') and the edge of a knife ('line'), seen
through the microscope

to objective reality. He published his views in the introduction to his *Micrographia*, the great work in which, with the lavish help of carefully executed copper engravings, he made his microscopic observations known to the world.

Hooke's line of thought is briefly as follows: In past ages men subscribed to the naive belief that what they have in their conscious-ness as thought pictures of the world, actually reproduces the real content of that world. The microscope now demonstrates, however, how much the familiar appearance of the world depends on the structure of our sense apparatus; for it reveals a realm just as real as that already known to us, but hitherto concealed from us because it is not accessible to the natural senses. Accordingly, if the microscope can penetrate through the veil of illusion which normally hides a whole world of potentially visible phenomena, it may be that it can even teach us something about the ideas we have hitherto formed concerning the nature of things. Perhaps it can bring us a step nearer the truth in the sphere of thought, as it so obviously has done in that of observation.

Of all the ideas that human reason can form, Hooke considered the simplest and the most fundamental to be the geometrical concepts of point and straight line. Undoubtedly we are able to think these, but the naive consciousness takes for granted that it also perceives them as objective realities outside itself, so that thoughts and facts correspond to each other. We must now ask, however, if this belief is not due to an optical deception. Let us turn to the microscope and see what point and line in the external world look like through it.

For his investigation Hooke chose the point of a needle and a knife-edge, as providing the best representatives among physical objects of point and straight line. The sketches he made show how Hooke made clear to his readers how little these two things, when observed through the microscope, resemble what is seen by the unaided eye. This fact convinced him that the apparent agreement between the world of perception and the world of ideas rests on nothing more solid than an optical limitation (Plate I)[1].

Compared with the more refined methods of present-day

thought, Hooke's procedure may strike us as somewhat primitive. Actually he did nothing more than has since been done times without number; for the scientist has become more and more willing to allow artifically evoked sense-perceptions to dictate the thoughts he uses in forming a scientific picture of the world.

In the present context we are concerned with the historical import of Hooke's procedure. This lies in the fact that, immediately after Descartes had satisfied himself that in thinking man had the one sure guarantee of his own existence, Hooke proved in a seemingly indubitable manner that thinking was entirely divorced from reality. It required only another century for philosophy to draw from this the unavoidable consequence. It appeared in the form of Hume's philosophic system, the outcome of which was universal scepticism.

As we shall see in due course, Hume's mode of reasoning continues to rule scientific thought even today, quite irrespective of the fact that science itself claims to have its philosophical parent in Kant, the very thinker who devoted his life's work to the refutation of Hume.

* * * * *

On the basis of his investigations into human consciousness Hume (1711-76) felt obliged to reason thus: My consciousness, as I know it, has no contact with the external world other than that of a mere outside onlooker. What it wins for its own content from the outer world is in the nature of single, mutually unrelated parts. Whatever may unite these parts into an objective whole within the world itself can never enter my consciousness; and any such unifying factor entertained by my thought can be only a self-constructed, hypothetical picture. Hume summed up his view in two axioms which he himself described as the alpha and omega of his whole philosophy. The first runs: 'All our distinct perceptions are distinct existences.' The other: 'The Mind never perceives any real connections between distinct existences.' (*Treatise of Human Nature*.)

If once we agree that we can know of nothing but unrelated thought pictures, because our consciousness is not in a position to relate these pictures to a unifying reality, then we have no right to ascribe, with Descartes and his school, an objective reality to the self. Even though the self may appear to us as the unifying agent among our thoughts, it must itself be a mental picture among mental pictures; and man can have no knowledge of any permanent reality outside this fluctuating picture-realm. So, with Hume, the onlooker-consciousness came to experience its own utter inability to achieve a knowledge of the objective existence either of a material world behind all external phenomena, or of a spiritual self behind all the details of its own internal content.

Accordingly, human consciousness found itself hurled into the abyss of universal scepticism. Hume himself suffered unspeakably under the impact of what he considered inescapable ideas — rightly described from another side as the 'suicide of human intelligence' — and his philosophy often seemed to him like a malady, as he himself called it, against whose grip he could see no remedy. The only thing left to him, if he was to prevent philosophical suicide from ending in physical suicide, was to forget in daily life his own conclusions as far as possible.

What Hume experienced as his philosophical malady, however, was the result not of a mental abnormality peculiar to himself, but of that modern form of consciousness which still prevails in general today. This explains why, despite all attempts to disprove Hume's philosophy, scientific thought has not broken away from its alpha and omega in the slightest degree.

A proof of this is to be found, for example, in the principle of Indeterminacy which has arisen in modern physics.

After the discovery by Galileo of the parallelogram of forces, it became the object of classical physics — unexpressed, indeed, until Newton wrote his *Principia* — to bring the unchanging laws ruling nature into the light of human consciousness, and to give them conceptual expression in the language of mathematical formulae. Since, however, science was obliged to restrict itself to what could be observed with a single, colour-blind eye, physics has taken as its main object of research the spatio-temporal relationships, and their changes, between discrete, ideally conceived, point-like particles. Accordingly, the mathematically formulable laws holding sway in nature came to mean the laws according to which the smallest particles in the material foundation of the world change their position with regard to each other. A science of this kind could logically maintain that, if ever it succeeded in defining both the position and the state of motion, in one single moment, of the totality of particles composing the universe, it would have discovered the law on which universal existence depends. This necessarily rested on the presupposition that it really was the ultimate particles of the physical world which were under observation. In the search for these, guided chiefly by the study of electricity, the physicists tracked down ever smaller and smaller units; and along this path scientific research has arrived at the following peculiar situation.

To observe any object in the sense world we need an appropriate medium of observation. For ordinary things, light provides this. In the sense in which light is understood today, this is possible because the wavelength of light is much smaller than the average magnitude of all microscopically visible objects. This ensures that they can be observed clearly by the human eye. Much smaller objects, however, will require a correspondingly shorter wavelength in the medium of observation. Now shorter wavelengths than those of visible light have been found in ultraviolet light and in X-rays; and these, accordingly, are now often used for minute physical research.

In this way, however, we are led by nature to a definite boundary; for we now find ourselves in a realm where the dimensions of the observation medium and the observed object are more or less the same. The result, unfortunately, is that when the light meets the object, it changes the latter's condition of movement, owing to the momentum of light which is an inevitable requirement of the quantum character which light takes in any interaction with matter. On the other hand, if a 'light' is used whose wavelength is too big to have any influence on the object's condition of movement, it precludes any exact determination of the object's location.

Thus, having arrived at the very ground of the world — that is, where the cosmic laws might be expected to reveal themselves directly — the scientist finds himself in the remarkable situation of only being able to determine accurately either the position of an observed object and not its state of motion, or its state of motion and not its position. The law he seeks, however, requires that both should be known at the same time. Nor is this situation due to the imperfection of the scientific apparatus employed, but to its very perfection, so that it appears to arise from the nature of the foundation of the world — in so far, at least, as modern science is bound to conceive it.

If it is true that a valid scientific knowledge of nature is possible only in the sphere open to a single-eyed, colour-blind observation, and if it is true — as science of this kind, at any rate, is obliged to believe — that all processes within the material foundation of the world depend on nothing but the movements of certain elementary particles of extremely small size, then the fact must be faced that the very nature of these processes rules out the discovery of any stable ordering of things in the sense of mathematically formulable laws. The discovery of such laws will then always be the last step but one in scientific investigation; the last will inevitably be the dissolution of such laws into chaos. For a consistent scientific thinking that goes this way, therefore, nothing is left but to recognise chaos as the only real basis of an apparently ordered world, a chaos on whose surface the laws that seem to hold sway are only the illusory picturings of the human mind. This, then, is the principle of Indeterminacy as it has been encountered in the course of investigation into the electrical processes within physical matter.

* * * * *

In the following way Professor Schrödinger, another leading thinker among modern theoretical physicists, explains the philosophical basis for the principle of Indeterminacy, which scientists have established in the meantime:[2]

'Every quantitative observation, every observation making use of measurement, is by nature discontinuous.... However far we go in the pursuit of accuracy we shall never get anything other than a finite series of discrete results.... The raw material of our quantitative cognition of nature will always have this primitive and discontinuous character.... It is possible that a physical system might be so simple that this meagre information would suffice to settle its fate; in that case nature would not be more complicated than a game of chess. To determine a position of a game of chess thirty-three facts suffice.... If nature is more complicated than a game of chess, a belief to which one tends to incline, then a physical system cannot be determined by a finite number of observations. But in practice a finite number of observations is all that we could make.'

Classical physics, the author goes on to show, held that it was possible to gain a real insight into the laws of the universe, because in principle an infinite number of such discrete observations would enable us to fill in the gaps sufficiently to allow us to determine the system of the physical world. Against this assumption modern physics must hold the view that an infinite number of observations cannot in any case be carried out in practice, and that nothing compels us to assume that even this would suffice to furnish us with the means for a complete determination, which alone would allow us to speak of 'law' in nature. 'This is the direction in which modern physics has led us without really intending it.'

What we have previously said will make it clear enough that in these words of a modern physicist we meet once more the two fundamentals of Hume's philosophy. It is just as obvious, however, that the very principle thus re-affirmed at the latest stage of modern physical science was already firmly established by Hooke, when he sought to prove to his contemporaries the unreality of human ideas.

Let us recall Hooke's motives and results. The human reason discovers that certain law-abiding forms of thought dwell within itself; these are the rules of mathematical thinking. The eye informs the reason that the same kind of law and order is present also in the outer world. The mind can think point and line; the eye reports that the same forms exist in nature outside. (Hooke could just as well have taken as his examples the apex and edge of a crystal.) The reason mistrusts the eye, however, and with the help of the microscope 'improves' upon it. What hitherto had been taken for a compact, regulated whole now collapses into a heap of unordered parts; behind the illusion of law a finer observation detects the reality of chaos!

Had science in its vehement career from discovery to discovery not forgotten its own beginnings so completely, it would not have needed its latest researches to bring out a principle which it had in fact been following from the outset — a principle which philosophy had already recognised, if not in quite the same formulation, in the eighteenth century. Indeterminacy, as we have just seen it explained by Schrödinger, is nothing but the exact continuation of Humean scepticism.

Chapter IV

THE COUNTRY THAT IS NOT OURS

The last two chapters have served to show the impasse into which human perception and thinking have come — in so far as they have been used for scientific purposes — by virtue of the relationship to the world in which man's consciousness found itself when it awoke to itself at the beginning of modern times. Now although the onlooker in man, especially in the earliest stage of our period, gave itself up to the conviction that a self-contained picture of the universe could be formed out of the kind of materials available to it, it nevertheless had a dim inkling that this picture, because it lacked all dynamic content, had no bearing on the real nature of the universe. Unable to find this reality within himself, the world-onlooker set about searching in his own way for what was missing, and turned to the perceptible world outside man. Here he came, all unexpectedly, upon... electricity. Scarcely was electricity discovered than it drew human thinking irresistibly into its own realm. Thereby man found himself, with a consciousness completely blind to dynamics, within a sphere of only too real dynamic forces. Today the world abounds in the results this has had for man's civilisation. The purpose of this chapter is to show how this situation was prepared right from the outset of the electrical discoveries.

* * * * *

First, let us recall how potent a role electricity has come to play in social life through the great discoveries which began at the end of the eighteenth century. To do this we need only compare the present relationship between production and consumption in the economic sphere with what it was before the power-machine, and especially the electrically driven machine, had been invented. Consider some major public undertaking in former times — say the construction of a great medieval cathedral. Almost all the work was done by human beings, with some help, of course, from domesticated animals. Under these circumstances the entire source of productive power lay in the will-energies of living beings, whose bodies had to be supplied with food, clothing and housing; and to provide these, other productive powers of a similar kind were required near the same place. Accordingly, since each of the power units employed in the work was simultaneously both producer and consumer, a certain natural limit was placed on the accumulation of productive forces in any one locality.

This condition of natural balance between production and consumption was profoundly disturbed by the introduction of the steam engine; but even so there were still some limits, though of a quite different kind, to local concentrations of productive power. For steam engines require water and coal at the scene of action, and these take up space and need continual shifting and replenishing. Owing to the very nature of physical matter, it cannot be heaped up where it is required in unlimited quantities.

All this changed directly man succeeded in producing energy electro-magnetically by the mere rotation of material masses, and in using the water-power of the earth — itself ultimately derived from the cosmic energies of the sun — for driving his dynamos. Not only is the source of energy thus tapped practically inexhaustible, but the machines produce it without consuming on their own account, apart from wear and tear, and so make possible the almost limitless accumulation of power in one place. For electricity is distinguished from all other power-supplying natural forces, living or otherwise, precisely in this, that it can be concentrated spatially with the aid of a physical carrier whose material bulk is insignificant compared with the energy supplied.

Through this property of electricity it has been possible for man to extend the range of his activity in all directions, far and near. So the balance between production and consumption, which in previous ages was more or less adequately maintained by natural conditions, has been entirely destroyed, and a major social-economic problem created.

In yet another way, and through quite another of its properties, electricity plays an important part in modern life. Not only does it compete with the human will; it also makes possible automatically intelligent operations quite beyond anything man can do on his own. There are innumerable examples of this in modern electrical technology; we need mention here only the computer and its many applications.

To an ever-increasing, quite uncontrolled degree — for to the mind of present-day man it is only natural to translate every new discovery into practice as soon and as extensively as possible — electricity enters decisively into our modern existence. If we take all its activities into account, we see arising amongst humanity a vast realm of labour units, possessed in their own way not only of will but of the sharpest imaginable intelligence. Although they are wholly remote from man's own nature, he more and more subdues his thoughts and actions to theirs, allowing them to take rank as guides and shapers of his civilisation.

Turning to the sphere of scientific research, we find electricity playing a role in the development of modern thinking remarkably similar to its part as a labour-force in everyday life. We find it associated with phenomena which, in Professor Heisenberg's words, expose their mutual connections to exact mathematical thinking more readily than do any other facts of nature; and yet the way in which these phenomena have become known has played fast and loose with mathematical thinking to an unparalleled degree. To recognise that in this sphere modern science owes its triumphs to a strange and often paradoxical mixture of outer accident and error in human thought, we need only review the history of the subject without prejudice.

* * * * *

The discovery of electricity has so far been accomplished in four clearly distinct stages. The first extends from the time when men first knew of electrical phenomena to the beginning of the natural scientific age; the second includes the seventeenth and the greater part of the eighteenth centuries; the third begins with Galvani's discovery and closes with the first observations of radiant electricity; and the fourth brings us to our own day. We shall here concern ourselves with a few outstanding features of each phase, enough to characterise the strange path along which man has been led by the discovery of electricity.

Until the beginning of modern times, nothing more was known about electricity, or of its sister force, magnetism, than what we find in Pliny's writings. There, without recognising a qualitative distinction between them, he refers to the faculty of rubbed amber and of certain pieces of iron to attract other small pieces of matter. It required the awakening of that overruling interest in material nature, characteristic of our own age, for the essential difference between electric and magnetic attraction to be recognised. The first to give a proper description of this was Queen Elizabeth's doctor, Gilbert. His discovery was soon followed by the construction of the first electrical machine by the German Guericke (also known through his invention of the air pump) which opened the way for the discovery that electricity could be transmitted from one place to another.

It was not, however, until the beginning of the eighteenth century that the crop of electrical discoveries began to increase considerably: among these was the recognition of the dual nature of electricity, by the Frenchman, Dufais, and the chance invention of the Leyden jar (made simultaneously by the German, von Kleist, and two Dutchmen, Musschenbroek and Cunaeus). The Leyden jar brought electrical effects of quite unexpected intensity within reach. Stimulated by what could be done with electricity in this form, more and more people now busied themselves in experimenting with so fascinating a force of nature, until in the second third of the century a whole army of observers was at work, whether by way of profession or of hobby, finding out ever new manifestations of its powers.

The mood that prevailed in those days among men engaged in electrical research is well reflected in a letter written by the Englishman, Walsh, after he had established the electric nature of the shocks given by certain fishes, to Benjamin Franklin, who shortly before had discovered the natural occurrence of electricity in the atmosphere:

'I rejoice in addressing these communications to You. He, who predicted and shewed that electricity wings the formidable bolt of the atmosphere, will hear with attention that in the deep it speeds a humbler bolt, silent and invisible; He, who analysed the electrical Phial, will hear with pleasure that its laws prevail in animate Phials; He, who by Reason became an electrician, will hear with reverence of an instinctive electrician, gifted in his birth with a wonderful apparatus, and with the skill to use it.' (Phil. Trans. 1773.)

Dare one believe that in electricity the soul of nature had been discovered? This was the question which at that time stirred the hearts of very many in Europe. Doctors had already sought to arouse new vitality in their patients by the use of strong electric shocks; attempts had even been made to bring the dead back to life by such means.

In a time like ours, when we are primarily concerned with the practical application of scientific discoveries, we are mostly accustomed to regard such flights of thought from a past age as nothing but the unessential accompaniment of youthful, immature science, and to smile at them accordingly as historical curiosities. This is a mistake, for we then overlook how within them was hidden an inkling of the truth, however wrongly conceived at the time, and we ignore the role which such apparently fantastic hopes have played in connection with the entry of electricity into human civilisation. (Nor are such hopes confined to the eighteenth century; as we shall see, the same impulse urged Crookes a hundred

THE COUNTRY THAT IS NOT OURS

years later to that decisive discovery which was to usher in the
latest phase in the history of science, a phase in which the investigating human spirit has been led to that boundary of the physical-
material world where the transition takes place from inert matter
into freely working energy.)

If there was any doubt left as to whether in nature the same
power was at work which, in animal and man, was hidden away
within the soul, this doubt seemed finally to have been dispelled
through Galvani's discovery that animal limbs could be made to
move electrically through being touched by two bits of different
metals. No wonder that 'the storm which was loosed in the world
of the physicists, the physiologists and the doctors through
Galvani's publication can only be compared with the one crossing
the political horizon of Europe at the same time. Wherever there
happened to be frogs and two pieces of different metals available,
everyone sought proof with his own eyes that the severed limbs
could be marvellously re-enlivened.'[1]

Like many of his contemporaries, Galvani was drawn by the
fascinating behaviour of the new force of nature to carry on
electrical experiments as a hobby alongside his professional
work, anatomical research. For his experiments he used the
room where his anatomical specimens were set out. So it happened
that his electrical machine stood near some frogs' legs, prepared
for dissection. By a further coincidence his assistant, while playing
with the machine, released a few sparks just when some of the
specimens were in such contact with the surface beneath them
that they were bound to react to the sudden alteration of the
electric field round the machine caused by its discharge. At
each spark the frogs' legs twitched. What Galvani saw with his
own eyes seemed to be no less than the union of two phenomena,
one observed by Franklin in the heights of the atmosphere, the
other by Walsh in the depths of the sea.

Galvani, as he himself describes, proceeded with immense
enthusiasm to investigate systematically what accident had thus
put into his hands.[2] He wanted first to see whether changes
occurring naturally in the electrical condition of the atmosphere

would call forth the same reaction in his specimens. For this purpose he fastened one end of an iron wire to a point high up outside his house; the lower end he connected with the nervous substance of a limb from one of his specimens, and to the foot of this he attached a second wire whose other end he submerged in a well. The specimen itself was either enclosed in a glass flask in order to insulate it, or simply left lying on a table near the well. And all this he did whenever a thunderstorm was threatening. As he himself reported: 'All took place as expected. Whenever the lightning flashed, all the muscles simultaneously came into repeated and violent twitchings, so that the movements of the muscles, like the flash of the lightning, always preceded the thunder, and thus, as it were, heralded its coming.' We can have some idea of what went on in Galvani's mind during these experiments if we picture vividly to ourselves the animal limbs twitching about every time the lightning flashed, as if a revitalising force of will had suddenly taken possession of them.

In the course of his investigations — he carried them on for a long time — Galvani was astonished to observe that some of his specimens, which he had hung on to an iron railing by means of brass hooks, sometimes fell to twitching even when the sky was quite clear and there was no sign of thunder. His natural conclusion was that this must be due to hitherto unnoticed electrical changes in the atmosphere. Observations maintained for hours every day, however, led to no conclusive result; when twitchings did occur it was only with some of the specimens, and even then there was no discoverable cause. Then it happened one day that Galvani, 'tired out with fruitless watching', took hold of one of the brass hooks by which the specimens were hung, and pressed it more strongly than usual against the iron railing. Immediately a twitching took place. 'I was almost at the point of ascribing the occurrence to atmospheric electricity,' Galvani tells us. All the same he took one of the specimens, a frog, into his laboratory and there subjected it to similar conditions by putting it on an iron plate, and pressing against this with the hook that was stuck through its spinal cord. Immediately the twitching occurred again. He tried with other metals and, for checking purposes, with non-metals as well. With some ingenuity he fixed up an arrangement, rather like that of an electric bell, whereby the limbs in contracting broke contact and in relaxing restored it, and so he managed to keep the frog in continuous rhythmical movement.

Whereas Galvani had been rightly convinced by his earlier observations that the movement in the specimens represented a reaction to an electric stimulus from outside, he now changed his mind. In the very moment of his really significant discovery he succumbed to the error that he had to do with an effect of animal electricity located somewhere in the dead creature itself, perhaps in the fashion of what had been observed in the electric fishes. He decided that the metal attachment served merely to set in motion the electricity within the animal.

Whilst Galvani persisted in this mistake until his death, Volta realised that the source of the electric force, as in the first of Galvani's observations, must still be sought outside the specimens, and himself rightly attributed it to the contacting metals. Guided by this hypothesis, Volta started systematic research into the Galvanic properties of metals, and presently succeeded in producing electricity once more from purely mineral substances, namely from two different metals in contact with a conductive liquid.

This mode of producing electricity, however, differed from any previously known in allowing for the first time the production of continuous electrical effects. It is this quality of the cells and piles constructed by Volta that laid open the road for the electric force to assume that role in human civilisation which we have already described. That Volta himself was aware of this essentially new factor in the Galvanic production of electricity is shown by his own report to the Royal Society:

'The chief of my results, and which comprehends nearly all the others, is the construction of an apparatus which resembles in its effects, viz. such as giving shocks to the arms, &c, the Leyden Phial, and still better electric batteries weakly charged; ... but which infinitely surpasses the virtue and power of these same batteries; as it has no need, like them, of being charged beforehand, by means of a foreign electricity; and as it is capable of giving the usual commotion as often as ever it is properly touched.'

Whilst Volta's success was based on avoiding Galvani's error, his apparatus nevertheless turned out inadvertently to be a close counterpart of precisely that animal organ which Galvani had in mind when misinterpreting his own discoveries! That Volta himself realised this is clear from the concluding words in his letter:

'This apparatus, as it resembles more the natural organ of the torpedo, or of the electrical eel, than the Leyden Phial or the ordinary electric batteries, I may call an artificial electric organ.'

This new method of producing continuous electric effects had far reaching results, one of which was the discovery of the magnetic properties of the electric current by the Dane, Oersted – once again a purely accidental discovery, moving directly counter to the assumptions of the discoverer himself. About to leave the lecture room where he had just been trying to prove the non-existence of such magnetic properties in the direction of the current (an attempt seemingly crowned with success), Oersted happened to glance once more at his demonstration bench. To his astonishment he noticed that one of his magnetic needles was out of alignment; evidently it was attracted by a magnetic field created by the current running through a wire he had just been using, which was still in circuit. Thus what had escaped Oersted throughout his planned researches – namely, that the magnetic force which accompanies an electric current must be sought in a direction at right angles to the current – a fortuitous event enabled him to detect.

These repeated strokes of chance and frequently mistaken interpretations of the phenomenon thus detected show that men were exploring the electrical realm as it were in the dark; it was a realm foreign to their ordinary ideas and they had not developed the forms of thought necessary for understanding it. (And this, as our further survey will show, is still true, even today.)

In our historical survey we come next to the researches of Faraday and Maxwell. Faraday was convinced that if electrical processes are accompanied by magnetic forces, as Oersted had shown, the reverse must also be true — magnetism must be accompanied by electricity. He was led to this correct conviction by his belief in the qualitative unity of all the forces of nature — a reflection, as his biography shows, of his strongly monotheistic, Old Testament faith. Precisely this view, however — which since Faraday natural science has quite consciously adopted as a leading principle — will reveal itself to us as a fundamental error.

It seems paradoxical to assert that the more consistently human thought has followed this error, the greater have been the results of the scientific investigation of electricity. Precisely this paradox, however, is characteristic of the realm of nature to which electricity belongs; and anyone earnestly seeking to overcome the illusions of our age will have to face the fact that the immediate effectiveness of an idea in practice is no proof of its ultimate truth.

Another eloquent example of the strange destiny of human thought in connection with electricity is to be found in the work of Clerk Maxwell, who, starting from Faraday's discoveries, gave the theory of electricity its mathematical basis. Along his purely theoretical line of thought he was led to the recognition of the existence of a form of electrical activity hitherto undreamt of — electro-magnetic vibrations. Stimulated by Maxwell's mathematical conclusions, Hertz and Marconi were soon afterwards able to demonstrate those phenomena which have led on the one hand to the electro-magnetic theory of light, and on the other to the practical achievements of wireless communication.

Once again, there is the paradoxical fact that this outcome of Maxwell's labours contradicts the very foundation on which he had built his theoretical edifice. For his starting-point had been to form a picture of the electro-magnetic field of force to which he could apply certain well-known formulae of mechanics. This he did by comparing the behaviour of the electrical force to the currents of an elastic fluid — that is, of a material substance. It is true that both he and his successors rightly emphasised that such a picture was not in any way meant as an explanation of electricity, but merely as an auxiliary concept in the form of a purely external analogy. Nevertheless, it was in the guise of a material fluid that he thought of this force, and that he could submit it to mathematical calculation. Yet the fact is that from this starting-point the strict logic of mathematics led him to the discovery that electricity is capable of behaviour which makes it appear qualitatively similar to ... light!

Whilst practical men were turning the work of Faraday and Maxwell to account by exploiting the mechanical working of electricity in power production, and its similarity to light in the wireless communication of thought, a new field of research, with entirely new practical possibilities, was suddenly opened up in the last third of the nineteenth century through the discovery of how electricity behaves in rarefied air. This brings us to the discovery of cathode rays and the phenomena accompanying them, from which the latest stage in the history of electricity originated. And here once more, as in the history of Galvani's discoveries, we encounter certain undercurrents of longing and expectation in the human soul which seemed to find an answer through this sudden, great advance in the knowledge of electricity — an advance which has again led to practical applications of the utmost significance for human society, though not at all in the way first hoped for.

Interest in the phenomena arising when electricity passes through gases with reduced pressure had simultaneously taken hold of several investigators in the seventies of the nineteenth century. But the decisive step in this sphere of research was taken by the English physicist, William Crookes (1832-1919). He was led on by a line of thought which seems entirely irrelevant; yet it was this which first directed his interest to the peculiar phenomena accompanying cathode rays; and they proved to be the starting-point of the long train of inquiry which has now culminated in the release of atomic energy.[3]

In the midst of his many interests and activities, Crookes was filled from his youth with a longing to find by empirical means the bridge leading from the world of physical effects to that of superphysical causes. He himself tells how this longing was awakened in him by the loss of a much-beloved brother. Before the dead body he came to the question, which thereafter was never to leave him, whether there was a land where the human individuality continues after it has laid aside its bodily sheath, and how was that land to be found. Seeing that scientific research was the instrument which modern man had forged to penetrate through the veil of external phenomena to the causes producing them, it was natural for Crookes to turn to it in seeking the way from the one world into the other.

It was after meeting with a man able to produce effects within the corporeal world by means of forces quite different from those familiar to science, that Crookes decided to devote himself to this scientific quest. Thus he first came into touch with that sphere of phenomena which is known as spiritualism, or perhaps more suitably, spiritism. Crookes now found himself before a special order of happenings which seemed to testify to a world other than that open to our senses; physical matter here showed itself capable of movement in defiance of gravity, manifestations of light and sound appeared without a physical source to produce them. Through becoming familiar with such things at seances arranged by his mediumistic acquaintance, he began to hope he had found the way by which scientific research could overstep the limits of the physical world. Accordingly, he threw himself eagerly into the systematic investigation of his new experiences, and so became the father of modern scientific spiritism.

Crookes had hoped that the scientists of his day would be positively interested in his researches. But his first paper in this field, 'On Phenomena called Spiritual', was at once and almost unanimously rejected by his colleagues, and as long as he concerned himself with such matters he suffered through their opposition. It passed his understanding as a scientist why anything should be regarded in advance as outside the scope of scientific research. After several years of fruitless struggle he broke off his investigations into spiritism, deeply disillusioned at his failure to interest official science in it. His own partiality for it continued, however (he served as President of the Society for Psychical Research from

1896 9), and he missed no opportunity of confessing himself a
pioneer in the search for the boundary land between the worlds
of matter and spirit. Through all his varied scientific work the
longing persisted to know more of this land.

Just as Crookes had once sought to investigate spiritism
scientifically, so in his subsequent scientific inquiries he was
always something of a spiritist. He admitted, indeed, that he
felt specially attracted by the strange light effects arising when
electricity passes through rarefied gases, because they reminded
him of certain luminous phenomena he had observed during his
spiritistic investigations. Besides this, there was the fact that
light here appeared to be susceptible to the magnetic force in a
way otherwise characteristic only of certain material substances.
Accordingly, everything combined to suggest to Crookes that
here, if anywhere, he was at the boundary between the physical
and the superphysical worlds. No wonder that he threw himself
into the study of these phenomena with enthusiasm.

He soon succeeded in evoking striking effects — light and
heat, and also mechanical — along the path of electricity passing
invisibly through the tube later named after him. Thus he proved
for the the first time visibly, so to say, the double nature —
material and supermaterial — of electricity. What Crookes himself
thought about these discoveries in the realm of the cathode
rays we may judge from the title, 'Radiant Matter', or 'The Fourth
State of Matter', which he gave to his first publication about them.
And so he was only being consistent when, in his lectures before
the Royal Institution in London, and the British Association in
Sheffield in 1879, after showing to an amazed scientific audience
the newly discovered properties of electricity, he came to the
climax of his exposition by saying: 'We have seen that in some of
its properties Radiant Matter is as material as this table, whilst
in other properties it almost assumes the character of Radiant
Energy. We have actually touched here the borderland where
Matter and Force seem to merge into one another, the shadowy
realm between Known and Unknown, which for me has always
had peculiar temptations.' And in boldly prophetic words, which

time has partly justified, he added, 'I venture to think that the greatest scientific problems of the future will find their solution in this Borderland, and even beyond; here, it seems to me, lie Ultimate Realities, subtle, far-reaching, wonderful.'

No one can read these words of Crookes without hearing again, as an undertone, the question which had forced itself on him at the bedside of his dead brother, long before. All that is left of the human being whom death has taken is a heap of substances, deserted by the force which had used them as the instrument of its own activity. Whither vanishes this force when it leaves the body, and is there any possibility of its revealing itself even without occupying such a body?

Stirred by this question, the young Crookes set out to find a world of forces which differ from the usual mechanical ones exercised by matter on matter, in that they are autonomous, superior to matter in its inert conglomeration, yet capable of using matter, just as the soul makes use of the body so long as it dwells within it. His aim was to secure proof that such forces exist, or, at any rate, to penetrate into the realm where the transition from matter to pure, matter-free force takes place. And once again, as in Galvani's day, electricity fascinated the eyes of a man who was seeking for the land of the soul. What spiritism denied, electricity seemed to grant.

The aversion to spiritism which Crookes met with in contemporary science was, from the standpoint of such a science, largely justified. Science, in the form in which Crookes himself conceived it, took for granted that the relationship of human consciousness to the world was that of external onlooking. Accordingly, if the scientist remained within the limits thus prescribed for consciousness, it was only consistent to refuse to make anything beyond these limits an object of scientific research.

On the other hand, it says much for the courage and open mindedness of Crookes that he refused to be held back from what was for him the only possible way of extending the boundaries of science beyond the given physical world. Moreover, it was only natural that in his search for a world of a higher order than

the physical he should, as a man of his time, first turn his attention
to spiritistic occurrences, for spiritism, as it had come over to
Europe from America in the middle of the nineteenth century,
was nothing but an attempt by the onlooker-consciousness to
learn something in its own way about the supersensible world.
The spiritist expects the spirit to reveal itself in outwardly perceptible phenomena as if it were part of the physical world.

Towards the end of his life Crookes confessed that if he
were able to begin again he would prefer to study telepathic
phenomena — the direct transference of thought from one person
to another — rather than the purely mechanical, or so-called
telekinetic, expressions of psychic forces. But although his interest
was thus turning towards a more interior field of psychic investigation, he remained true to his times in still assuming that knowledge about the world, whatever it might be, could be won only by
placing oneself as a mere onlooker outside the object of research.

*   *   *   *   *

The stream of new discoveries which followed Crookes' work
justified his conviction that in cathode ray phenomena we have to
do with the frontier region of physical nature. Still, the land that
lies on the other side of this frontier is not the one Crookes had
been looking for throughout his life. For, instead of finding the
way into the land whither man's soul disappears at death, Crookes
had inadvertently crossed the border into another land — a land
which the twentieth-century scientist is impelled to call 'the
country that is not ours'.

The realm thrown open to science by Crookes' observations,
which human knowledge now entered as if taking it by storm,
was that of the radioactive processes of the mineral stratum of
the earth. Many new and surprising properties of electricity were
discovered there — yet the riddle of electricity itself, instead of
coming nearer, withdrew into ever deeper obscurity.

The very first step into this newly discovered territory made the riddles still more bewildering. As we have said, Maxwell's use of a material analogy as a means of formulating mathematically the properties of electro-magnetic fields of force had led to results which brought electricity into close conjunction with light. In his own way Crookes focused, to begin with, his attention entirely on the light-like character of electric effects in a vacuum. It was precisely these observations, however, as continued by J.J. Thomson and others, which presently made it necessary to see in electricity nothing else than a special manifestation of inert mass.

* * * * *

The developments leading up to this stage are recent and familiar enough to be briefly summarised. The first step was once more an accident, when Röntgen (or rather one of his assistants) noticed that a bunch of keys, laid down by chance on top of an unopened box of photographic plates near a cathode tube, had produced an inexplicable shadow-image of itself on one of the plates. The cathode tube was apparently giving off some hitherto unknown type of radiation, capable of penetrating opaque substances. Röntgen was an experimentalist, not a theorist; his pupils used to say privately that in publishing this discovery of X-rays he attempted a theoretical explanation for the first and only time in his life — and got it wrong!

However, this accidental discovery had far-reaching consequences. It drew attention to the fluorescence of minerals placed in the cathode tube; this inspired Becquerel to inquire whether naturally fluorescent substances gave off anything like X-rays, and eventually — yet again by accident — he came upon certain uranium compounds. These were found to give off a radiation similar to X-rays, and to give it off naturally and all the time. Soon afterwards the Curies succeeded in isolating the element, radium, an element which was found to be undergoing a continuous natural disintegration. The way was now clear for that long series of experiments on atomic disintegration which led finally to the splitting of the nucleus and the construction of the atomic bomb.

* * * * *

A typical modern paradox emerges from these results. By restricting his cognitive powers to a field of experience in which the concept of force as an objective reality was unthinkable, man has been led on a line of practical investigation the pursuit of which was bound to land him amongst the force-activities of the cosmos. For what distinguishes electric and sub-electric activities from all other forces of physical nature so far known to science, is that for their operation they have no need of the resistance offered by space-bound material bodies; they represent a world of pure dynamics into which spatial limitations do not enter.

Equally paradoxical is the situation of theoretical thinking in face of that realm of natural being which practical research has lately entered. We have seen that this thinking, by virtue of the consciousness on which it is founded, is impelled always to clothe its ideas in spatial form. Wherever anything in the pure spatial adjacency of physical things remains inexplicable, resort is had to hypothetical pictures whose content consists once more of nothing but spatially extended and spatially adjacent items. In this way matter came to be seen as consisting of molecules, molecules of atoms, and atoms of electrons, protons, neutrons, and so forth.

Where we have arrived along this path is brought out in a passage in Eddington's *The Nature of the Physical World*. There, after describing the modern picture of electrons dancing round the atomic nucleus, he says: 'This spectacle is so fascinating that we have perhaps forgotten that there was a time when we wanted to be told what an electron is. This question was never answered. No familiar conceptions can be woven round the electron; it belongs to the waiting list.' The only thing we can say about the electron, if we are not to deceive ourselves, Eddington concludes, is: *'Something unknown is doing we don't know what'*.

This situation has become still more acute through the potent consequences which the practical application of electrons and of other minute parts of the atom has brought about. For not only does nearly every new discovery call in question the views prompted by its predecessor, but there is the upsetting fact that in this realm all happenings appear to follow the principle of Indeterminacy which we mentioned in the last chapter in connection with the views of Hooke and Hume. For in the innermost core of matter and therefore, as is believed, at the very bottom of nature, no determinate processes are to be found, but only such as can be computed as occurring with this or that degree of probability. In this connection there has arisen what is perhaps the greatest and saddest paradox characteristic of this field of research. It is the fate of Albert Einstein.

Once, when Einstein was asked whether he believed in God, his answer was that he believed 'in Spinoza's God, who reveals Himself in the harmonies of all existence, but not in a God who concerns Himself with the destinies and actions of human beings'. His whole work of research was thus guided by his conviction that the universe obeys absolute laws in the sense of a 'pre-established harmony' (Leibniz) which can be expressed in mathematical language. Along this way of thinking he was led to conceive mass as condensed energy and to indicate the amount of energy represented by a certain quantity of mass. When nuclear fission became possible, Einstein's conclusions proved right. Moreover, these very conclusions had been, right from the start, instrumental in establishing the belief that such an interference with matter was possible. Yet the phenomena found along this line of research were of a character which, as already said, seem to confirm Indeterminacy. This, however, stands in flat contradiction to Einstein's own basic view concerning the nature of the universe. As a confession to this unshakable view of his, he cried to the atomic physicists at the end of his life: 'I cannot believe that God plays dice with the world!' We shall come back to this after having dealt with Goethe's theory of Metamorphosis.

* * * * *

Ever since more has become known of the vicissitudes suffered by some of the scientists whose labours in the field of nuclear physics have conjured up the present precarious situation in the world, modern man has been led unawares to a conception of the tragic in life which was almost lost in the era of prevailing intellectualism, the word 'tragedy' having come to be used mostly as a synonym for 'sad event', 'calamity', 'serious event', even 'crime' (*The Oxford English Dictionary*). In its original meaning, however, springing from the dramatic poetry of ancient Greece, the word combines the concept of calamity with that of inevitable action by the hero. If anything can be called tragic in our day in the true sense of the word, then certainly it is the lives and labours of these men, whether they be Albert Einstein, Robert Oppenheimer, or any of the others in the same boat. Accordingly, the term 'tragic' occurs more and more often in the relevant literature.

This reappearance of the original conception of tragedy, however, requires from modern man an attitude towards the tragic in life different from the one that was adequate for man in ancient Greece. At that time the author of a tragic action was not held to be personally responsible for it, since he was caught in a nexus of circumstances which had neither been created nor could be changed by him (Orestes, Oedipus, etc). Today, when man finds himself in a state of self-awakened consciousness, his meeting with tragedy is a challenge to him to investigate its cause in order to become master of it. For him, therefore, the question arises as to the actual source of the tragic in human life.

There is an utterance, remarkably often heard in our day, that 'man's moral development has not kept pace with his intellectual development'. How, it is asked, can man's emotional catch up with his intellectual advance? Yet one seldom finds

attention paid to the other problem which, correspondingly
worded, reads: 'Man's cognitional development has not kept
pace with his scientific discoveries.' Nevertheless, this fact really
accounts for our present trouble. It was a matter of course that
during the centuries of European development, until the beginning of the age of natural science, the first of the two problems
held foremost place in man's mind. For the other problem has
become acute only with the setting in of the modern age. In the
preceding period man's soul in its religious striving was directed
to the account in the Bible which tells of the original deviation
of human nature from its God-planned condition — i.e. the event
known as the 'Fall'. What appears in man as the weakness of his
will and the disorder of his emotional nature was ascribed to this
primeval event. But it seems forgotten in present-day religious
life that man's original 'sin' consisted in his succumbing to a power
which helped him to an illumination of his consciousness which,
in relation to the divine plan, was premature. In the pictorial
language of the Bible this is described as the eating from the
Tree of *Knowledge*. Medieval thought, correctly characterising
this power, gave it the name of LUCIFER (Light-bearer). As a
result of this happening, the Bible tells us, man became mortal.
The same is said in modern language, as a result of pure scientific
observation, by stating that man's thinking and perceiving activity
is based on processes of disintegration in his body (Chapter II).
According to the Bible, man lost his primordial state of life — he
was expelled from Paradise — in order that he should not eat of
the Tree of Life. Today we note: man's consciousness, bound up
with his dying nerve system, is incapable of penetrating to the
region of his corporeal life where his will is rooted.

The development of man's intellectual faculty took place
with no particular effort of his own, because it had been set going
by a power working into him from without, a power whose aim
it was to deflect his mind from the relative immaturity of the
other parts of his being. Today, we experience this fact in outer
civilisation as a determining factor of mankind's destiny.

As already said, this is only one side of the problem. If we express this side by briefly saying: 'Man's Knowing has outrun his Doing', then the other side would have to be expressed by saying: 'Man's Doing has outrun his Knowing' (Knowing, in the sense of his cognitional faculty). Certainly, both these problems are inter-connected, but the second has nevertheless an origin of its own in the history of the human race. Of this, too, the literary documents of old, including the Bible, bear witness. Before quoting some of them we will turn to one of a more recent time, because it will help us to appreciate the other ones.

This is the place to deal with the passage in Goethe's poetical work of which we said in our first chapter that Goethe had there fulfilled Heisenberg's demand that he should have stated that the whole of Newtonian physics was 'from the devil'. This utterance occurs in the second part of *Faust*, in the first scene of the fourth act. This act is that part of the entire drama which Goethe wrote last of all, in the last year of his life, after having previously decided not to write it at all, but to leave here a gap in the whole work. What he expresses through it shows such a prophetic gaze into our own time that one can understand it required a special decision for him to confide such things to the poem. Moreover, they could no longer be clothed in classical imagery, as are the happenings of the preceding act. Now he had to turn to much older revelations.

In its major part this act shows Faust entering – with the help of Mephistopheles – into the high-level political life of his day. It is in a sense the climax of the service rendered to him by Mephistopheles during the various stages of his life. Faust helps the Emperor to defeat his enemies by employing quasi-magical powers which Mephisto supplies: the three Mighty Men, giant-like beings with super-human powers. Mephistopheles also assists directly by creating certain bewildering hallucinations in the enemy's ranks. These happenings, however, are preceded by something which seems to stand in no relation to what follows, but in reality it does so most intimately. The act opens with Faust and Mephistopheles meeting among high mountains and with a controversy between the two about the origin of the

mountain ranges of the earth. In this dispute Faust represents
Goethe's own view, Mephisto the customary one, though he puts
it into his own language. Both these views will occupy us in a
later part of this book. At present we are interested in the words
Faust uses when ending their conversation:

> *Es ist doch auch bemerkenswert zu achten,*
> *Zu sehn, wie Teufel die Natur betrachten.*

> There is indeed remarkable attraction
> In seeing a devil's view of Nature's action.

This scene is followed immediately by the aforementioned
political events.

Obviously, throughout this act Goethe wants to express
nothing less than this: the very spirit that teaches man to regard
nature in the manner of matter-bound science is capable of putting
into man's hands super-human forces of a quasi-magical nature
which will enable him to wage war efficiently. At the same time,
Goethe makes it clear that these forces are not health-bearing
ones, even when used for peaceful purposes. As the last act of the
drama shows (in the tragedy of Philemon and Baucis), he who
attempts to engage in constructive social work with the help of
such forces is bound to cause social misery, and so does not
actually help to diminish the total sum of human distress. This
fate, in the end, falls on Faust himself. For while he delights in
observing his work of social upbuilding, one of four grey women
appears by his side. She, being W O R R Y — the other three are
W A N T, G U I L T, and D I S T R E S S — is the only one who has access
to this outwardly wealthy and powerful man. With the words:

> *Die Menschen sind im ganzen Leben blind;*
> *Nun, Fauste, werde dus am Ende!*

> Throughout their lives are mortals blind;
> Thou, Faustus, shalt become it at life's ending!

she breathes on him and he becomes blind.

There are three places in the dialogue between Faust and Mephisto on the origin of the mountains where the text has marginal notes pointing to certain parts in the Bible. One, facing the passage where Mephisto stirs up in Faust the lust for political power, refers to Christ's temptation in the desert (Matthew, iv). Another, facing Mephistopheles' geological explanations, refers to the passage in one of the epistles of St. Paul (Eph., vi, 12) where Paul says:

> We have not to battle with flesh and blood,

but:

> with the Very-Beginners (Archai)
> with the Manifesters (Exusiai)
> with the Cosmic Regents in the Darkness
>   of this World
> with the spirit-actions of the heaven-indwelling
>   powers of Evil.[4]

The power of evil to which Paul points here is one that manifests in the first place through natural forces and by this means interferes with man's soul. It is a power representative of Darkness, as Lucifer is of Light. In the ancient Persian mythology it bore the name of A H R I M A N; the Bible calls it S A T A N. Goethe's marginal note shows that he reckons Mephistopheles and spirits of his kind as belonging to this category of cosmic powers. In precisely this sense, Mephistopheles introduces himself when he first appears before Faust (in the first part of the drama) by calling himself 'part of the Darkness which brought forth the Light — the Light which now disputes her ancient rank with Mother Night'. It is in the sense of these powers that Goethe makes Mephisto explain the origin of the mountains. It is from their realm that the forces arise with whose help Faust sways political events.

The scene in which the 'three Mighty Ones' first appear bears as a marginal note, 'II, Samuel xxiii, 8'. There, indeed, we learn of three 'mighty men' whom David employs in battle against the Philistines. That the Philistines, too, kept such giant beings in their service is known from the story of David's fight with Goliath, which apparently means that weak human forces, if skilfully used, get the better of such a gigantic power. If we ask about the origin of such Mighty Ones, we are led again to the beginning of the Bible, where the sixth chapter of Genesis says (in as literal translation as possible): 'The Giants (Mighty Ones) were on earth in those days when the sons of the Gods came unto the daughters of men, and they bare the Heroes to them that in grey times were "Men of Name" (Fame).' The deeds of the generation thus engendered led to the natural catastrophe known to all mythologies of mankind as the 'Great Flood'.

At this place the Bible speaks of yet another 'Fall', which, however, differs significantly from the one reported previously. Firstly, it is a fall of beings of a rank higher than man down to man's estate. Secondly, the two sexes play an opposite role. The following instance from the literature of our own day may show that possibilities of this kind, though they seem to be far removed from customary scientific thought, require to be heeded. Not long ago a book appeared in Germany under the title *Ex Ovo*, in which the author, Peter Bamm, deals with the fact that through the development of modern science man has become able to exert influence on the human soul by means of chemical substances without really knowing what he is doing. For he knows neither what *substance* nor what *soul* really is. He therefore acts in double blindness. In trying to answer the question of how it was possible for man to get into this situation, Bamm conceives a 'second Fall' at the beginning of the age of natural science; it resembles the Biblical Fall in one sense and contrasts it in another. Both, says Bamm, are the result of human 'curiosity', the first of the 'curiosity of the woman', the second of the 'curiosity of the man', meaning by the latter that intellectual curiosity as the driving power of scientific research which he rightly regards as the male part of man's soul in contrast to the female emotional part. The consistency with which Goethe created his *Faust* is shown by the fact that he causes the Mephistophelian power to exert its influence

on the man and the woman to become the victim of it, in contra-
distinction to Lucifer's way of proceeding in Paradise.

We have embarked upon these observations with a view to
finding the source of that sense of the 'tragic' which has re-entered
present-day civilisation as a result of science and its technical
applications. We spoke of the concept 'tragic' as applying originally
to the situation of a human being who through his actions creates
suffering out of circumstances which he has neither created nor
is able to avoid. This is precisely the character of the event described in the sixth chapter of Genesis. A new attitude towards
the tragic, however, emerges with St. Paul. He wants to direct
people's minds towards a battle with the Powers of Darkness
which man is to go through willingly in a future time, best translated as 'the onerous day'. With this aim in view he gives, in the
pictorial language of his day, various pieces of advice which we
need not consider here. For the word that matches our own time
was spoken by Goethe in the passage where he anticipates our
essential problem. By breathing on Faust, 'Worry' puts him into
a condition in which, as she says, other men dwell all their lives.
Hence they are not aware of it, whereas Faust is meant to become
conscious of it. Under the impact of this experience he makes
the turn-about that is essential for Faustian man in our time,
accompanying it with the words that are essential for our whole
age:

> *Die Nacht scheint tiefer tief hereinzudringen,*
> *Allein im Innern leuchtet helles Licht.*

> Night presses round me deep and deeper still,
> And yet within me beams a radiant light.

It will be the purpose of the further pages of this book to
show how in the present age of spirit-blindness one can, in the
field of science, attain to seeing with the inner light.

PART TWO

GOETHEANISM – WHENCE AND WHITHER?

Chapter V

THE ADVENTURE OF REASON

In 1790, a year before Galvani's monograph, *Concerning the Forces of Electricity*, appeared, Goethe published his *Metamorphosis of Plants*, which represents the first step towards the practical overcoming of the limitations of the onlooker-consciousness in science. Goethe's paper was not destined to raise such a storm as soon followed Galvani's publication. And yet the fruit of Goethe's endeavours is no less significant than Galvani's discovery, for the progress of mankind. For in Goethe's achievement lay the seed of that form of knowing which man requires, if in the age of the electrification of civilisation he is to remain master of his existence.

* * * * *

Among the essays in which Goethe in later years gave out some of the results of his scientific observation in axiomatic form, is one called 'Intuitive Judgment' (*'Anschauende Urteilskraft'*), in which he maintains that he has achieved in practice what Kant had declared to be forever beyond the scope of the human mind. Goethe refers to a passage in the *Critique of Judgment*, where Kant defines the limits of human cognitional powers as he had observed them in his study of the peculiar nature of the human reason. We must first go briefly into Kant's own exposition of the matter.[1]

Kant distinguishes between two possible forms of reason, the *intellectus archetypus* and the *intellectus ectypus*. By the first he means a reason 'which being, not like ours, discursive, but intuitive, proceeds from the synthetic universal (the intuition of the whole as such) to the particular, that is, from the whole to the parts'.

According to Kant, such a reason lies outside human possibilities. In contrast to it, the *intellectus ectypus* peculiar to man is restricted to taking in through the senses the single details of the world as such; with these it can certainly construct pictures of their totalities, but these pictures never have more than a hypothetical character and can claim no reality for themselves. Above all, it is not given to such a thinking to think 'wholes' in such a way that through an act of thought alone the single items contained in them can be conceived as parts springing from them by necessity. (To illustrate this, we may say that, according to Kant, we can certainly comprehend the parts of an organism, say of a plant, and out of its components make a picture of the plant as a whole; but we are not in a position to think that 'whole' of the plant which conditions the existence of its organism and brings forth its parts by necessity.) Kant expresses this in the following way:

'For external objects as phenomena an adequate ground related to purposes cannot be met with; this, although it lies in nature, must be sought only in the supersensible substrata of nature, from all possible insight into which we are cut off. Our understanding has then this peculiarity as concerns the judgment, that in cognitive understanding the particular is not determined by the universal and cannot therefore be derived from it.'

The attempt to prove whether or not another form of reason than this (the *intellectus archetypus*) is possible — even though declared to be beyond man — Kant regarded as superfluous, because the fact was enough for him 'that we are led to the Idea of it — which contains no contradiction — in contrast to our discursive understanding, which has need of images (*intellectus ectypus*), and to the contingency of its constitution.'

Kant here brings forward two reasons why it is permissible to conceive of the existence of an extra-human, archetypal reason. On the one hand he admits that the existence of our own reason in its present condition is of a contingent order, and thus does not exclude the possible existence of a reason differently constituted. On the other hand, he allows that we can think of a form of reason which in every respect is the opposite of our own, without meeting any logical inconsistency.

From these definitions emerges a conception of the properties of man's cognitional powers which agrees exactly with those on which, as we have seen, Hume built up his whole philosophy. Both allow to the reason a knowledge-material consisting only of pictures — that is, of pictures evoked in consciousness through sense-perception, and received by it from the outer world in the form of disconnected units, whilst denying it all powers, as Hume expressed it, ever 'to perceive any real connections between distinct existences'.

This agreement between Kant and Hume must at first sight surprise us, when we recall that, as already mentioned, Kant worked out his philosophy precisely to protect the cognising being of man from the consequences of Hume's thought. For, as he himself said, it was his becoming acquainted with Hume's *Treatise* that 'roused him out of his dogmatic slumber' and obliged him to reflect on the foundations of human knowing. We shall understand this apparent paradox, however, if we take it as a symptom of humanity's close imprisonment in recent centuries within the limits of its onlooker consciousness.

In his struggle against Hume, Kant was not concerned to challenge his opponent's definition of man's reasoning power. His sole object was to show that, if one accepted this definition, one must not go as far as Hume in the application of this power. All that Kant could aspire to do was to protect the ethical from attack by the intellectual part of man, and to do this by proving that the former belongs to a world into which the latter has no access. For with his will man belongs to a world of purposeful doing, whereas the reason, as our quotations have shown, is incapable even in observing external nature, of comprehending the wholes within nature which determine natural ends. Still less can it do this in regard to man, a being who in his actions is integrated into higher purposes.

Kant's deed is significant in that it correctly drew attention to that polar division in human nature which, after all, was already established in Kant's own time. Kant demonstrated also that to win insight into the ethical nature of man with the aid of the isolated intellect alone implied a trespass beyond permissible limits. In order to give the doing part of the human being its necessary anchorage, however, Kant assigned it to a moral world-order entirely external to man, to which it could be properly related only through obedient submission.

In this way Kant became the philosopher of that division between knowledge and faith which to this day is upheld in both the ecclesiastical and scientific spheres of our civilisation. Never-theless, he did not succeed in safeguarding humanity from the consequences of Hume's philosophy; for man cannot live indefin-itely in the belief that with the two parts of his own being he is bound up with two mutually unrelated worlds. The time when this was feasible is already over, as may be seen from the fact that ever greater masses of men wish to determine their behaviour according to their own ideas, and as they see no alternative in the civilisation around them but to form ideas by means of the discur-sive reason which inevitably leads to agnosticism, they determine their actions accordingly. Meanwhile, the ethical life as viewed by Kant accordingly shrinks ever further into a powerless, hole-and-corner existence.

* * * * *

It is Goethe's merit to have first shown that there is a way out of this impasse. He had no need to argue theoretically with Kant as to the justification of denying man any power of under-standing apart from the discursive, and of leaving the faculty of intuitive knowledge to a divinity somewhere outside the world of man. For Goethe was his own witness that Kant was mistaken in regarding man's present condition as his lasting nature. Let us hear how he expresses himself on this fact at the beginning of his essay written as an answer to Kant's statement:

'It is true, the author here seems to be pointing to an intellect not human but divine. And yet, if in the moral sphere we are supposed to lift ourselves up to a higher region through faith in God, Virtue and Immortality, so drawing nearer to the Primal Being, why should it not be likewise in the intellectual? By contemplation (*Anschauen*) of an ever-creative nature, may we not make ourselves worthy to be spiritual sharers in her productions? I at first, led by an inner urge that would not rest, had quite unconsciously been seeking for the realm of Type and Archetype, and my attempt had been rewarded: I had been able to build up a description, in conformity with Nature herself. Now therefore nothing more could hinder me from braving what the Old Man of the King's Hill[2] himself calls the *Adventure of Reason.*'

Goethe started from the conviction that our senses as well as our intellect are gifts of nature, and that, if at any given moment they prove incapable through their collaboration of solving a riddle of nature, we must ask her to help us to develop this collaboration adequately. Thus there was no question for him of any restriction of sense perception in order to bring the latter in line with the existing power of the intellect, but rather to learn to make an ever fuller use of the senses and to bring our intellect into line with what they tell. 'The senses do not deceive, but the judgment deceives', is one of his basic utterances concerning their respective roles in our quest for knowledge and understanding. As to the senses themselves, he was sure that 'the human being is adequately equipped for all true earthly requirements if he trusts his senses, and so develops them as to make them worthy of trust'.

There is no contradiction in the statement that we have to trust our senses, and that we have to develop them to make them trustworthy. For, 'nature speaks upwards to the known senses of man, downwards to unknown senses of his'. Goethe's path was aimed at wakening faculties, both perceptual and conceptual, which lay dormant in himself. His experience showed him that 'every process in nature, rightly observed, wakens in us a new organ of cognition'. Right observation, in this respect, consisted in a form of contemplating nature which he called a 're-creating

(creating in the wake) of an ever-creative nature' (*Nachschaffen einer immer schaffenden Natur*).

* * * * *

We should do Goethe an injustice if we measured the value of his scientific work by the amount of factual knowledge he contributed to one or other sphere of research. Although Goethe did bring many new things to light, as has been duly recognised in the scientific fields concerned, it cannot be gainsaid that other scientists in his own day, working along the usual lines, far exceeded his total of discoveries. Nor can it be denied that, as critics have pointed out, he occasionally went astray in reporting his observations. These things, however, do not determine the value or otherwise of his scientific labours. His work draws its significance not so much from the 'what', to use a Goethean expression, as from the 'how' of his observations, that is, from his way of investigating nature. Having once developed this method in the field of plant observation, Goethe was able, with its aid, to establish a new view of animal nature, to lay the basis for a new meteorology, and, by creating his theory of light and colour, to provide a model for a research in the field of physics, free from onlooker-restrictions.

In the scientific work of Goethe his botanical studies have a special place. As a living organism, the plant is involved in an endless process of becoming. It shares this characteristic, of course, with the higher creatures of nature, and yet between it and them there is an essential difference. Whereas in animal and man a considerable part of the life-processes conceal themselves within the organism, in order to provide a basis for inner soul processes, the plant brings its inner life into direct and total outer manifestation. Hence the plant, better than anything, could become Goethe's first teacher in his exercise of re-creating nature.

It is for the same reason that we shall here use the plant for introducing Goethe's method. The following exposition, however, does not aim at rendering in detail Goethe's own botanical researches, expounded by him in two extensive essays, *Morphology* and *The Metamorphosis of Plants*, as well as in a series of smaller writings. There are several excellent translations of the chief paper, the *Metamorphosis*, from which the English-speaking reader can derive sufficient insight into Goethe's way of expressing his ideas; a pleasure as well as a profit which he should not deny himself.

Our own way of procedure will have to be such that Goethe's method, and its fruitfulness for the general advance of science, come as clearly as possible into view.[3] Botanical details will be referred to only as far as seems necessary for this purpose.

The data for observation, from which in Goethe's own fashion we shall start, have been selected as best for our purpose, quite independently of the data used by Goethe himself. Our choice was determined by the material available when these pages were being written. The reader is free to supplement our studies by his own observation of other plants.

*   *   *   *   *

Figures 1 and 2 show two series of leaves which are so arranged as to represent definite stages in the growth-process of the plant concerned. In each sequence shown the leaves have been taken from a single plant, in which each leaf-form was repeated, perhaps several times, before it passed over into the next stage. The leaves on Fig. 1 come from a Sidalcea (of the mallow family), those on Fig. 2 from a Delphinium. We will describe the forms in sequence, so that we may grasp as clearly as possible the transition from one to another as presented to the eye.

Starting with the right-hand leaf at the bottom of Fig. 1, we let our eye and mind be impressed by its characteristic form, seeking to take hold of the pattern after which it is shaped. Its edge bears numerous incisions of varying depths which, however, do not disturb the roundness of the leaf as a whole. If we re-create in our imagination the 'becoming' of such a leaf, that is, its gradual growth in all directions, we receive an impression of

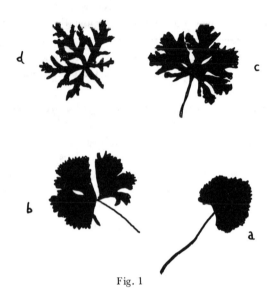

Fig. 1

Fig. 2

these incisions as 'negative' forms, because, at the points where they occur, the multiplication of the cells resulting from the general growth has been retarded. We observe that this holding back follows a certain order.

We now proceed to the next leaf in the same Figure and observe that, whilst the initial plan is faithfully maintained, the ratio between the positive and negative forms has changed. A number of incisions, hardly yet indicated in the first leaf, have become quite conspicuous. The leaf begins to look as if it were breaking up into a number of subdivisions.

In the next leaf we find this process still further advanced. The large incisions have almost reached the centre, while a number of smaller ones at the periphery have also grown deeper into the leaf. The basic plan of the total leaf is still maintained, but the negative forms have so far got the upper hand that the original roundness is no longer obvious.

The last leaf shows the process in its extreme degree. As we glance back and along the whole series of development, we recognise that the form of the last leaf is already indicated in that of the first. It appears as if the form has gradually come to the fore through certain forces which have increasingly prevented the leaf from filling in the whole of its ground-plan with matter. In the last leaf the common plan is still visible in the distribution of the veins, but the fleshy part of the leaf has become restricted to narrow strips along these veins. In this metamorphosis the basic form of the leaf appears step by step. After the achievement of the top leaf, the plant 'leaps into the calyx stage'.

The metamorphosis of the delphinium leaf (Fig. 2) is of a different character. Here the plant begins with a highly elaborate form of the leaf, while in the end nothing remains but the barest indication of it. The impression received from this series of leaves is that of a gradual withdrawal of the magnificent form, revealed in its fullness only in the first leaf. This kind of metamorphosis Goethe described as 'softly stealing into the calyx stage'.

A more intense impression of what these metamorphoses actually mean is achieved by altering our mode of contemplation in the following way. After repeated and careful observation of the different forms on either of the plates, we build up inwardly, as a memory picture, the shape of the first leaf, and then transform this mental image successively into the images of the ensuing forms until we reach the final stage. The same process can also be tried retrogressively, and so repeated forward and backward.

This is how Goethe studied the *doing* of the plant, and it is by this method that he discovered the spiritual principle of all plant life, and succeeded also in throwing a first light on the inner life-principle of animals.

* * * * *

We chose the transformation of leaf forms into one another as the starting-point of our observations, because the principle of metamorphosis appears here in a most conspicuous manner. This principle, however, is not confined to this part of the plant's organism. In fact, all the different organs which the plant produces within its life cycle — foliage, calyx, corolla, organs of fertilisation, fruit and seed — are metamorphoses of one and the same organ.

Man has long learnt to make use of this law of metamorphosis in the plant for what is called *doubling* the flower of a certain species. Such a flower crowds many additional petals within its original circle, and these petals are nothing but metamorphosed stamens; this, for instance, is the difference between the wild and the cultivated rose. The multitude of petals in the latter is obtained by the transformation of a number of the former's innumerable stamens. (Note the intermediate stages between the two, often found inside the flower of such plants.)

This falling back from the stage of an organ of fertilisation to that of a petal shows that the plant is capable of *regressive metamorphosis*, and we may conclude from this that in the normal sequence the different organs are transformed from one another by way of *progressive metamorphosis*. It is evident that the regressive type occurs only as an abnormality, or as a result of artificial cultivation. Plants once brought into this condition frequently show a general state of unrest, so that other organs also are inclined to fall back to a lower level. Thus we may come across a rose, an outer petal of which appears in the form of a leaf of the calyx (sepal), or one of the sepals is found to have grown into an ordinary rose leaf.

We now extend our mental exercise to the plant's whole organism. By a similar mental effort as applied to the leaf-formations we strive to build up a complete plant. We start with the seed, from which we first imagine the cotyledons unfolding, letting this be followed by the gradual development of the entire green part of the plant, its stem and leaves, until the final leaves change into the sepals of the calyx. These again we turn into the petals of the flower, until via pistil and stamens the fruit and seed are formed.

By pursuing in this way the living doing of the plant from stage to stage we become aware of a significant rhythm in its total life cycle. This, when first discovered by Goethe, gave him the key to an understanding of nature's general procedure in building living organisms, and in maintaining life in them.

The plant clearly divides into three major parts: firstly, the one that extends from the cotyledons to the calyx, the green part of the plant, that is, where the life principle is most active; secondly, the one comprising the flower itself with the organs of fertilisation, where the vitality of the plant gives way to other principles; and lastly, the fruit and seed, which are destined to be discharged from the mother organism. Each of these three contains two kinds of organs: first, organs with the tendency to grow into width — leaf, flower and fruit; second, organs which are outwardly smaller and simpler, but have the function of preparing the decisive leaps in the plant's development: these are the calyx, the stamens, etc, and the seed.

In this succession, Goethe recognised a certain rhythm of expansion and contraction, and he found that the plant passes through it three times during any one cycle of its life. In the foliage the plant expands, in the calyx it contracts; it expands again in the flower and contracts in the pistil and stamens; finally, it expands in the fruit and contracts in the seed.

The deeper meaning of this threefold rhythm will become clear when we consider it against the background of what we observed in the metamorphosis of the leaf. Take the mallow leaf; its metamorphosis shows a step-wise progression from coarser to finer forms, whereby the characteristic plan of the leaf comes more and more into view, so that in the topmost leaf it reaches a certain stage of perfection. Now we observe that in the calyx this stage is not improved on, but that the plant reverts to a much simpler formation.

Whilst in the case of the mallow the withdrawal from the stage of the leaf into that of the calyx occurs with a sudden leap, we observe that the delphinium performs this process by degrees. Whilst the mallow reaches the highly elaborate form of the leaf only in the final stage, the delphinium leaps forth at the outset, as it were, with the fully accomplished leaf, and then protracts its withdrawal into the calyx over a number of steps, so that this process can be watched with our very eyes. In this type of meta-morphosis the last leaf beneath the calyx shows a form that differs little from that of a calyx itself, with its simple sepals. Only in its general geometrical arrangement does it still remind us of the original pattern.

In a case like this, the stem-leaves, to use Goethe's expression, 'softly steal into the calyx stage'.[4] In the topmost leaf the plant has already achieved something which, along the other line of metamorphosis, is tackled only after the leaf plan itself has been gradually executed. In this case the calyx stage, we may say, is attained at one leap.

Whatever type of metamorphosis is followed by a plant (and there are others as well, so that we may even speak of meta-morphoses between different types of metamorphosis!) they all obey the same basic rule, namely, that before proceeding to the next higher stage of the cycle, the plant sacrifices something already achieved in a preceding one. Behind the inconspicuous sheath of the calyx we see the plant preparing itself for a new creation of an entirely different order. As successor to the leaf, the flower appears to us time and again as a miracle. Nothing in the lower realm of the plant predicts the form, colour, scent and all the other properties of the new organ produced at this stage. The completed leaf, preceding the plant's withdrawal into the calyx, represents a triumph of structure over matter. Now, in the flower, matter is overcome to a still higher degree. It is as if the material substance here becomes transparent, so that what is immaterial in the plant may shine through its outer surface.

* * * * *

In this 'climbing up the spiritual ladder' Goethe learned to recognise one of nature's basic principles. He termed it *Steigerung* (heightening). Thus he saw the plant develop through Meta-morphosis and Heightening towards its consummation. Implicit in the second of these two principles, however, there is yet another natural principle for which Goethe did not coin a specific term, although he shows through other utterances that he was well aware of it, and of its universal significance for all life. We propose to call it here the principle of Renunciation.

In the life of the plant this principle shows itself most con-spicuously where the green leaf is heightened into the flower. While progressing from leaf to flower the plant undergoes a decisive ebb in its vitality. Compared with the leaf, the flower is a dying organ. This dying, however, is of a kind we may aptly call a 'dying into being'. Life in its mere vegetative form is here seen withdrawing in order that a higher manifestation of the spirit may take place. The same principle can be seen at work in the insect kingdom, when the caterpillar's tremendous vitality passes over into the short-lived beauty of the butterfly. In the human being it is responsible for that metamorphosis of organic processes which occurs on the path from the metabolic to the nervous system, and which we came to recognise as the precondition for the appearance of consciousness within the organism.

What powerful forces must be at work in the plant organism

at this point of transition from its green to its coloured parts! They enforce a complete halt upon the juices that rise up right into the calyx, so that these bring nothing of their life-bearing activity into the formation of the flower, but undergo a complete transmutation, not gradually, but with a sudden leap.

After achieving its masterpiece in the flower, the plant once more goes through a process of withdrawal, this time into the tiny organs of fertilisation. (We shall return later to this essential stage in the life cycle of the plant, and shall then clear up the misinterpretation put upon it ever since scientific biology began.) After fertilisation, the fruit begins to swell; once more the plant produces an organ with a more or less conspicuous spatial extension. This is followed by a final and extreme contraction in the forming of the seed inside the fruit. In the seed the plant gives up all outer appearance to such a degree that nothing seems to remain but a small, insignificant speck of organised matter. Yet this tiny, inconspicuous thing bears in it the power of bringing forth a whole new plant.

*   *   *   *   *

In these three successive rhythms of expansion and contraction the plant reveals to us the basic rule of its existence. During each expansion, the active principle of the plant presses forth into visible *appearance*; during each contraction it withdraws from outer embodiment into what we may describe as a more or less pure state of *being*. We thus find the spiritual principle of the plant engaged in a kind of breathing rhythm, now appearing, now disappearing, now assuming power over matter, now withdrawing from it again.

In the fully developed plant this rhythm repeats itself three times in succession and at ever higher levels, so that the plant, in climbing from stage to stage, each time goes through a process of withdrawal before appearing at the next. The greater the creative power required at a certain stage, the more nearly complete must be the withdrawal from outer appearance. This is why the most extreme withdrawal of the plant into the state of being takes place in the seed, when the other plant prepares itself for its transition from one generation to another. Even earlier, the flower stands towards the leaves as something like a new generation springing from the small organ of the calyx , as does the fruit to the flower when it arises from the tiny organs of reproduction. In the end, however, nothing appears outwardly so unlike the actual plant as the little seed which, at the expense of all appearance, has the power to renew the whole cycle.

Through studying the plant in this way Goethe grew aware also of the significance of the nodes and eyes which the plant develops as points where its vital energy is specially concentrated; not only the seed, but the eye also, is capable of producing a new, complete plant. In each of these eyes, formed in the axils of the leaves, the power of the plant is present in its entirety, very much as in each single seed.

In other ways, too, the plant shows its capacity to act as a whole at various places of its organism. Otherwise, no plant could be propagated by cuttings; in any little twig cut from a parent plant, all the manifold forces operative in the gathering, transmuting, forming of matter, that are necessary for the production of root, leaf, flower, fruit, etc., are potentially present, ready to leap into action provided we give it suitable outer conditions. Other plants, such as gloxinia and begonia, are known to have the power of bringing forth a new, complete plant from each of their leaves. From a small cut applied to a vein in a leaf, which is then embedded in earth, a root will soon be seen springing downward, and a stalk with leaves rising upward.

A particular observation made by Goethe in this respect is of interest for methodological reasons. In the introduction to his treatise *Metamorphosis of Plants*, when referring to the regressive metamorphosis of stamens into petals as an example of an *irregular* metamorphosis, he remarks that 'experiences of this kind of metamorphosis will enable us to disclose what is hidden from us in the regular way of development, and to see clearly and visibly what we should otherwise only be able to infer'. In this remark Goethe expresses a truth that is valid in many spheres of life, both human and natural. It is frequently a pathological aberration in an organic entity that allows us to see in physical appearance things that do not come outwardly to the fore in the more balanced condition of normal development, although they are equally part of the regular organic process.

An enlightening experience of this kind came to Goethe's aid when one day he happened to see a 'proliferated' rose (*durchgewachsene Rose*), that is, a rose from whose centre a whole new plant had sprung. Instead of the contracted seed pod, with the attached, equally contracted, organs of fertilisation, there appeared a continuation of the stalk, half red and half green, bearing in succession a number of small reddish petals with traces of anthers. Thorns could be seen appearing further up, petals half-turned into leaves, and even a number of fresh nodes from which little imperfect flowers were budding. The whole phenomenon, in all its irregularity, was one more proof for Goethe that the plant in its totality is potentially present at each point of its organism.[5]

* * * * *

Goethe's observation of the single plant *in statu agendi* had trained him to recognise things of quite different outer appearance as identical in their inner nature. Leaf, sepal, petal, etc., much as they differ outwardly, yet showed themselves to him as manifestations of one and the same spiritual archetype. His idea of Metamorphosis enabled him to reduce what in outer appearance seems incompatibly different to its common formative principle. His next step was to observe the different appearances of one and the same species in different regions of the earth, and thus to watch the capacity of the species to respond in a completely flexible way to the various climatic conditions, yet without concealing its inner identity in the varying outer forms. His travels in Switzerland and Italy gave him opportunity for such observations, and in the Alpine regions especially he was delighted at the variations in the species which he already knew so well from his home in Weimar. He saw their proportions, the distances between the single parts, the degree of lignification, the intensity of colour, etc., varying with the varied conditions, yet never concealing the identity of the species.

Having once advanced in his investigations from metamorphosis in the parts of the single plant to metamorphosis among different representatives of single plant species, Goethe had to take only one further, yet decisive, step in order to recognise how *every* member of the plant kingdom is the manifestation of a single formative principle common to them all. He was thus faced with the momentous task of preparing his spirit to think an idea from which the plant world in its entire variety could be derived.

Goethe did not take such a step easily, for it was one of his scientific principles never to think out an idea prematurely. He was well aware that he who aspires to recognise and to express in idea the spirit which reveals itself through the phenomena of the sense-world must develop the art of waiting — of waiting, however, in a way intensely active, whereby one looks again and yet again, until what one looks at begins to speak and the day at last dawns when, through tireless 're-creation of an ever-creating nature', one has grown ripe to express her secrets openly. Goethe was a master in this art of active waiting.

* * * * *

It was in the very year of Galvani's chance discovery, which opened the way to the overwhelming invasion of mankind by the purely physical forces of nature, that Goethe came clearly to see that he had achieved the goal of his labours. We can form some picture of the decisive act in the drama of his seeking and finding from letters written during the years 1785-7.

In the spring of 1785 he writes to a friend in a way that shows him fully aware of his new method of studying nature, which he recognised was a *reading* of her phenomena: 'I can't tell you how the Book of Nature is becoming readable to me. My long practice in spelling has helped me; it now suddenly

works, and my quiet joy is inexpressible.' Again in the summer of
the following year: 'It is a growing aware of the Form with which
again and again nature plays, and, in playing, brings forth manifold
life.'

Then Goethe went on his famous journey to Italy which was to
bear significant fruit for his inner life, both in art and in science.
At Michaelmas, 1786, he reports from his visit to the botanical
garden in Padua that 'the thought becomes more and more living
that it may be possible out of one form to develop all plant
forms'. At this moment Goethe felt so near to the basic conception
of the plant for which he was seeking, that he already christened
it with a special name. The term he coined for it is *Urpflanze*,
literally rendered *archetypal plant*, or *ur-plant*, as we propose
quite simply to call it.[6]

It was the rich tropical and sub-tropical vegetation in the
botanical gardens in Palermo that helped Goethe to his decisive
observations. The peculiar nature of the warmer regions of the
earth enables the spirit to reveal itself more intensively than is
possible in the temperate zone. Thus in tropical vegetation many
things come before the eye which otherwise remain undisclosed,
and then can be detected only through an effort of active thought.
From this point of view, tropical vegetation is 'abnormal' in the
same sense as was the proliferated rose which confirmed for
Goethe's physical perception that inner law of plant-growth which
had already become clear to his mind.

During his sojourn in Palermo in the spring of 1787 Goethe
writes in his notebook: 'There must be one (ur-plant): how
otherwise could we recognise this or that formation to be a
plant unless they were all formed after one pattern?' Soon after
this, he writes in a letter to the poet Herder, one of his friends in
Weimar:

'Further, I must confide to you that I am quite close to the
secret of plant creation, and that it is the simplest thing imaginable.
The ur-plant will be the strangest creature in the world, for which
nature herself should envy me. With this model and the key to
it one will be able to invent plants *ad infinitum*; they would be

consistent; that is to say, though non-existing, they would be capable of existing, being no shades or semblances of the painter or poet, but possessing truth and necessity. The same law will be capable of extension to all living things.'

* * * * *

To become more familiar with the conception of the ur-plant, let us bring the life cycle of the plant before our inner eye once again. There, all the different organs of the plant — leaf, blossom, fruit, etc. — appears as the metamorphic revelations of the one, identical active principle, a principle which gradually manifests itself to us by way of successive heightening from the cotyledons to the perfected glory of the flower. Amongst all the forms which thus appear in turn, that of the leaf has a special place; for the leaf is that organ of the plant in which the ground-plan of all plant existence comes most immediately to expression. Not only do all the different leaf forms arise, through endless changing, out of each other, but the leaf, in accordance with the same principle, also changes itself into all the other organs which the plant produces in the course of its growth.

It is by precisely the same principle that the ur-plant reveals itself in the plant kingdom as a whole. Just as in the single plant organism the different parts are a graduated revelation of the ur-plant, so are the single kinds and species within the total plant world. As we let our glance range over all its ranks and stages (from the single-celled, almost formless alga to the rose and beyond to the tree), we are following, step by step, the revelation of the ur-plant. Barely hinting at itself in the lowest vegetable species, it comes in the next higher stages into ever clearer view, finally streaming forth in full glory in the magnificence of the manifold blossoming plants. Then, as its highest creation, it brings forth the tree, which, itself a veritable minature earth, becomes the basis for innumerable single plant growths.

It has struck biologists of Goethe's own and later times that contrary to their method he did not build up his study of the plant by starting with its lowest form, and so the reproach has been levelled against him of having unduly neglected the latter. Because of this, the views he had come to were regarded as scientifically unfounded. Goethe's notebooks prove that there is no justification for such a reproach. He was in actual fact deeply interested in the lower plants, but he realised that they could not contribute anything fundamental to the spiritual image of the plant as such which he was seeking to attain. To *understand* the plant he found himself obliged to pay special attention to examples in which it came to its most perfect expression. For what was hidden in the *alga* was made manifest in the *rose*. To demand of Goethe that in accordance with ordinary science he should have explained nature 'from below upwards' is to misunderstand the methodological basis of all his investigations.

Seen with Goethe's eyes, the plant kingdom as a whole appears to be a single mighty plant. In it the ur-plant, while pressing into *appearance*, is seen to observe the very rule which we have found governing its action in the single plant — that of repeated expansion and contraction.[7] Taking the tree in the sense already indicated, as the state of highest expansion along the ur-plant's way of entering into spatial manifestation, we note that tree-formation occurs successively at four different levels — as fern-tree (also the extinct tree-form of the horsetail) at the stage of the cryptogams, as coniferous tree at the stage of the gymnosperms, as palm tree at the stage of the monocotyledons, and lastly in the form of the manifold species of the leaf-trees at the highest level of the plant kingdom, the dicotyledons. All these tree-formations have come successively into existence, as geological research has shown; the ur-plant achieved these various tree-formations successively, thus giving up again its state of expansion each time after having reached it at a particular level, in order to renew its creative play at the next higher one.

From the concept of the ur-plant Goethe soon learned to develop another concept which was to express the spiritual principle working in a particular plant species, just as the ur-plant was the spiritual principle covering the plant kingdom as a whole. He called it the *type*. In the manifold types which are thus seen active in the plant world we meet offspring, as it were, of the mother, the 'ur-plant', which in them assumes differentiated modes of action.

* * * * *

Our observations have reached a point where we may consider that stage in the life cycle of the single plant where, by means of the process of pollination, the seed acquires the capacity to produce out of itself a new example of the species. Our discussion of this will bring home the fundamental difference in idea that arises when, instead of judging a process from the standpoint of the mere onlooker, we try to comprehend it through re-creating it inwardly.

Biological science of our day takes it for granted that the process uniting pollen with seed in the plant is an act of fertilisation analogous to that which occurs among the higher organisms of nature. Now it is not to be gainsaid that to external observation this comparison seems obvious, and that it is therefore only natural to speak of the pollen as the male, and of the ovule as the female, element, and of their union as entirely parallel to that between the sexes in the higher kingdoms of nature.

Goethe confesses that at first he himself 'had credulously put up with the ruling dogma of sexuality'. He was first made aware of the invalidity of this analogy by Professor Schelver who, as Superintendent of the Jena Botanical Institute, was working under Goethe's direction and had trained himself in Goethe's method of observing plants. This man had come to see that if one held strictly to the Goethean practice of using nothing for the explanation of the plant but what one could read from the plant itself, one must not ascribe to it any sexual process. He was convinced that for a Goethean kind of biology it must be possible to find, even for the process of pollination, an idea derived from nothing but the two principles of plant life: growth and formation.

Goethe immediately recognised the rightness of this thought,

and set about the task of relating the pollination process to the
picture of the plant which his investigations had already yielded.
His way of reporting the result shows how fully conscious he was
of its revolutionary nature. Nor was he in any doubt as to the kind
of reception it would be given by official biology.

In observing the growth of the plant, Goethe had perceived
that this proceeds simultaneously according to two different
principles. On the one hand the plant grows in an axial direction
and thereby produces its main and side stems. To this growth
principle Goethe gave the name 'vertical tendency'. Were the
plant to follow this principle only, its lateral shoots would all
stand vertically one above the other. But observation shows that
the different plant species obey very different laws in this respect,
as may be seen if one links up all the leaf buds along any plant
stem; they form a line which winds spiral fashion around it.
Each plant family is distinguishable by its own characteristic
spiral, which can be represented either geometrically by a diagram,
or arithmetically by a fraction. If, for example, the leaves are
so arranged in a plant that every fifth leaf recurs on the same
side of the stem, while the spiral connecting the five successive
leaf-buds winds twice round the stem, this is expressed in botany
by the fraction 2/5. To distinguish this principle of plant growth
from the vertical tendency, Goethe used the term 'spiral tendency'.

To help towards a clear understanding of both tendencies,
Goethe describes an exercise which is characteristic of his way of
schooling himself in what he called exact sensorial fantasy. He
first looks out for a phenomenon in which the 'secret' of the
spiral tendency is made 'open'. This he finds in such a plant as
the convolvulus; in this kind of plant the vertical tendency is
lacking, and the spiral principle comes obviously into outer view.
Accordingly, the convolvulus requires an external support, around
which it can wind itself. Goethe now suggests that after looking
at a convolvulus as it grows upwards around its support, one
should first make this clearly present to one's inner eye, and then
again picture the plant's growth without the vertical support,
allowing instead the upward-growing plant inwardly to produce a

vertical support for itself. By way of inward re-creation (which the reader should not fail to carry out himself) Goethe attained a clear experience of how, in all those plants which in growing upwards produce their leaves spiral-wise around the stem, the vertical and spiral tendencies work together.

In following the two growth-principles, Goethe saw that the vertical comes to a halt in the blossom: the straight line here shrinks together, so to say, into a point, surviving only in the ovary and pistil as continuations of the plant's stalk. The spiral tendency, on the other hand, is to be found in the circle of the stamens arranged around these; the process which in the leaves strove outwards in spiral succession around a straight line is now telescoped on to a single plane. In other words, the vertical-spiral growth of the plant here separates into its two components. And when a pollen grain lands on a pistil and joins with the ovule prepared in the ovary, the two components are united again. Out of the now complete seed a new and complete plant can arise.

Goethe understood that he would be taught a correct conception of this process only by the plant itself. Accordingly, he asked himself where else in the growing plant something like separation and reunion could be seen. This he found in the branching and reuniting of the veins in the leaves, known as *anastomosis*.

In the dividing of the two growth-principles in the plant through the formation of carpel and pistil, on the one hand, and the pollen-bearing stamens on the other, and in their reunion through the coming together of the pollen with the seed, Goethe recognised a metamorphosis of the process of anastomosis at a higher level. His vision of it caused him to term it 'spiritual anastomosis'.

Goethe held a lofty and comprehensive view of the significance of the male and female principles as spiritual opposites in the cosmos. Among the various manifestations of this polarity in earthly nature he found one, but one only, in the duality of the sexes as characteristic of man and animal. Nothing compelled him, therefore, to ascribe it in the same form to the plant. This enabled him to discover how the plant bore the same polarity in plant fashion.

In the neighbourhood of Weimar, Goethe often watched a vine slinging its foliaged stem about the trunk and branches of an elm tree. In this impressive sight nature offered him a picture of 'the female and male, the one that needs and the one that gives, side by side in the vertical and spiral directions'. Thus his artist's eye clearly detected in the upward striving of the plant a decisively masculine principle, and in its spiral winding an equally definite feminine principle. Since in the normal plant both principles are inwardly connected, 'we can represent vegetation as a whole as being in a secret androgynous union from the root up. From this union, through the changes of growth, both systems break away into open polarity and so stand in decisive opposition to each other, only to unite again in a higher sense.'

Thus Goethe found himself led to ideas regarding the male and female principles in the plant, which were the exact opposite of those one obtains if, in trying to explain the process of pollination, one does not keep to the plant itself but imports an analogy from another kingdom of nature. For in continuance of the vertical principle of the plant, the pistil and carpel represent the male aspect in the process of spiritual anastomosis, and the mobile, wind- or insect-borne pollen, in continuing the spiral principle, represents the female part.

If the process of pollination is what the plant tells us it is, then the question arises as to the reason for the occurrence of such a process in the life cycle of the fully developed plant. Goethe himself has not expressed himself explicitly on this subject. But his term *spiritual anastomosis* shows that he had some definite idea about it. Let us picture in our mind what happens physically in the plant as a result of pollination and then try to read from this picture, as from a hieroglyph, what act of the spiritual principle in the plant comes to expression through it.

Without pollination there is no ripening of the seed. Ripening means for the seed its acquisition of the power to bring forth a new and independent plant organism through which the species continues its existence within nature. In the life cycle of the plant this event takes place after the organism has reached its highest degree of physical perfection. When we now read these facts in the light of the knowledge that they are deeds of the activity of the *type*, we may describe them as follows:

Stage by stage the type expends itself in ever more elaborate forms of appearance, until in the blossom a triumph of form over matter is reached. A mere continuation of this path could lead to nothing but a loss of all connection between the plant's superphysical and physical component parts. Thus, to guarantee for the species its continuation in a new generation, the formative power of the type must find a way of linking itself anew to some part of the plant's materiality. This is achieved by the plant's abandoning the union between its two polar growth-principles and re-establishing it again, which in the majority of cases takes place even in such a way that the bearers of the two principles originate from two different organisms.

By picturing the process in this way we are brought face to face with a rule of nature which, once we have recognised it, proves to hold sway at all levels of organic nature. In general terms it may be expressed as follows:

In order that spiritual continuity may be maintained within the coming and going multitude of nature's creations, the physical stream must suffer discontinuity at certain intervals.

In the case of the plant this discontinuity is achieved by the breaking asunder of the male and female growth-principles. When they have reunited, the type begins to abandon either the entire old plant or at least part of it, according to whether the species is an annual or a perennial one, in order to concentrate on the tiny seed, setting, as it were, its living seal on it.

* * * * *

Our pursuit of Goethe's way of observing the life of the plant has brought us to a point where it becomes possible to rectify a widespread error concerning his position as an evolutionary theorist.

Goethe has been honourably mentioned as a predecessor of

Darwin. The truth is, that the idea of evolution emerging from Goethe's mode of regarding nature is the exact opposite of the one held by Darwin and − in whatever modified form − by his followers. A brief consideration of the Darwinian concepts of inheritance and adaptation will show this.

Goethe's approach to his conception of the type is clear evidence that he did not undervalue the factor of adaptation as a formative element in nature; we have seen that he became acquainted with it in studying the same plant species under different climatic conditions. In his view, however, adaptation appears not as the passive effect of a blindly working, external cause, but as the response of the spiritual type to the conditions meeting it from outside.

The same applies to the concept of inheritance. Through inheritance Goethe saw single, accessory characteristics of a species being carried over from one generation to the next; but never could the re-appearance of the basic features of the species itself be explained in this way. He was sufficiently initiated into nature's methods to know that she was not in need of a continuity of the stream of physical substance, in the sense of the theory of inheritance, to guarantee a continuance of the features of the species through successive generations, but that it was her craft to achieve such continuance by means of physical discontinuity.

* * * * *

We opened this chapter with a description of the epistemological contrast between Goethe and Kant, following Goethe's own account in his essay, *Intuitive Judgment*. In this sense, it is true, Goethe was not able to express himself on his achievements in understanding organic nature at the time when he accomplished them. Indeed, between the publications of his *Metamorphosis of Plants* in 1790 and this essay, thirty years elapsed; and they covered his friendship with Schiller, which played a momentous role in this development.

Goethe was not temperamentally given to reflecting deliberately on his own cognitional process. Moreover, the excess of reflection going on around him in the intellectual life of his younger days inclined him to guard himself with a certain anxiety against philosophical cogitations. His words to a friend — 'Dear friend, I have done it well, and never reflected about thinking' — bring this home to us. If in his later years Goethe could become to some degree epistemologically conscious of his spiritual achievements, as, for instance, his essay on *Intuitive Judgment* shows, he owed this to his friendship with Schiller, who became for him a kind of soul mirror, in which he could see the reflection of his own processes of consciousness. Indeed, at their first personal encounter, significant as it was for their whole later relationship, Schiller — though all unconsciously — performed a decisive service of this kind for him. Goethe himself speaks of the occasion in his essay *Happy Encounter* (*Glückliches Ereignis*), written twelve years after Schiller's death.

The occasion was, outwardly regarded, fortuitous: both men were leaving a lecture on natural science at the University of Jena, Schiller having been present as Professor of History in the University, and Goethe as its patron and as a Weimar Minister of State. They met at the door of the lecture hall and went out into the street together. Schiller, who had been wanting to come into closer contact with Goethe for a long time, used the opportunity to begin a conversation. He opened with a comment on the lecture they had just heard, saying that such a piecemeal way of handling nature could not bring the layman any real satisfaction. Goethe, to whom this remark was heartily welcome, replied that such a style of scientific observation 'was uncanny even for the initiated, and that there must certainly be another way altogether, which did not treat of nature as divided and in pieces, but presented her as working and alive, striving out of the whole into the parts'.

Schiller's interest was at once aroused by this remark, although as a thorough Kantian he could not conceal his doubts whether the kind of thing indicated by Goethe was within human capacity. Goethe began to explain himself further, and so the discussion proceeded, until the speakers arrived at Schiller's house. Quite absorbed in his description of plant metamorphosis, Goethe went in with Schiller and climbed the stairs to the latter's study. Once there, he seized pen and paper from Schiller's writing desk, and to bring his conception of the ur-plant vividly before his companion's eyes he made 'a symbolic plant appear with many a characteristic stroke of the pen'.

Although Schiller had listened up to this point 'with great interest and definite understanding', he shook his head as Goethe finished, and said — Kantian that he was at that time: 'That is no experience, this is an idea.' These words were very disappointing to Goethe. At once his old antipathy towards Schiller rose up, an antipathy caused by much in Schiller's public utterances which he had found distasteful.

Once again he felt that Schiller and he were 'spiritual antipodes, removed from each other by more than an earth diameter.' However, Goethe restrained his rising annoyance, and answered Schiller in a tranquil but determined manner: *'I am glad to have ideas without knowing it, and to see them with my very eyes.'*

Although at this meeting Goethe and Schiller came to no real agreement, the personal relationship formed through it did not break off: both had become aware of the value of each to the other. For Goethe his first meeting with Schiller had the significant result of showing him that 'thinking about thought' could be fruitful. For Schiller this significance consisted in his having met in Goethe a human intellect which, simply by its existing properties, invalidated Kant's philosophy. For him Goethe's mind became an object of empirical study on which he based the beginnings of a new philosophy free from onlooker-restrictions.

An essay, written by Goethe about the same time as the one just quoted, shows how he came to think at a later date about the raising of human perception into the realm of ideas. In this essay, entitled *Discovery of an Excellent Predecessor,*[8] Goethe comments on certain views of the botanist, K.F. Wolff, regarding the relationships between the different plant organs, which seemed to be similar to his own, and at which Wolff had arrived in his own way.

Wolff had risen up as an opponent of the so-called preformation theory, still widespread at that time, according to which the entire plant with all its different parts is already present in embryonic physical form in the seed, and simply grows out into space through physical enlargement. Such a mode of thought seemed inadmissible to Wolff, for it made use of an hypothesis 'resting on an extra-sensible conception, which was held to be thinkable, although it could never be demonstrated from the sense world'. Wolff laid it down as a fundamental principle of all research that 'nothing may be assumed, admitted or asserted that has not been actually seen and cannot be made similarly visible to others'. Thus in Wolff we meet with a phenomenologist who in his way tried to oppose certain trends of contemporary biological thinking. As such, Wolff had made certain observations which caused him to ascribe to the plant features quite similar to those which Goethe had grasped under the conception of progressive and regressive metamorphosis. In this way Wolff had grown convinced that all plant organs are transformed leaves. True to his own principle, he had then turned to the microscope for his eyes to confirm what his mind had already recognised.

The microscope gave him the confirmation he expected by showing that all the different organs of the plant develop out of identical embryonic beginnings. In his absolute reliance on physical observation, however, he tried to go further than this and to detect in this way the reason why the plant does not always bring forth the same organ. He saw that the vegetative strength in the plant diminishes in proportion as its organism enters upon its later stages. He therefore attributed the differentiated evolution of plant organs from identical beginnings to an ever weaker process of development in them.

Despite his joy in Wolff as someone who in his own fashion had arrived at certain truths which he himself had also discovered, and despite his agreement with Wolff's phenomenalistic principle, Goethe could in no way accept his explanation of *why* metamorphosis took place in plants. He said: 'In plant metamorphosis Wolff saw how the same organ continuously draws together, makes itself smaller; he did not see that this contraction alternates with an expansion. He saw that the organ diminishes in volume, but not that at the same time it ennobles itself, and so, against reason, he attributed decline to the path towards perfection.' What was it, then, which had prevented Wolff from seeing things aright? 'However admirable may be Wolff's method, through which he has achieved so much, the excellent man never thought that there may be a difference between seeing and seeing, that the eyes of the spirit have to work in perpetual living connection with those of the body, for one otherwise risks seeing and yet seeing past a thing (*zu sehen und doch vorbeizusehen*).'

* * * * * *

These considerations have served to show how Goethe came to be aware of the fruit of knowledge which his striving for a *natural* observation of nature had yielded. Henceforth he knew that one can see ideas with one's eyes, and that in addition to the eye-of-the-body, which serves the physical sense of sight, man possesses also an eye-of-the-spirit, capable of seeing ideas. Both 'eyes', it is true, are part of one integral whole, but there is this essential difference between them: the bodily eye functions automatically, whereas the activity of the spiritual eye depends on the exertion of the will. However much anyone may look at with the aid of the former, he will remain blind for the spirit which manifests through sense-phenomena unless he calls into action his spiritual eye. It was the Goethe equipped with this understanding who could put into Faust's mouth the words quoted in the preceding chapter, when Faust, while stricken blind physically, declares his experience of the continued shining of the 'inner light'.

It is this Goethe who saw with deep concern the danger arising for mankind from the fact that — as we put it — man's Doing was outrunning his Knowing. A field of scientific research which enabled Goethe to discern this danger most clearly was that of microscopy, by means of which, for instance, Wolff had made his discoveries, but which at the same time had prevented him from finding the true *idea* belonging to his observations. Goethe's concern over this state of affairs speaks from his utterance: 'Microscopes and telescopes, in actual fact, confuse man's innate clarity of mind.' Goethe certainly had no aversion in principle to the use of the microscope (or, for that matter, of the telescope), but he saw clearly that, in relation to the rapidly increasing use of these instruments, the human mind in its intellectual condition was much too passive for it not to become their mere servant.

This is the moment for returning to Hooke's observations, discussed in Chapter III. In the light of what we have just seen, Hooke's case – dating from the very beginnings of microscopical investigation – is symptomatic in just the same way as Wolff's. As was then intimated, we shall be able to say how Goethe would have judged Hooke's attempt to answer with the help of the microscope the questions about the relation between human thinking and external reality. He would undoubtedly have pointed out that there would be no such thing as a knife with its line-like edge unless man were able to think the concept 'line', nor a needle with its point-like end unless he were able to think the concept 'point'. In fact, knife and needle are products of a human action which is guided by these two concepts respectively. As such they are embodiments, though more or less imperfect ones, of these concepts.

Seeing Hooke's case in this light enables us to make a fundamental observation concerning the **difference** in the relation between Idea and Object at the different levels of the phenomenal world. As we have seen, a characteristic of organic entities is that they are actively indwelt by their ideas as form-giving and form-sustaining principles. Inorganic entities must be understood as being what they are through an external relation to their corresponding ideas. This is pre-eminently true of all purely man-made things. A machine is in its own way the manifestation of an idea, but the idea of it resides in the mind of the man who built it. Hence, a mechanism can be taken to bits and re-assembled any number of times, provided we are familiar with its 'idea'. An organism does not permit this. When we dismember it, we have

— in Goethe's words — 'the single parts in our hand; missing, alas is the spiritual band'. One thing, however, both organic and inorganic entities have in common: Their ideas can be found only by turning one's attention to the coming-into-being of the object. Hooke's error, like that of his own and the succeeding age, consisted in the opinion that to test the relation of thought to the sense-world one had to turn to the object in its finished state. Correspondingly, even Kant, when turning to conceive the supersensible counterpart of sense-given things, could not imagine it except as a 'thing in itself' (*Ding an sich*). Yet, the spirit does not consist in 'things', but has its very being in a continuous 'doing'. Anyone who tries to find the thought of a straight line, by looking at a knife, as Hooke did — i.e. at the finished object — must arrive at the statement that there is nothing in the outer world corresponding to our thoughts. In Goethe's words, he has 'seen past the thing'. For to find it, one must look at the knife-maker's 'doing', guided by the concept of a straight line. Goethe himself developed a clear distinction between these two ways of observing the world, ascribing one to what he called 'Intellect' (*Verstand*), the other to 'Reason' (*Vernunft*). He says: 'The Reason is directed to things in the course of becoming; the Intellect to things that have become.'[9] Goethe's writings abound in juxtapositions of Intellect and Reason in this sense.

* * * * *

Wolff's case, as much as Hooke's, shows in a symptomatic way how man in his onlooker-state was bound to develop illusory concepts from correct observations, and how the Goethean approach helps to dispel these illusions. We shall have repeated opportunity to illustrate this point. One other example, however, may be dealt with here because of its representative character. It will show in particular the truth of Goethe's statement, quoted earlier, that, in so far as we dwell in illusions about the world of the senses, the fault must not be sought in our senses, but in our power of judgment (p. 77).

When the newly-born scientific mind of man, restricted as it was to one-eyed colour-blind onlooking, set out to attain to objective statements about nature, it obviously had to turn to the reading of pointers of one kind or another. Eddington, in connection with his delineation of the physicist's field of experience, accordingly calls the physical and related sciences 'pointer-reading' sciences. In fact, all pointer instruments devised since the beginning of science, have as their model man himself, restricted to colourless, non-stereoscopic vision. For all that is left to him in this condition is to focus points in space and to register changes in their positions. Indeed, the perfect scientific observer is himself the arch-pointer-instrument. Now, it is possible to establish exactly when and in which field pointer-reading began. This was when Galileo, whom we have already come to know as the arch-spectator, constructed the first thermometer — actually a thermoscope, i.e. a contrivance which shows changes of temperature, but with no scale to measure them.

Our primary knowledge of the existence of something we call 'warmth' or 'cold' is due to a particular *sense of warmth* which modern research has recognised as a clearly definable sense. But the experiences gained through this sense lie outside the sphere of the spectator. In order to obtain an objective picture of the behaviour of warmth and its effects in the physical world, man in the spectator-state had to resort to certain instruments which, through the movements of a pointer, enable him to register changes in the thermal condition of physical objects. In contrast to the 'objective' results of pure pointer-reading, a merely 'subjective' value was ascribed to the experiences given by the sense of warmth. The following experiment and its conceptual evaluation, often found in textbooks on elementary physics as an introduction to the chapter on Heat, are held to justify this verdict.

If you plunge your hands first into two separate bowls, one filled with hot water and the other with cold, and then plunge them together into a bowl of tepid water, this will feel cold to the hand coming from the hot water and warm to the hand coming from the cold, whereas two thermometers which are put through the same procedure will both register the same temperature of the tepid water. This is meant to show the superiority of the 'objective' recording of the instrument over the 'subjective' experiences mediated by our sense of warmth.

Let us test this procedure by carrying out the same experiment with the help of thermometrical instruments in the original form first used by Galileo. By doing so we proceed in a truly Goethean manner. For he always took care to arrange experiments in such a way as to divest them of all accessories which prevent the phenomenon from appearing in its primary form.

For our test we can use ordinary thermometers with the scales expunged. If we carry out the experiment with two such instruments, we at once become aware of something which usually escapes us, because our attention is fixed on the scale-reading. For we now notice that the two instruments, when transferred from the hot and cold water into the tepid water, behave quite differently. In one the column will fall; in the other it will rise. This is precisely what our sense of warmth registers as the change which our hands undergo respectively during the same procedure!

The circumstances are by no means changed if we change the thermoscopes back into ordinary thermometers by fitting them each with a scale and marking a zero as a point of reference. By thus emphasising a zero level we merely save ourselves the trouble of repeatedly getting the column down to this level, for instance by plunging the instrument into melting ice. As a result, our attention is now drawn to the final position of the indicator and we forget what it actually indicates — the outcome of a movement from one level to another. In reality, *thermometrical measurements are always measurements of a change of level.*

Hence we see that in the ordinary operation with the thermometers, and when we use our hands in the prescribed manner, we are dealing with the zero level in two quite different ways. While in the two instruments the zero level is the same, in accordance with the whole idea of thermometric measurement, we make a special arrangement so as to expose our hands to two different

levels. So we need not be surprised if these two ways yield different results. If, after placing two thermometers without scales in
hot and cold water, we were to assign to each its own zero in
accordance with the respective height of its column, and then
graduate them from this reference point, they would necessarily
record different levels when exposed to the tepid water, in just
the same way as hands do. Our two hands, moreover, will receive
the same sense-impression from the tepid water, if we keep them
in it long enough.

Seen in this light, the original experiment, designed to show
the subjective character of the impressions gained through the
sense of warmth, reveals itself as a piece of self-deception by the
onlooker-consciousness. The truth of the matter is that, in so
far as there is any subjective element in the experience and measurement of heat, it does not lie on the side of our sense of warmth,
but in our judgment of the significance of thermometrical readings.
In fact, our test of the alleged proof of the absolute superiority of
pointer-readings over the impressions gained by our senses gives us
proof of the correctness of Goethe's statement, quoted earlier,
that the senses do not deceive, but the judgment deceives.

The purpose of this illustration is not to depreciate the method
of pointer-reading. Whenever quantitative observations are required,
we cannot dispense with pointer-instruments, for the direct
impressions of our senses do not yield quantitative comparisons.
What we have to discard is simply the idea that physical measurement is absolutely superior to immediate sense-perception for
achieving an objective apprehension of the world. For it is this
misconception that has led scientific research to the point where
a scientist himself is constrained to say: 'In natural science the
object of investigation is not nature as such, but nature exposed
to man's mode of enquiry.' (W. Heisenberg.) Goethe, who foresaw
this, expresses his concern at this prospect by saying: 'It is a
calamity that the use of the experiment has severed nature from
man, so that he is content to understand nature merely through
what artificial instruments reveal, and by so doing even restricts
her achievements.' This remark must not be taken to imply that

Goethe rejected experiments altogether as a means of investigation. As a foundation for his theory of colour he himself carried out a great many experiments for years, and in his Essay, *The Experiment as Mediator between Subject and Object*,[10] he analyses in a most positive sense the role of the experiment. What he regarded as dangerous was only the one-sided manner of experimenting that he saw developing, and the importance attached to it for a true understanding of nature. In the last words of the quotation something more, even, is expressed. For they actually say that by this means man prevents nature from doing as much for him as in principle she could do. Apparently Goethe expected that a science which did not sever nature from man would be able to open up opportunities for her to achieve quite other things than those to which she is restricted if she is approached merely through pointer-readings. Later parts of this book will show that this can indeed happen.

* * * * *

Observation of the life of the plant has given us a foundation for developing Goethe's method. In doing so we followed his own procedure. As we said to start with, the plant, because to a unique degree it can be watched in the process of becoming, could serve Goethe better than anything as his first teacher. As we have now seen, his method is not restricted to the investigation of the organic world. On the contrary, much will be gained by applying it to the inorganic sciences. Goethe himself showed this with his theory of colour, which will therefore occupy us in due course.

In Goethe's essay, *History of my Botanical Studies*, which he wrote in later life as an account of his labours in the field of science, he says: 'Thus not through an extraordinary spiritual gift, not through momentary inspiration, unexpected and unique, but through consistent work, did I eventually achieve such satis-factory results.' These words show how anxious he was to make it rightly understood that this faculty of reading in the Book of Nature, as he knew it, was the result of a systematic training and therefore could be acquired by anyone ready to apply such training to himself.

In a review of a contemporary work on psychology[11] (which he valued highly) Goethe uses a special term for a spiritual faculty which he regarded as the prerequisite for creative action, in art as well as in science. He calls it, *exact sensorial fantasy*.[12] This is indeed the faculty he first developed by studying the plant in his own way. Let us remember how we made acquaintance with the principle of metamorphosis. First of all, we had to use exact sense-perception for forming a clear picture of the single leaf-forms. Next, we needed the power of memory in order to retain them. Then we tried to transform these into one another. In this way we carried out something in our mind which had not been imparted to it by the sense-data. Now, in addition to the image-forming power of memory, we possess another power, enabling us to form and transform mental images independently of the sense-world. This is fantasy. By re-creating inwardly the transition from one leaf-form into another, however, we apply this faculty to images first gained by means of exact sense-perception. What we are really doing is to endow objective memory, which by nature is static, with the dynamic properties of fantasy, while endowing mobile fantasy, which by nature is subjective, with the objective character of memory. It is the union of these two polar faculties of the soul which gives rise to the new organ of cognition for which Goethe aptly coined the term 'exact sensorial fantasy'.

From our earlier descriptions of man's psycho-physical make-up (Chapter II) we may recall that the nervous system provides the basis for memory, and the blood, the basis for fantasy. Exact sensorial fantasy, therefore, appears to be based on a newly-created collaboration of the two. We also know from the same considerations, that in the little child no such polarisation, in body or in soul, has yet emerged. Thus we see that training along Goethe's lines aims at nothing less than restoring within oneself a condition which is natural in early childhood.

We shall hear more about this; it touches on the very foundations of the new pathway to science.

Chapter VI

'ALWAYS STAND BY FORM'

In this and the following chapter we shall concern ourselves with a number of personalities from the more or less recent past of the cultural life of Britain, each of whom was a spiritual kinsman of Goethe, and so a living illustration of the fact that the true source of knowledge in man must be sought, and can be found, outside the limits of his modern adult consciousness. Whilst none of them was a match for Goethe as regards universality and scientific lucidity, they are all characteristic of an immediacy of approach to certain essential truths, which in the sense we mean is not found in Goethe. It enabled them to express one or the other of these truths in a form that makes them suitable as signposts on our own path of exploration. We shall find repeated opportunity in the later pages of this book to remember just what these men saw and thought.

The present chapter will be devoted to two of them: John Ruskin (1819-1900) and Luke Howard (1772-1864). Both are characterised by a certain artistic approach to natural phenomena, derived from their religious or artistic experience of the sense-world, which enabled them to be true readers in the book of nature. They will thus be helpful to us in our attempt to establish an up-to-date method of apprehending nature's phenomena through reading them.

In discussing Howard, particularly, we shall find ourselves led into another sphere of Goethe's scientific work. For it will mean recognising the importance of Howard's findings for Goethe's meteorological studies, enhanced by the personal contact between the two men which was brought about by their common interests and similar approach to nature. We shall thus come as a matter of course to speak of Goethe's thoughts about meteorology, and this again will give opportunity to introduce a leading concept of Goethean science in addition to those brought forward already.

Of Ruskin only so much will appear in the present chapter as is necessary to show him as an exemplary reader in the book of nature. He will then be a more or less permanent companion in our investigations.

* * * * *

The following words of Ruskin from *The Queen of the Air* reveal him at once as a true reader in the book of nature:

'Over the entire surface of the earth and its waters, as influenced by the power of the air under solar light, there is developed a series of changing forms, in clouds, plants and animals, all of which have reference in their action, or nature, to the human intelligence that perceives them.' (II, 89).

Here Ruskin in an entirely Goethean way points to *form* in nature as the element in her that speaks to human intelligence — meaning by form, as other utterances of his show, all those qualities through which the natural object under observation reveals itself to our senses as a whole.

By virtue of his pictorial-dynamic way of regarding nature, Ruskin was quite clear that the scientists' one-eyed seeking after external forces and the mathematically calculable interplay between them can never lead to a comprehension of life in nature. For in such a search man loses sight of the real signature of *life*: form as a dynamic element. Accordingly, in his *Ethics of the Dust*, Ruskin does not answer the question: 'What is Life?' with a scientific explanation, but with the laconic injunction: 'Always stand by Form against Force.' This he later enlarges pictorially in the words: 'Discern the moulding hand of the potter commanding the clay from the merely beating foot as it turns the wheel.' (Lect. X.)

In thus opposing form and force to each other, Ruskin is actually referring to two kinds of forces. There exist those forces which resemble the potter's foot in producing mere numerically regulated movements (so that this part of the potter's activity can be replaced by a power-machine), and others which, like the potter's hand, strive for a certain end and so in the process create definite forms. Ruskin goes a step further still in *The Queen of the Air*, where he speaks of selective order as a mark of the spirit:

'It does not merely crystallise indefinite masses, but it gives to limited portions of matter the power of gathering, selectively, other elements proper to them, and binding these elements into their own peculiar and adopted form . . . .

'For the mere force of junction is not spirit, but the power that catches out of chaos, charcoal, water, lime and what not, and fastens them into given form, is properly called "spirit"; and we shall not diminish, but strengthen our cognition of this creative energy by recognising its presence in lower states of matter than our own.' (II, 59.)[1]

When Ruskin wrote this passage, he could count on a certain measure of agreement from his contemporaries that the essence of man himself is spirit, though certainly without any very exact notion being implied. This persuaded him to fight on behalf of the spirit, lest its activity on the lower levels of nature should not be duly acknowledged. Today, when the purely physical conception of nature has laid hold of the entire man, Ruskin might have given his thought the following turn: ' . . . and we shall certainly attain to no real insight into this creative force (of the spirit) at the level of man, unless we win the capacity to recognise its activity in lower states of matter.'

What Ruskin is really pointing towards is the very thing for which Goethe formed the concept 'type'. And just as Ruskin, like Goethe, recognised the signature of the spirit in the material processes which work towards a goal, so he counted as another such signature what Goethe called *Steigerung*, though certainly without forming such a universally valid idea of it:

'The Spirit in the plant — that is to say, its power of gathering dead matter out of the wreck round it, and shaping it into its own chosen shape — is of course strongest in the moment of flowering, for it then not only gathers, but forms, with the greatest energy.' It is characteristic of Ruskin's conception of the relationship between man's mind and nature that he added: 'And where this life is in it at full power, its form becomes invested with aspects that are chiefly delightful to our own senses.' (II, 60.)

Obviously, a mind capable of looking at nature in this way could not accept such a picture of evolution as was put forward by Ruskin's contemporary, Darwin. So we find Ruskin, in *The Queen of the Air*, opposing the Darwinistic conception of the preservation of the species as the driving factor in the life of nature:

'With respect to plants as animals, we are wrong in speaking as if the object of life were only the bequeathing of itself. The flower is the end and proper object of the seeds, not the seed of the flower. The reason for the seed is that flowers may be, not the reason of flowers that seeds may be. The flower itself is the creature which the spirit makes; only, in connection with its perfectedness, is placed the giving birth to its successor.' (II, 60.)

For Ruskin the true meaning of life in all its stages lay not in the maintenance of physical continuity from generation to generation, but in the ever-renewed, ever more enhanced revelation of the spirit.

He was never for a moment in doubt regarding the inevitable effect of such an evolutionary theory as Darwin's on the general social attitude of humanity. Men would be led, he realised, to see themselves as the accidental products of an animal nature based on the struggle for existence and the preservation of the species.

Enough has been said to stamp Ruskin as a reader in the book of nature, capable of deciphering the signature of the spirit in the phenomena of the sense world.

* * * * *

Outwardly different from Ruskin's and yet spiritually comparable, is the contribution made by his older contemporary, Luke Howard, to the foundation of a science of nature based on intuition. Whereas Ruskin throws out a multitude of aphoristic utterances about many different aspects of nature, which will provide us with further starting-points for our own observations and thought, Howard is concerned with a single sphere of phenomena, that of cloud formation. On the other hand, his contribution consists of a definite discovery which he himself methodically and consciously achieved, and it is the content of this discovery, together with the method of research leading to it, which will supply us ever and again with a model for our own procedure. At the same time, as we have indicated, he will help us to become familiar with Goethe, and to widen our knowledge of the basic scientific concepts formed by him.

Anyone interested today in weather phenomena is acquainted with the terms used in cloud classification — Cirrus, Cumulus, Stratus, and Nimbus. These have come so far into general use that it is not easy to realise that, until Howard's paper, *On the Modification of Clouds*, appeared in 1803, no names for classifying clouds were available. Superficially, it may seem that Howard had done nothing more than science has so often done in grouping and classifying and naming the contents of nature. In fact, however, he did something essentially different.

In the introduction to his essay, Howard describes the motives which led him to devote himself to a study of meteorological phenomena:

'It is the frequent observation of the countenance of the sky, and of its connection with the present and ensuing phenomena, that constitutes the ancient and popular meteorology. The want of this branch of knowledge renders the prediction of the philosopher (who in attending his instruments may be said to examine the pulse of the atmosphere), less generally successful than those of the weather-wise mariners and husbandmen.'

When he thus speaks of studying the 'countenance of the sky', Howard is not using a mere form of speech; he is exactly describing his own procedure, as he shows when he proceeds to justify it as a means to scientific knowledge. The clouds with their ever-moving, ever-changing forms are not, he says, to be regarded as the mere 'sport of the winds', nor is their existence 'the mere result of the condensation of vapour in the masses of the atmosphere which they occupy'. What comes to view in them is identical, in its own realm, with what the changing expression of the human face reveals of 'a person's state of mind or body'. It would hardly be possible to represent oneself more clearly as a genuine reader in the book of nature than by such words. What is it but Ruskin's 'Stand by Form against Force' that Howard is here saying in his own way?

* * * * *

Before entering into a further description of Howard's system, we must make clear why we disregard the fact that modern meteorology has developed the scale of cloud formation far beyond Howard, and why we shall keep to his own fourfold scale.

It is characteristic of Goethe that, on becoming acquainted with Howard's work, he at once gave a warning against subdividing his scale without limit. Goethe foresaw that the attempt to insert too many transitory forms between Howard's chief types would result only in obscuring that view of the essentials which Howard's original classification had opened up. Obviously, for a science based on mere onlooking there is no objection to breaking up an established system into ever more subdivisions in order to keep it in line with an increasingly detailed outer observation. This, indeed, modern meteorology has done with Howard's system, with the result that, today, the total scale is made up of ten different stages of cloud-formation.

Valuable as this tenfold scale may be for certain practical purposes, it must be ignored by one who realises that through Howard's fourfold scale nature herself speaks to man's intuitive judgment. Let us, therefore, turn to Howard's discovery, undisturbed by the extension to which modern meteorology has subjected it.

* * * * *

Luke Howard, a chemist by profession, knew well how to

value the results of scientific knowledge above traditional folk-knowledge. He saw the superiority of scientifically acquired knowledge in the fact that it was universally communicable, whereas folk-wisdom is bound up with the personality of its bearer, his individual observations and his memory of them. Nevertheless, the increasing mathematising of science, including his own branch of it, gave him great concern, for he could not regard it as helpful in the true progress of man's *understanding* of nature. Accordingly, he sought for a method of observation in which the practice of 'the weatherwise mariner and husband-man' could be raised to the level of scientific procedure. To this end he studied the changing phenomena of the sky for many years, until he was able so to read its play of features that it disclosed to him the archetypal forms of cloud-formation under-lying all change. To these he gave the now well-know names (in Latin, so that they might be internationally comprehensible):

Cirrus: Parallel, flexuous or divergent fibres extensible in any and all directions.
Cumulus: Convex or conical heaps, increasing upwards from a horizontal base.
Stratus: A widely extended, continuous, horizontal sheet, increasing from below.
Nimbus: The rain cloud.

Let us, on the background of Howard's brief definitions, try to form a more exact picture of the atmospheric dynamics at work in each of the stages he describes.

Among the three formations of cirrus, cumulus and stratus, the cumulus has a special place as representing in the most actual sense what is meant by the term 'cloud'. The reason is that both cirrus and stratus have characteristics which in one or the other direction tend away from the pure realm of atmospheric cloud-formation. In the stratus, the atmospheric vapour is gathered into a horizontal, relatively arched layer around the earth, and so anticipates the actual water covering below, which extends spher-

PLATE II

ically around the earth's centre. Thus the stratus arranges itself in a direction which is already conditioned by the earth's field of gravity. In the language of physics, the stratus forms an equipotential surface in the gravitational field permeating the earth's atmosphere.

As the exact opposite of this we have the cirrus. If in the stratus the form ceases to consist of distinct particulars, because the entire cloud-mass runs together into a single layer, in the cirrus the form begins to vanish before our eyes, because it dissolves into the surrounding atmospheric space. In the cirrus there is present a tendency to expand; in the stratus to contract.

Between the two, the cumulus, even viewed simply as a form-type, represents an exact mean. In how densely mounded a shape does the majestically towering cumulus appear before us, and yet how buoyantly it hovers aloft in the heights! If one ever comes into the midst of a cumulus cloud in the mountains, one sees how its myriads of single particles are in ceaseless movement. And yet the whole remains stationary, on windless days preserving its form unchanged for hours. More recent meteorological research has established that in many cumulus forms the entire mass is in constant rotation, although seen from outside, it appears as a stable, unvarying shape. Nowhere in nature may the supremacy of form over matter be so vividly observed as in the cumulus cloud. And the forms of the cumuli themselves tell us in manifold metamorphoses of a state of equilibrium between expansive and contractive tendencies within the atmosphere.

Our description of the three cloud-types of cirrus, cumulus and stratus, makes it clear that we have to do with a self-contained symmetrical system of forms, within which the two outer, dynamically regarded, represent the extreme tendencies of expansion and contraction, whilst in the middle forms these are held more or less in balance. By adding Howard's nimbus formation to this system, we destroy its symmetry. Actually, in the nimbus we have cloud in such a condition that it ceases to be an atmospheric phenomenon in any real sense of the word; for it now breaks up into single drops of water, each of which, under the pull of gravity, makes its own independent way to the earth. The symmetry is restored as soon as we realise that the nimbus, as a frontier stage below the stratus, has a counterpart in a corresponding frontier stage above the cirrus. To provide insight into this upper frontier stage, of which neither Howard nor Goethe was at that time in a position to develop a clear enough conception to deal with it scientifically, is one of the aims of this book.

* * * * *

In order to understand what prompted Goethe to accept, as he did, Howard's classification and terminology at first glance, and what persuaded him to make himself its eloquent herald, we must note from what point Goethe's labours for a natural understanding of nature had originated.

In his *History of my Botanical Studies* Goethe mentions, besides Shakespeare and Spinoza, Linnaeus as one who had most influenced his own development. Concerning Linnaeus, however, this is to be understood in a negative sense. For when Goethe, himself searching for a way of bringing the confusing multiplicity of plant phenomena into a comprehensive system, met with the Linnaean system, he was, despite his admiration for the thoroughness and ingenuity of Linnaeus's work, repelled by his method. Thus by way of reaction, his thought was brought into its own creative movement: 'As I sought to take in his acute, ingenious analysis, his apt, appropriate, though often arbitrary laws, a cleft was set up in my inner nature: what he sought to hold forcibly apart could not but strive for union according to the inmost need of my own being.'

Linnaeus's system agonised Goethe because it demanded from him 'to memorise a ready-made terminology, to hold in readiness a certain number of nouns and adjectives, so as to be able, whenever any form was in question, to employ them in apt and skilful selection, and so to give it its characteristic designation and appropriate position.' Such a procedure appeared to Goethe as a kind of mosaic, in which one ready-made piece is set next to another in order to produce out of a thousand details the semblance of a picture; and this was 'in a certain way repugnant' to him. What Goethe awoke to when he met Linnaeus's attempt at systematising the plant kingdom was the old problem of whether the study of nature should proceed from the parts to the whole or from the whole to the parts.

Seeing, therefore, how it became a question for Goethe, at the very beginning of his scientific studies, whether a *natural* classification of nature's phenomena could be achieved, we can understand why he was so overjoyed when, towards the end of his life, in a field of observation which had meanwhile caught much of his interest, he met with a classification which showed, down to the single names employed, that it had been read off from reality.

The following is a comprehensive description of Goethe's meteorological views, which he gave a few years before his death in one of his conversations with his secretary, Eckermann:

'I compare the earth and her hygrosphere[2] to a great living being perpetually inhaling and exhaling. If she inhales, she draws the hygrosphere to her, so that, coming near her surface, it is condensed to clouds and rain. This state I call water-affirmative (*Wasser-Bejahung*). Should it continue for an indefinite period, the earth would be drowned. This the earth does not allow, but exhales again, and sends the watery vapours upwards, when they are dissipated through the whole space of the higher atmosphere. These become so rarefied that not only does the sun penetrate them with its brilliancy, but the eternal darkness of infinite space is seen through them as a fresh blue. This state of the hygrosphere I call water-negative (*Wasser Verneinung*). For just as under the contrary influence, not only does water come profusely from above, but also the moisture of the earth cannot be dried and dissipated — so, on the contrary, in this state not only does no moisture come from above, but the damp of the earth itself flies upwards; so that, if this should continue for an indefinite period, the earth, even if the sun did not shine, would be in danger of drying up.' (11th April 1827)

Goethe's notes of the results of his meteorological observations show how in them, too, he followed his principle of keeping strictly to the phenomenon. His first concern is to bring the recorded measurements of weather phenomena into their proper order of significance. To this end he compares measurements of atmospheric temperatures and local density with barometric measurements. He finds that the first two, being of a more local and accidental nature, have the value of 'derived' phenomena, whereas the variations in the atmosphere revealed by the barometer are the same over wide areas and therefore point to fundamental changes in the general conditions of the earth. Measurements made regularly over long periods of time finally lead him to recognise in the barometric variations of atmospheric pressure the basic meteorological phenomenon.

In all this we find Goethe carefully guarding himself against 'explaining' these atmospheric changes by assuming some kind of purely mechanical cause, such as the accumulation of air-masses over a certain area or the like. Just as little would he permit himself lightly to assume influences of an extra-terrestrial nature, such as those of the moon. Not that he would have had anything against such things, if they had rested on genuine observation. But his own observations, as far as he was able to carry them, told him simply that the atmosphere presses with greater or lesser intensity on the earth in more or less regular rhythms. He was not abandoning the phenomenal sphere, however, when he said that these changes are results of the activity of earthly gravity, or when he concluded from this that barometric variations were caused by variations in the intensity of the field of terrestrial gravity, whereby the earth sometimes drew the atmosphere to it with a stronger, and sometimes with a weaker, pull.

He was again not departing from the realm of the phenomenal when he looked round for other indications in nature of such an alternation of drawing in and letting forth of air, and found them in the respiratory processes of animated beings. (To regard the earth as a merely physical structure was impossible for Goethe, for he could have done this only by leaving out of account the life visibly bound up with it.) Accordingly, barometric measurements became for him the sign of a breathing process carried out by the earth.

Alongside the alternating phases of contraction and expansion within the atmosphere, Goethe placed the fact that atmospheric density decreases with height. Observation of differences in cloud formation at different levels, of the boundary of snow formation, etc, led him to speak of different 'atmospheres' or of atmospheric circles or spheres, which when undisturbed are arranged concentrically round the earth. Here also he saw, in space, phases of contraction alternating with phases of expansion.

* * * * *

It was while on his way with the Grand Duke of Weimar to visit a newly-erected meteorological observatory that Goethe, in the course of informing his companion of his own meteorological ideas, first heard of Howard's writings about the formation of clouds. The Duke had read a report of them in a German scientific periodical, and it seemed to him that Howard's cloud system corresponded with what he now heard of Goethe's thoughts about the force relationships working in the different atmospheric levels. He had made no mistake. Goethe, who immediately obtained Howard's essay, recognised at first glance in Howard's cloud scale the law of atmospheric changes which he himself had discovered. He found here what he had always missed in the customary practice of merely tabulating the results of scientific measurements. And so he took hold of the Howard system with delight, for it 'provided him with a thread which had hitherto been lacking'.

Moreover, in the names which Howard had chosen for designating the basic cloud forms, Goethe saw the dynamic element in each of them coming to immediate expression in human speech.[3] He therefore always spoke of Howard's system as a 'welcome terminology'.

All this inspired Goethe to celebrate Howard's personality and his work in a number of verses in which he gave a description of these dynamic elements and a paraphrase of the names, moulding them together into an artistic unity. In a few accompanying verses he honoured Howard as the first to 'distinguish and suitably name' the clouds.[4]

The reason why Goethe laid so much stress on Howard's terminology was because he was very much aware of the power of names to help or hinder men in their quest for knowledge. He himself usually waited a long time before deciding on a name for a natural phenomenon or a connection between phenomena which he had discovered. The Idea which his spiritual eye had observed had first to appear so closely before him that he could clothe it in a thought-form proper to it. Seeing in the act of name-giving an essential function of man (we are reminded of what in this respect the Biblical story of creation says of Adam),[5] Goethe called man 'the first conversation which Nature conducts with God'.

It is characteristic of Goethe that he did not content himself with knowing the truth which someone had brought forward in a field of knowledge in which he himself was interested, but that he felt his acquaintance with this truth to be complete only when he also knew something about the personality of the man himself. So he introduces his account of his endeavours to know more about Howard, the man, with the following words: 'Increasingly convinced that everything occurring through man should be regarded in an ethical sense, and that moral value is to be estimated only from a man's way of life, I asked a friend in London to find out if possible something about Howard's life, if only the simplest facts.' Goethe was uncertain whether the Englishman was still alive, so his delight and surprise were considerable when from Howard himself he received an answer in the form of a short autobiographical sketch, which fully confirmed his expectations regarding Howard's ethical personality.

Howard's account of himself is known to us, as Goethe included a translation of it in the collection of his own meteorological studies. Howard in a modest yet dignified way described his Christian faith, his guide through all his relationships, whether to other men or to nature.[6] A man comes before us who, untroubled by the prevailing philosophy of his day, was able to advance to the knowledge of an objective truth in nature, because he had the ability to carry religious experience even into his observation of the sense world.

In view of all this, it is perhaps not too much to say that in the meeting between Howard and Goethe by way of the spiritual bridge of the clouds, something happened that was more than a mere event in the personal history of these two men.

* * * * *

At this point in our discussion it is appropriate to introduce another leading concept of Goethean nature observation, which was for him — as it will be for us — of particular significance for carrying over the Goethean method of research from the organic into the inorganic realm of nature. This is the concept of the ur-phenomenon (*Ur-phänomen*). In this latter realm, nature no longer brings forth related phenomena in the ordering proper to them; hence we are obliged to acquire the capacity of penetrating to this ordering by means of our own realistically trained observation and thought.

From among the various utterances of Goethe regarding his general conception of the ur-phenomenon, we here select a passage from that part of the historical section of his *Theory of Colour* where he discusses the method of investigation introduced into science by Bacon. He says:

'In the range of phenomena, all had equal value in Bacon's eyes. For although he himself always points out that one should collect the particulars only to select from them and to arrange them, in order finally to attain to Universals, yet too much privilege is granted to the simple facts; and before it becomes possible to attain to simplification and conclusion by means of induction (the very way he recommends), life vanishes and forces get exhausted. He who cannot realise that one instance is often worth a thousand, bearing all within itself; he who proves unable to comprehend and esteem what we called ur-phenomena, will never be in a position to advance anything, either to his own, or to others' joy and profit.'

What Goethe says here calls for the following comparison. We can say that nature seen through Bacon's eyes appears as if painted on a two-dimensional surface, so that all its facts are seen alongside each other at exactly the same distance from the observer. Goethe, on the other hand, ascribed to the human spirit the power of seeing the phenomenal world in all its three dimensional multiplicity; that is, of seeing it in perspective and distinguishing between foreground and background.[7] Things in the foreground he called ur-phenomena. Here the idea creatively determining the relevant field of facts comes to its purest expression. The sole task of the investigator of nature, he considered, was to seek for the ur-phenomena and to bring all other phenomena into relation with them; and in the fulfilment of this task he saw the means of fully satisfying the human mind's need to theorise. He expressed this in the words, 'Every fact is itself already theory.' In Goethe's meteorological studies we have a lucid example of how he sought and found the relevant ur-phenomenon. It is the breathing-process of the earth as shown by the variations of barometric pressure.

Chapter VII

EXCEPT WE BECOME ...

When, in Chapter V, we first introduced Goethe's term, 'exact
sensorial fantasy', we found that the acquisition of this organ
of cognition means in actual fact a restoring within oneself of a
condition of body and soul which is native to man, but is lost
in the course of growing away from the state of early childhood.
The two representatives of British cultural life who will speak
to us in this chapter are witnesses, each in his way, to the fact
that man's path to wisdom-filled apprehension of the world is
the path towards recovery of this lost state of childhood. They
are Thomas Reid (1710-96), the Scottish philosopher, and Thomas
Traherne (1638-74), the English mystic, thinker and poet. What
they have experienced, discovered and achieved implies a conception of childhood to which, in a particular way, William
Wordsworth also bears witness. He, too, therefore, will form
part of our discussion.

* * * * *

Thomas Reid figures in the history of modern philosophy as
the first teacher of the unusual doctrine that man's 'common
sense' has been the true root of all philosophy that deserves this
name.[1] After having served for some years as a minister of the
Church of Scotland, Reid became professor of philosophy at the
University of Aberdeen, whence he was called to Glasgow as the
successor of Adam Smith. Through his birth in Strachan, Kincardine, he belonged to the same part of Scotland from which
Kant's ancestors had come.

Reid, like his contemporary Kant, felt his philosophical

conscience stirred by Hume's *Treatise of Human Nature*, and, like Kant, set himself the task of opposing it. Unlike Kant, however, whose philosophic system was designed to arrest man's reason before the abyss into which Hume threatened to cast it, Reid contrives to detect the bridge that leads safely across this abyss. Even though it was not granted to him actually to set foot on this bridge (this, in his time, only Goethe managed to do), he was able to describe it in a manner especially helpful for our own purpose.

The first of the three books in which Reid set out the results of his labours appeared in 1764 under the title, *Inquiry into the Human Mind on the Principles of Common Sense*. The other two, *Essays on the Intellectual Powers of Man* and *Essays on the Active Powers of Man*, appeared twenty years later. In these books Reid had in view a more all-embracing purpose than in his first work. The achievement of this purpose, however, required a greater spiritual power than was granted to him. Comparing this later with his earlier work, Reid's biographer, A. Campbell Fraser, says:

'Reid's *Essays* form, as it were, the inner court of the temple of which the Aberdonian *Inquiry* is the vestibule. But the vestibule is a more finished work of constructive skill than the inner court, for the aged architect appears at last as if embarrassed by accumulated material. The *Essays*, greater in bulk, perhaps less deserve a place among modern philosophical classics than the *Inquiry*, notwithstanding its narrower scope, confined as it is to man's perception of the extended world, as an object lesson on the method of appeal to common sense.'

Whilst the ideas of Kant, by which he tried in his way to oppose Hume's philosophy, have become within a short space of time the common possession of men's minds, it was the fate of Reid's ideas to find favour among only a restricted circle of friends. Moreover, they suffered decisive misunderstanding and distortion through the efforts of well-meaning disciples. This was because Kant's work was a late fruit of an epoch of human development which had lasted for centuries and in his time began to draw to its close, while Reid's work represents a seed of a new epoch yet to come. Here lies the reason also for his failure to develop his philosophy beyond the achievements contained in his first work. It is on the latter, therefore, that we shall chiefly draw for presenting Reid's thoughts.

* * * * *

The convincing nature of Hume's argumentation, together with the absurdity of the conclusions to which it led, aroused in Reid a suspicion that the premises on which Hume's thoughts were built, and which he, in company with all his predecessors, had assumed quite uncritically, contained some fundamental error. For as a Christian, a philosopher, and a man in possession of common sense, Reid had no doubt as to the absurdity and destructiveness of the conclusions to which Hume's reasoning had led him.

'For my own satisfaction, I entered into a serious examination of the principles upon which this sceptical system is built; and was not a little surprised to find that it leans with its whole weight upon a hypothesis, which is ancient indeed, and hath been very generally received by philosophers, but of which I could find no solid proof. The hypothesis I mean is, That nothing is perceived but what is in the mind which perceives it: That we do not really perceive the things that are external, but only certain images and pictures of them imprinted upon the mind, which are called *impressions* and *ideas*.

'If this be true, supposing certain impressions and ideas to exist presently in my mind, I cannot, from their existence, infer the existence of anything else; my impressions and ideas are the only existence of which I can have any knowledge or conception; and they are such fleeting and transitory beings, that they can have no existence at all, any longer than I am conscious of them. So that, upon this hypothesis, the whole universe about me, bodies and spirits, sun, moon, stars, and earth, friends and relations, all things without exception, which I imagined to have a permanent existence whether I thought of them or not vanish at once:

'And, like the baseless fabric of this vision...
Leave not a rack behind.

'I thought it unreasonable, upon the authority of philosophers,
to admit a hypothesis which, in my opinion, overturns all philosophy, all religion and virtue, and all common sense: and finding,
that all the systems which I was acquainted with, were built upon
this hypothesis, I resolved to enquire into this subject anew,
without regard to any hypothesis.'

The following passage from the first chapter of the *Inquiry*
reveals Reid as a personality who was not dazzled to the same
extent as were his contemporaries by the onlooker-consciousness:

'If it [the mind] is indeed what the *Treatise of Human Nature*
makes it, I find I have been only in an enchanted castle, imposed
upon by spectres and apparitions. I blush inwardly to think how
I have been deluded; I am ashamed of my frame, and can hardly
forbear expostulating with my destiny: Is this thy pastime, O
Nature, to put such tricks upon a silly creature, and then to take
off the mask, and show him how he hath been befooled? If this is
the philosophy of human nature, my soul enter thou not into her
secrets. It is surely the forbidden tree of knowledge; I no sooner
taste it, than I perceive myself naked, and stript of all things — yea
even of my very self. I see myself, and the whole frame of nature,
shrink into fleeting ideas, which, like Epicurus's atoms, dance
about in emptiness.

'But what if these profound disquisitions into the first principles of human nature, do naturally and necessarily plunge a man
into this abyss of scepticism? May we not reasonably judge from
what hath happened? Descartes no sooner began to dig in this
mine, than scepticism was ready to break in upon him. He did
what he could to shut it out. Malebranche and Locke, who dug
deeper, found the difficulty of keeping out this enemy still to
increase; but they laboured honestly in the design. Then Berkeley,
who carried on the work, despairing of securing all, bethought
himself of an expedient: By giving up the material world, which
he thought might be spared without loss, and even with advantage,

he hoped by an impregnable partition to secure the world of spirits. But, alas! the *Treatise of Human Nature* wantonly sapped the foundation of this partition and drowned all in one universal deluge.' (Chapter I, Sections VI-VII.)

What Reid so pertinently describes here as the 'enchanted castle' is nothing else than the human head, which knows of no occurrence beyond its boundaries, because it has forgotten that it is only the end-product of a living existence outside of, and beyond, itself. We see here that Reid is gifted with the faculty of entering this castle without forfeiting his memory of the world outside; and so even from within its walls, he could recognise its true nature. To a high degree this helped him to keep free of those deceptions to which the majority of his contemporaries fell victim, and to which so many persons are still subject today.

It is in this way that Reid could make it one of the cardinal principles of his observations to test all that the head thinks by relating it to the rest of human nature and to allow nothing to stand, which does not survive this test. In this respect the argument he sets over against the Cartesian, *'cogito ergo sum'* is characteristic: ' "I am thinking," says he, "therefore I am": and is it not as good reasoning to say, I am sleeping, therefore I am? If a body moves, it must exist, no doubt; but if it is at rest, it must exist likewise.'

The following summarises the position to which Reid is led when he includes the *whole* human being in his philosophical inquiries.

Reid admits that, when the consciousness that has become aware of itself surveys that which lies within its own horizon, it finds nothing else there but transient pictures. These pictures in themselves bring to the mind no experience of a lasting existence outside itself. There is no firm evidence of the existence of either an outer material world to which these pictures can be related, or of an inner spiritual entity which is responsible for them. To be able to speak of an existence in either realm is impossible for a philosophy which confines its attention solely to the mere picture content of the waking consciousness.

But man is not only a percipient being; he is also a being of will, and as such he comes into a relationship with the world which can be a source of rich experience. If one observes this relationship, one is bound to notice that it is based on the self-evident assumption that one possesses a lasting individuality, whose actions deal with a lasting material world. Any other way of behaviour would contradict the common sense of man; where we meet with it we are faced with a lunatic.

Thus philosophy and common sense seem to stand in irreconcilable opposition to each other. But this opposition is only apparent. It exists so long as philosophy thinks it is able to come to valid conclusions without listening to the voice of common sense, believing itself to be too exalted to need to do so. Philosophy, then, does not realise 'that it has no other root but the principles of Common Sense; it grows out of them, and draws its nourishment from them: severed from this root, its honours wither, its sap is dried up, it dies and rots.' (I. 5.)

At the moment when the philosophical consciousness ceases to regard itself as the sole foundation of its existence and recognises that it can say nothing about itself without considering the source from which it has evolved, it attains the possibility of seeing the content of its experience in a new light. For it is no longer satisfied with considering this content in the completed form in which it presents itself. Rather does it feel impelled to investigate the process which gives rise to this content as an end-product (the 'impressions' and 'ideas' of Hume and his predecessors).

Reid has *faith* in the fact — for his common sense assures him of it — that a lasting substantiality lies behind the world of the senses, even if for human consciousness it exists only so long as impressions of it are received via the bodily senses. Similarly, he has faith in the fact that his consciousness, although existing but intermittently, has as its bearer a lasting self. Instead of allowing this intuitively given knowledge to be shaken by a mere staring at fugitive pictures, behind which the real existence of self and world is hidden, he seeks instead in both directions for the origin of the pictures and will not rest until he has found the lasting causes of their transient appearances.

In one direction Reid finds himself led to the outer boundary of the body, where sense perception has its origin. This prompts him to investigate the perceptions of the five known senses: smelling, tasting, hearing, touching and seeing, which he discusses in this order. In the other direction he finds himself led — and here we meet with a special attribute of Reid's whole philosophical outlook — to the realm of human speech. For speech depends upon an inner, intelligent human activity, which, once learnt, becomes a lasting part of man's being, quite outside the realm of his philosophising consciousness, and yet forming an indispensable instrument for this consciousness.

The simplest human reasoning, prompted only by common sense, and the subtlest philosophical thought, both need language for their expression. Through his ability to speak, man lifts himself above an instinctive animal existence, and yet he develops this ability at an infantile stage, when, in so far as concerns the level of his consciousness and his relationship to the world, he hardly rises above the level of the animal. It requires a highly developed intelligence to probe the intricacies of language, yet complicated tongues were spoken in human history long before man awoke to his own individual intelligence. Just as each man learnt to think through speaking, so did humanity as a whole. Thus speech can become a means for acquiring insight into the original form of human intelligence. For in speech the common sense of man, working unconsciously within him, meets the fully awakened philosophical consciousness.[2]

The way in which the two paths of observation have here been set out must not give rise to the expectation that they are discussed by Reid in a similarly systematic form. For this, Reid lacked the sufficient detachment from his own thoughts. As he presents his observations in the *Inquiry* they seem to be nothing but a systematic description of the five senses, broken into continually by linguistic considerations of the kind indicated above. So, for example, many of his more important statements about language are found in his chapter on 'Hearing'.

Our task will be to summarise Reid's work, taking from his description, so often full of profound observations, only what is essential to illustrate his decisive discoveries. This requires that (keeping to Mr. Fraser's picture) we consider separately the two pillars supporting the roof of the temple's forecourt; speech and sense-impressions. We will start with speech.

* * * * *

Reid notes as a fundamental characteristic of human language that it includes two distinct elements: first, the purely acoustic element, represented by the sheer succession of sounds, and secondly the variety of meanings represented by various groups of sounds, meanings which seem to have nothing to do with the sounds as such. This state of language, where the sound-value of the word and its value as a *sign* to denote a *thing signified by it*, have little or nothing to do with one another, is certainly not the primeval one. In the contemporary state of language, which Reid calls *artificial language*, we must see a development from a former condition, which Reid calls *natural language.* So long as this earlier condition obtained, man expressed in the sound itself what he felt impelled to communicate to his fellows. In those days sound was not merely an abstract sign, but a gesture, which moreover was accompanied and supported by the gestures of the limbs.

Even today, man, at the beginning of his life, still finds himself in that relationship to language which was natural to all men in former times. The little child acquires the ability to speak through the imitation of sounds, becoming aware of them long before it understands the meaning accorded to the various groups of sounds in the artificial state of contemporary adult speech. That the child's attention should be directed solely to the sound, and not to the abstract meaning of the individual words, is indeed the pre-requisite of learning to speak. If, says Reid, the child were to understand immediately the conceptual content of the words it hears, it would never learn to speak at all.

When the adult of today uses language in its artificial state, words are only signs for things signified by them. As he speaks, his attention is directed exclusively towards this side of language; the pure sound of the words he uses remains outside the scope of his awareness. The little child, on the other hand, has no understanding of the meaning of words, and therefore lives completely in the experience of pure sound. In the light of this, Reid comes to the conclusion, so important for what follows, that with the emergence of a certain form of consciousness, in this case that of the intellectual content of words, another form submerges, a form in which the experience of the pure sound prevails. The adult, while in one respect ahead of the child, yet in another is inferior, for the effect of this change is a definite impoverishment in soul-experience. Reid puts this as follows:

'It is by natural signs chiefly that we give force and energy to language; and the less language has of them, it is the less expressive and persuasive .... Artificial signs signify, but they do not express; they speak to the understanding, as algebraic characters may do, but the passions and the affections and the will hear them not: these continue dormant and inactive, till we speak to them in the language of nature, to which they are all attention and obedience.'

We have followed Reid so far in his study of language, because it is along this way that he came to form the concepts that were to serve him as a key for his all-important findings in the realm of sense-experience. These are the concepts which bear on the connection between the sign and the thing signified; the distinction between the artificial and the natural state of language; and the disappearance of certain primeval human capacities for experience, of which Reid says that they are brought by the child into the world, but fade as his intellectual capacities develop.

* * * * *

As soon as one begins to study Reid's observations in the realm of sense-experience, one meets with a certain difficulty, noticeable earlier but not so strikingly. The source of it is that Reid was obliged to relate the results of his observations only to the five senses known in his day, whereas in fact his observations embrace a far greater field of human sense-perception. Thus a certain disharmony creeps into his descriptions and makes his statements less convincing, especially for someone who does not penetrate to its real cause.

However this may be, it need not concern us here; what matter to us are Reid's actual observations. For these led him to the important distinction between two factors in our act of acquiring knowledge of the outer world, each of which holds an entirely different place in ordinary consciousness. Reid distinguishes them as 'sensation' and 'perception'. It is through the latter that we become aware of the object as such. But we are mistaken if we regard the content of this perception as identical with the sum total of the sensations which are caused in our consciousness by the particular object. For these sensations are qualitatively something quite different, and, although without them no perception of the object is possible, they do not by themselves convey a knowledge of the thing perceived. Only, because our attention is so predominantly engaged by the object under perception, we pay no heed to the content of our sensation.

To take an example, the impressions of roundness, angularity, smoothness, roughness, colour, etc, of a table contain, all told, nothing that could assure us of the existence of the object 'table' as the real content of the external world. How, then, do we receive the conviction of the latter's existence? Reid's answer is, *by entering into an immediate intuitive relationship with it.* It is true that to establish this relationship we need the stimuli coming from the impressions which our mind receives through the various senses. Yet this must not induce us to confuse the two.

When nature speaks to man through his senses, something occurs exactly analogous to the process when man communicates with man through the spoken word. In both cases the perception, that is, the result of the process of perception, is something quite other than the sum of sensations underlying it. Per-ceiving by means of the senses is none other than a re-ceiving of nature's language; and this language, just like human language, bears two entirely different elements within it. According as one or the other element prevails in man's intercourse with nature, this intercourse will be either 'natural' or 'artificial' — to use the terms by which Reid distinguished the two stages of human speech.

Just as every human being must once have listened only to the pure sound of the spoken word on a wholly sentient level in order to acquire the faculty of speaking, so also, in order to learn nature's language, the soul must once have been totally surrendered to the pure impressions of the senses. And just as with time the spoken word becomes a symbol for that which is signified by it, the consciousness turning to the latter and neglecting the actual sound-content of the word, so also in its intercourse with nature the soul, with its growing interest in the thing signified, turns its attention more and more away from the actual experiences of the senses.

From this it follows that a philosophy which seeks to do justice to man's whole being must not be satisfied with examining the given content of human consciousness, but must strive to observe the actual process to which this content owes its emergence. In practice this means that a philosopher who understands his task aright must strive to reawaken in himself a mode of experience which is naturally given to man in his early childhood. Reid expresses this in the *Inquiry* in the following way:

'When one is learning a language, he attends to the sounds, but when he is master of it, he attends only to the sense of what he would express. If this is the case, we must become as little children again, if we will be philosophers: we must overcome habits which have been gathering strength ever since we began to think; habits, the usefulness of which atones for the difficulty it creates for the philosopher in discovering the first principles of the human mind.'

We must become as little children again, if we will be true philosophers. This is not the first time that we have come across such a demand. When we discussed Goethe's concept, *exact sensorial fantasy,* we found that striving for this faculty of cognition means working for the restoration within oneself of a condition of the soul which had been ours in early childhood.

What Reid states in these words, Goethe actually carried out. We are therefore not astonished to find Goethe thinking favourably of the whole trend of philosophy as represented by Reid. Among his papers there is a note entitled *Deutsche Philosophie*, where he mentions the 'Scottish philosopher Reid' and his follower, Stewart, as representatives of the 'Scottish doctrine' which he contrasts favourably with the German philosophy of his time. What appealed to him was their attempt 'to reconcile *Sensualismus* and *Spiritualismus*;[3] to expound the conformity of the Real with the Ideal; and thereby to bring about a more perfect state of human thinking and acting.

How close to Goethe Reid was led by his method of observation and thought is shown by the following passage in his *Inquiries* where he deals with the question of the apprehension of natural law by the human mind. He, too, was an opponent of the method of 'explaining' phenomena by means of abstract theories spun out of sheer thinking, and more than once in his writings he inveighs against it in his downright, humorous way.[4]

His conviction that human thinking ought to remain within the realm of directly experienced observation is shown in the following words: 'In the solution of natural phenomena, all the length that the human facilities can carry us is only this, that from particular phenomena, we may, by induction, trace out general phenomena, of which all the particular ones are necessary conclusions.'[5] As an example of this, he takes gravity, leading the reader from one phenomenon to the next without ever abandoning them, and concluding the journey by saying: 'The most general phenomena we can reach are what we call laws of nature. So that laws of nature are nothing else but the most general facts relating to the operations of nature, which include a great many particular facts under them.' Clearly, Reid's 'most general facts' are nothing else but what Goethe termed 'ur-phenomena'.

In the passage which includes 'we must become as little children again if we will be philosophers', this phrase appears almost in passing, and Reid never came back to it again. And yet in it is contained the *Open Sesame* which gives access to the hidden spirit-treasures of the world. In this unawareness of Reid's of the importance of what he thus had found we must see the reason for his incapacity to develop his philosophy beyond its first beginnings. This handicap arose from the fact that in all his thinking he was guided by a picture of the being of man which — as a child of his time, dominated by the contemporary religious outlook — he could never realise distinctly. Yet without a clear conception of this picture no justice can be done to Reid's concept of common sense. Our next task, therefore, must be to evoke this picture as clearly as we can.

* * * * *

The following passage in Reid's *Inquiry* provides a key for the understanding of his difficulty in conceiving an adequate picture of man's being. In this passage, Reid maintains that all art is based on man's experience of the natural language of things, and that in every human being there lives in inborn artist who is more or less crippled by man's growing accustomed to the state of artificial language in his intercourse with the world. In continuation of the passage quoted on page 133 Reid says:

'It were easy to show, that the fine arts of the musician, the painter, the actor, and the orator, so far as they are expressive; although the knowledge of them requires in us a delicate taste, a nice judgment, and much study and practice; yet they are nothing else but the language of nature, which we brought into the world with us, but have unlearned by disuse and so find the greatest difficulty in recovering it.

'Abolish the use of articulate sounds and writing among mankind for a century, and every man would be a painter, an actor, and an orator. We mean not to affirm that such an expedient is practicable; or if it were, that the advantage would counterbalance the loss; but that, as men are led by nature and necessity to converse together they will use every means in their power to make themselves understood; and where they cannot do this by artificial signs, they will do it as far as possible by natural ones:

and he that understands perfectly the use of natural signs, must
be the best judge in all expressive arts.'

* * * * *

When Reid says that there are certain characteristics — and
these just of the kind whose development truly ennobles human
life — *which the soul brings with it into the world*, a picture of
man is evoked in us in which the supersensible part of his being
appears as an entity whose existence reaches further back than
the moment of birth and even the first beginnings of the body.
Now such a conception of man is in no way foreign to humanity,
in more ancient times it was universally prevalent, and it still lives
on today, if merely traditionally, in the eastern part of the world.
It is only in the West that from a certain period it ceased to be
held. This was the result of a change which entered into human
memory in historical times, just as the re-dawning of the old
knowledge of man's pre-existence, of which Reid is a symptom,
is a result of another corresponding alteration in the memory-
powers of man in modern times.

For men of old it was characteristic that alongside the impressions they received in earthly life through the senses (which
in any case were far less intense than they are today), they remembered experiences of a purely supersensible kind, which gave
them assurance that before the soul was knit together with a
physical body it had existed in a cosmic state purely spiritual
in nature. The moment in history when this kind of memory
disappeared is that of the transition from the philosophy of
Plato to that of Aristotle. Whereas Plato was convinced by clear
knowledge that the soul possesses characteristics implanted in it
before conception, Aristotle recognised a bodiless state of the
soul only in the life after death. For him the beginning of the
soul's existence was identical with that of the body.

The picture of man, taught for the first time by Aristotle,
still required about twice four hundred years — from the fourth
pre-Christian to the fourth post-Christian century — before it

became so far the common possession of men that the Church Father Augustine (354-430) could base his teaching on it — a teaching which moulded man's outlook on himself for the coming centuries right up to our own time.

The following passage from Augustine's *Confessions* shows clearly how he was compelled to think about the nature of the little child:

'This age, whereof I have no remembrance, which I take on others' words, and guess from other infants that I have passed, true though the guess be, I am yet loath to count in this life of mine which I live in this world. For no less than that which I lived in my mother's womb, is it hid from me in the shadows of forgetfulness. But if I was shapen in iniquity and in sin my mother did conceive me, where, I beseech thee, O my God, where, Lord, or when, was I thy servant guiltless? But lo! that period I pass by; and what have I to do with that of which I can recall no vestige?'[6]

On the grounds of such experience, Augustine was unable to picture man's being in any other way than by seeing him, from the first moment of his life, as subject to the condition of the human race which resulted from the Fall. Thus he exclaims in his *Confessions*: 'Before Thee, O God, no one is free from sin, not even the child which has lived but a single day on the earth.' In so far as there was any question of the soul's arising from this fallen state, it was deemed unable to attain this by any effort of its own, but to depend on the gifts of grace which the Church was able to dispense through the Sacraments.

Compare with this the present-day scientific conception of human nature, as it dominates the thought of specialist and layman alike. Here man appears, both in body and soul, as a sum of inherited characteristics, of characteristics, that is to say, which have been passed on by way of sexual propagation and gradually emerge into full manifestation as the individual grows up. Apart from this inherited predestination the soul is held to present itself, in Locke's classical phrase, as a *tabula rasa* upon which are stamped all manner of external impressions.

The similarity between this modern picture of man and the earlier theological one is striking. In both cases the central assumption is that human development from child to man consists in the unfolding of certain inherited characteristics which are capable of further specific modification under influences proceeding from outside. The only difference between the two pictures is that in the modern one the concepts of heredity and adaptation have been formed without special application to the ethical characteristics of the soul.

It is clear that from both Augustine's and the modern scientific viewpoint there is no sense in requiring — as Reid did — those who seek the truth about themselves and the world to recover a condition which had been theirs as children. Nor from this point of view is there any justification to call on a Common Sense, innate in man, to sit in judgment on the philosophical efforts of the adult reason.

*　*　*　*　*

That even in the days of Augustine the original conception of human nature had not disappeared entirely, is shown by the appearance of Augustine's opponent Pelagius, called the 'arch-heretic'. To consider him at this point in our discussion will prove helpful for our understanding of Reid's historic position in the modern age.

What interests us here in Pelagius's doctrine (leaving aside all questions concerning the meaning of the Sacraments, etc.), is the picture of man which must have lived in him for him to teach as he did.

Leaving his Irish-Scottish homeland and arriving about the year 400 in Rome, where on account of the unusual purity of his being he soon came to be held in the highest esteem, Pelagius found himself obliged to come out publicly against Augustine. For in Augustine's doctrine of man's total depravity and of the consequent bondage of the will he could not but see danger for the future development of Christian humanity. How radically he diverged from Augustine in his view of man we may see from such of his leading thoughts as follow:

'Each man begins his life in the same condition as Adam.'

'All good or evil for which in life we are deserving of praise or blame is done by ourselves and is not born with us.'

'Before the personal will of man comes into action there is nothing in him but what God has placed there.'

'It is therefore left to the free will of man whether he falls into sin, as also whether through following Christ he raises himself out of it again.'

Pelagius could think in this way because he came from a part of Europe where the older form of human memory, already at that time almost extinct in the South, was in some degree still active. For him it was therefore a matter of direct experience that the development of man from childhood onwards was connected with a diminution of certain original capacities of the soul. Yet he was so far a child of his age as to be no longer capable of seeing whence these capacities originated.

To provide the necessary corrective to Augustine's doctrine of inheritance, Pelagius would have had to be able to see in the first years of life both a beginning of the earthly and a termination of the pre-earthly existence of the soul. The imperfections of his picture of man, however, led him to underestimate, even to deny, the significance of heredity and so of original sin in human life. For an age which no longer had any direct experience of the soul's pre-natal life, the doctrines of Augustine were undoubtedly more appropriate than those of Pelagius; Augustine was in fact the more modern of the two.

And now, if we move forward a dozen centuries and compare Thomas Reid and Immanuel Kant from this same point of view, we find the same conception of man again triumphant. But there is an essential difference: Kant carried all before him because he based himself on an age-old view of human nature, whereas Reid, uncomprehended up to our own day, pointed to a picture of man only just then dawning on the horizon of the future. Just as through Pelagius there sounded something like a last call to European humanity not to forget the cosmic nature of the soul, so through Reid the memory of this nature announced its first faint renewal. It is common to both that their voices lacked the clarity to make themselves heard among the other voices of their times; and with both the reason was the same: neither could perceive in fullness — the one no longer, the other not yet — the picture of man which ensouled their ideas.

The certainty of Reid's philosophical instinct — if such an expression be allowed — and at the same time his tragic limitations, due to an inability to understand fully the origin of this instinct, come out clearly in the battle he waged against the 'idea' as his immediate predecessors understood it. We know that Plato introduced this word into the philosophical language of mankind. In Greek ἰδέα (from ἰδεῖν, to see) means something of which one knows that it exists, because one sees it. It was therefore possible to use the word 'to see' as Plato did, because in his day it covered both sensible and supersensible perception. For Plato, knowing consisted in the soul's raising itself to perceiving the objective, world-forming IDEAS, and this action comprised at the same time a recollection of what the soul had seen while it lived, as an Idea among Ideas, before its appearance on earth.

As long as Plato's philosophy continued to shape their thought, men went on speaking more or less traditionally of Ideas as real supersensible beings. When, however, the Aristotelian mode of thinking superseded the Platonic, the term 'Idea' ceased to be used in its original sense; so much so that, when Locke and other modern philosophers resorted to it in order to describe the content of the mind, they did so in complete obliviousness of its first significance.

It is thus that in modern philosophy, and finally in ordinary modern usage, 'idea' came to be a word with many meanings. Sometimes it signifies a sense-impression, sometimes a mental representation, sometimes the thought, concept or essential nature of a thing. The only thing common to these various meanings is an underlying implication that an idea is a purely subjective item in human consciousness, without any assured correspondence to anything outside.

It was against this view of the idea that Reid took the field, going so far as to label the philosophy holding it the 'ideas system'. He failed to see, however, that in attacking the abstract use of the term he was actually in a position to restore to it its original, genuine meaning. If, instead of simply throwing the word overboard, he had been able to make use of it in its real meaning, he would have expressed himself with far greater exactitude and consistency.[7] He was prevented from doing this by his apparent ignorance of the earlier Greek philosophers, Plato included. All he seems to have known of their teachings came from inferior, second-hand reports of a later and already decadent period.

* * * * *

We now turn to the two other representatives of British spiritual life, Wordsworth and Traherne, both of whom witness to the fact that the emergence of Reid's philosophy on the stage of history was by no means an accidental event but that it represents a symptom of a general reappearance of the long-forgotten picture of man, in which birth no more than death sets up an absolute limit to human existence.

Wordsworth's work and character are so well known that there is no need to speak of them here in detail.[8] For our purpose we shall pay special attention only to his *Ode on Intimations of Immortality from Recollections of Early Childhood*, where he shows himself in possession of a memory (at any rate at the time when he wrote the poem) of the pre-natal origin of the soul, and of a capacity for experiencing, at certain moments, the frontier which the soul crosses at birth.

If, despite the widespread familiarity of the Ode, we here quote certain passages from it, we do so because, like many similar things, it has fallen victim to the intellectualism of our time in being regarded merely as a piece of poetic fantasy. We shall take the poet's words as literally as he himself uttered them. We read:

'Our birth is but a sleep and a forgetting:
The Soul that rises with us, our life's Star,
    Hath had elsewhere its setting,
    And cometh from afar:
    Not in entire forgetfulness,
    And not in utter nakedness,
But trailing clouds of glory do we come
    From God who is our home:
Heaven lies about us in our infancy!
Shades of the prison house begin to close
    Upon the growing Boy.
But he beholds the light, and whence it flows,
    He sees it in his joy;
The Youth, who daily farther from the east
    Must travel, still is Nature's Priest,
    And by the vision splendid
    Is on his way attended.'

And later:

'Hence in a season of calm weather
    Though inland far we be,
Our Souls have sight of that immortal sea
    Which brought us hither,
    Can in a moment travel thither,
And see the Children sport upon the shore,
And hear the mighty waters rolling evermore.'

The fact that Wordsworth in his later years gave no further
indication of such experiences need not prevent us from taking
quite literally what he says here. The truth is that an original
faculty faded away with increasing age, somewhat as happened
with Reid when he could no longer continue his philosophical
work along its original lines. Wordsworth's Ode is the testament
of the childhood forces still persisting but already declining within
him; it is significant that he set it down in about the same year of
life (his thirty-sixth) as that in which Traherne died and in which
Goethe, seeking renewal of his being, took flight to Italy.

* * * * *

In Appendix I the reader will find an account of the remarkable events that led at the end of the last century, to the discovery of Traherne's writings, which had remained unknown for more than two hundred years, and to the identification of the author of the unnamed manuscripts; a brief survey of Traherne's life and spiritual development is also included. These matters are dealt with in greater detail by Traherne's discoverer, Bertram Dobell, in the introduction to his edition of Traherne's poems, and by Gladys I. Wade in her work, *Thomas Traherne*. Our gratitude for the labours of these two writers, which have provided mankind with the knowledge of the character and the work of this unique personality, cannot hinder us, however, from stating that both were prevented by the premises of their own view of the world from rightly estimating that side of Traherne which is importnat for us in this book, and with which we shall specially concern ourselves in the following pages.

Of the two works of Traherne which Dobell rescued from oblivion, on both of which we shall draw for our exposition, one contains his poems, the other his prose writings. The title of the latter is *Centuries of Meditations*. The title page of one of the two manuscripts containing the collection of the poetical writings introduces these as *Poems of Felicity, Containing Divine Reflections on the Native Objects of an Infant-Eye*. As regards the title 'Centuries of Meditations' we are ignorant of the meaning Traherne may have attached to it, and what he meant by calling the four parts of the book, 'First, 'Second', etc., Century. The book itself represents a manual of devotion for meditative study by the reader.

Let our first quotation be one from the opening paragraph of the third 'Century' in which Traherne introduces himself as the bearer of certain uncommon powers of memory and, arising from these powers, a particular mission as a teacher:

'Those pure and virgin apprehensions I had from the womb, and that divine light wherewith I was born are the best unto this

day, wherein I can see the Universe. By the gift of God they
attended me into the world, and by His special favour I remember
them till now. Verily they seem the greatest gifts His wisdom
could bestow, for without them all other gifts had been dead and
vain. They are unattainable by books, and therefore I will teach
them by experience.' (III, 1.)

We find Traherne speaking here of original perceptions of a
non-sensory character and of how he was able to remember them
throughout his life. We can therefore infer that this mode of
perception did not last beyond a certain time. Traherne himself
knew when and under what circumstances it actually ceased,
though it lived on in his recollection. He tells us this in a poem,
Dumnesse, of which we will here quote the essential parts:[9]

'Sure Man was born to Meditat on Things
And to Contemplat the Eternal Springs
Of God and Nature, Glory, Bliss and Pleasure;
That Life and Love might be his Heavenly Treasure:
And therefore Speechless made at first, that he
Might in himself profoundly Busied be:
And not vent out, before he hath t'ane in
Those Antidots that guard his Soul from Sin.
    Wise Nature made him Deaf too, that he might
Not be disturbd, while he doth take Delight
In inward Things, nor be depravd with Tongues,
Nor injurd by the Errors and the Wrongs
That *Mortal Words* convey ....
    This, my Dear friends, this was my Blessed Case;
For nothing spoke to me but the fair Face
Of Heav'n and Earth, before my self could speak,
I then my Bliss did, when my Silence, break.
My Non-Intelligence of Human Words
Ten thousand Pleasures unto me affords;...
Then did I dwell within a World of Light,
Distinct and Separat from all Mens Sight,
Where did I feel strange Thoughts, and such Things see

That were, or seemd, only reveald to Me.
There I saw all the World Enjoyd by one;
There I was in the World alone;
No Business Serious seemd but one; No Work
But one was found; and that did in me lurk.
   D'ye ask me What? It was with Cleerer Eys
To see all Creatures full of Deities;
Especially Ones self: And to Admire
The Satisfaction of all True Desire
Twas to be Pleasd with all that God had done;
Twas to Enjoy even *All* beneath the Sun:
Twas with a Steddy and immediat Sense
To feel and measure all the Excellence
Of Things: Twas to inherit Endless Treasure,
And to be filld with Everlasting Pleasure:
To reign in Silence and to Sing alone
To see, love, Covet, hav, Enjoy and Prais, in one:
To Prize and to be ravishd: to be true,
Sincere and Single in a Blessed View
To prize and prais. Thus was I pent within
A Fort, Impregnable to any Sin:
Till the Avenues being Open laid,
Whole Legions Enterd, and the Forts Betrayd.
   Before which time a Pulpit in my Mind,
A Temple, and a Teacher I did find,
With a large Text to comment on. No Ear,
But Eys them selvs were all the Hearers there.
And evry Stone, and evry Star a Tongue,
And evry Gale of Wind a Curious Song.
The Heavens were an Oracle, and spake
Divinity: The Earth did undertake
The office of a Priest; And I being Dum
(Nothing besides was dum;) All things did com
With Voices and Instructions; but when I
Had gained a Tongue, their Power began to die. . . .
   Yet the first Words mine Infancy did hear,

The Things which in my Dumness did appear,
Preventing all the rest, got such a root
Within my Heart, and stick so close unto't
It may be Trampld on, but still will glow;
And Nutriment to *Soyl* it self will owe.
The first Impressions are Immortal all.
And let Mine Enemies hoop, Cry, roar, or Call,
Yet these will whisper if I will but hear,
And penetrat the Heart, if not the Ear.'

The parts of the poem we have omitted are mainly those
in which Traherne engages in moral condemnation of the world
whence human language first sounded towards him when he was
a little child. For in his retrospect he interpreted the effect on the
infant's consciousness of the acquisition of speech as having come
from the sin-filled contents of the words spoken in his surroundings.
Such an explanation can be dispensed with by anyone who has
realised that this is the effect of speech itself when the language
changes over, in Reid's words, from its 'natural' to its 'artificial'
condition.

A particular note, especially significant in our context, is
struck by Traherne in the following memory-picture of the nature
of his soul during his early years on earth:

'Certainly Adam in Paradise had not more sweet and curious
apprehensions of the world, than I when I was a child. All appeared
new, and strange at first, inexpressibly rare and delightful and
beautiful. I was a little stranger, which at my entrance into the
world was saluted and surrounded with innumerable joys. My
knowledge was Divine. I knew by intuition those things which since
my Apostacy, I collected again by the highest reason. I was entertained like an Angel with the works of God in their splendour
and glory, I saw all in the peace of Eden; Heaven and Earth did
sing my Creator's praises, and could not make more melody to
Adam, than to me. All Time was Eternity, and a perpetual Sabbath.
Is it not strange, that an infant should be the heir of the whole
world, and see those mysteries which the books of the learned

never unfold?' (III, 1, 2.)

* * * * *

In a different form the same experience comes to expression in the opening lines of Traherne's poem, *Wonder*:

'How like an Angel came I down!
How bright are all things here!
When first among his Works I did appear
O how their G L O R Y did me crown!
The World resembled his E T E R N I T I E,
In which my Soul did Walk;
And evry Thing that I did see
Did with me talk.'

The picture of man thus sketched by Traherne is as close to Reid's as it is remote from Augustine's. This remoteness comes plainly to expression in the way Traherne and Augustine regard the summons of Christ to His disciples to become as little children, a summons to which Reid was led, as we have seen, on purely philosophical grounds. Let us first of all recall the words of Christ as recorded by Matthew in his 18th and 19th chapters:

'And Jesus called a little child unto him, and set him in the midst of them, and said: Verily I say unto you, except ye be converted, and become as little children, ye shall not enter into the kingdom of Heaven. Whosoever therefore shall humble himself as this little child, the same is the greatest in the kingdom of Heaven.' (xviii, 2-4.)

'Suffer the little children and forbid them not to come unto me: for of such is the kingdom of Heaven.' (xix, 14.)

Augustine refers to these words when he concludes that examination of his childhood memories which he undertook in order to prove the depravity of the soul from its first day on earth. He says: 'In the littleness of children didst Thou, our king, give us a symbol of humility when Thou didst say: Of such is the kingdom of Heaven.'

If we glance back from what Augustine says here to the original passages in the Gospel just quoted, we see what a remarkable alteration he makes. Of the first passage only the last sentence is taken, and this in Augustine's mind is fused into one with the second passage. Thereby the admonition of Christ through one's own effort *to become* as one once was as a child disappears completely. The whole passage thus takes on a meaning corresponding to that passive attitude to the divine will inculcated by Augustine and opposed by Pelagius, and it is in this sense that the words of Christ have sunk into the consciousness of Western Christianity and are usually taken today.

We may see how differently this injunction of Christ lived in Traherne's consciousness from the following passage out of his *Centuries*:

'Our Saviour's meaning, when He said, *ye must be born again and become a little child that will enter into the Kingdom of Heaven*, is deeper far than is generally believed. It is not only in a careless reliance upon Divine Providence, that we are to become little children, or in the feebleness and shortness of our anger and simplicity of our passions, but in the peace and purity of all our soul. Which purity also is a deeper thing than is commonly apprehended.' (III, 5.)

With Traherne also the passage in question has been fused together with another utterance of Christ, from John's account of Christ's conversation with Nicodemus:

'Verily, verily I say unto you, except a man be born again, he cannot see the Kingdom of God.' (John iii, 3.)

What conception of the infant condition of man must have existed in a soul for it to unite these two passages from the Gospels in this way? Whereas for Augustine it is because of its small stature and helplessness that the child becomes a symbol for the spiritual smallness and helplessness of man as such, compared with the overwhelming power of the divine King, for Traherne it is the child's nearness to God which is most present to him, and which must be regained by the man who strives for inner perfection.

Traherne could bear in himself such a picture of man's infancy because, as he himself emphasises, he was in possession of an unbroken memory of the experiences which the soul enjoys before it awakens to earthly sense-perception. The following passage from the poem, *My Spirit*, gives a detailed picture of the early state in which the soul has experiences and perceptions quite different from those of its later life. (We may recall Reid's indication of how the child receives the natural language of things.)

> 'An Object, if it were before
> Mine Ey, was by Dame Nature's Law
>   Within my Soul: Her Store
> Was all at once within me; all her Treasures
> Were my immediat and internal Pleasures;
> Substantial Joys, which did inform my Mind.

> '... I could not tell
> Whether the Things did there
>   Themselvs appear,
> Which in *my Spirit truly* seem'd to dwell:
> Or whether my conforming Mind
> Were not ev'n all that therein shin'd.'

Further detail is added to this picture by the description, given in the poem *The Praeparative*, of the soul's non-experience of the body at that early stage. The description is unmistakably one of an experience during the time between conception and birth.

> 'My Body being dead, my Limbs unknown;
>   Before I skill'd to prize
>   Those living Stars, mine Eys;
> Before or Tongue or Cheeks I call'd mine own,
>   Before I knew these Hands were mine,
> Or that my Sinews did my Members join;
>   When neither Nostril, Foot, nor Ear,

As yet could be discern'd or did appear;
   I was within
A House I knew not; newly cloath'd with Skin.

Then was my Soul my only All to me,
    A living endless Ey,
    Scarce bounded with the Sky,
Whose Power, and Act, and Essence was to see;
   I was an inward Sphere of Light,
Or an interminable Orb of Sight,
    Exceeding that which makes the Days,
A *vital* Sun that shed abroad its Rays:
    All Life, all Sense,
A naked, simple, pure Intelligence.'

In the stanza following upon this, Traherne makes a statement which is of particular importance in the context of our present discussion. After some additional description of the absence of all bodily needs he says:

'Without disturbance then I did receiv
   The tru Ideas of all Things.'

The manuscript of this poem shows a small alteration in Traherne's hand in the second of these two lines. Where we now read 'true Ideas', there originally stood 'fair Ideas'. 'Fair' described Traherne's experience as he immediately remembered it; the later alteration to 'true' shows how well aware he was that his contemporaries might miss what he meant by 'Idea', through taking it in the sense that had already become customary in his time, namely, as a mere product of man's own mental activity.

* * * * *

At the beginning of our discussion of Traherne we spoke of him as having, among other attributes, those of a mystic. We may now distinguish him from all other mystics who deserve the name by calling him a 'mystic of thought'. For all evidence here advanced shows him as the herald of a divine, idea-filled Reason in which man participates before his birth and during the first period of his life on earth, and which to re-acquire is man's highest goal. Accordingly, Traherne regarded himself definitely as a philosopher commissioned to proclaim the doctrine of the true nature of thought. It is therefore not surprising that no fewer than four of his poems bear the title, *Thoughts*. The first of them begins with the lines:

> Ye brisk Divine and Living Things.
> Ye great Exemplars, and ye Heavenly Springs,
> Which I within me see;
> Ye Machines Great,
> Which in my Spirit God did Seat,
> Ye Engines of Felicitie.... [10]

'Thoughts' — another poem says — 'are the Angels which we send abroad to visit all the parts of God's abode.' They are described as 'Elijah's fiery Charet that conveys the soul, even here, to the eternal joys'. Thought 'is the fine and curious flower which we return and offer every hour'.[11] Of the last-named function of thought he speaks in his *Centuries* in a way that marks him as the bearer of a cognitional attitude of a kind which, for our time was first substantiated and taught in all detail by Rudolf Steiner. Traherne says:

'The thought of the World whereby it is enjoyed is better than the World. So is the idea of it in the Soul of Man, better than the World in the esteem of God .... The world within you is an offering returned, which is infinitely more acceptable to God Almighty, since it came from Him, that it might return to Him. Wherein the mystery is great. For God hath made you able to create worlds in your own mind which are more precious unto Him than those which He created .... Besides all which in its own nature also a Thought of the World, or the World in a Thought, is more excellent than the World, because it is spiritual and nearer unto God. The material World is dead and feeleth nothing, but this spiritual world, though it be invisible, hath all dimensions, and is a divine and living Being, the voluntary Act of an obedient Soul.' (II, 90.)

Traherne has not been spared the fate of having his true being and spiritual mission misunderstood by the very people who out of real love for him took on the task of making him known to their own and future generations. Miss Wade, it is true, took great pains to do justice to Traherne the mystic. But she was fascinated by that side of him which shows him as striving to lift himself up through strict self-training from the experience of the abyss to the stage of beatific vision.[12] Hence she shuts her eyes to the fact that, in spite of the genuine experiences he underwent, Traherne was granted throughout his life the remembrance of the cosmic consciousness of his early childhood, and that this accompanied him through all the struggles of his soul. For her, the picture of Childhood which Traherne says plainly was based on objective experience, is a purely ideal-poetical one. It was her inability to overcome in herself the Augustinian picture of man that prompted her to interpret Traherne in this way. While seeing, she 'saw past the thing'. For Traherne himself was after all (without knowing it) a true 'Pelagian'.

Dobell, after his own manner, fared no differently. Even the precaution which led Traherne to alter the text of his poem, *The Praeparative*, as described above did not save him from being mininterpreted in precisely the way he feared — by the very critic who discovered him. It is because of the symptomatic character of this misinterpretation that we must deal with it here.

In his attempt to classify the philosophical mode of thought behind Traherne's writings, Dobell, to his own amazement, comes to the conclusion that Traherne had anticipated Bishop Berkeley (1684-1753). They seemed to him so alike that he does not hesitate to call Traherne a 'Berkeleyan before Berkeley was born'. In proof of this he refers to the poems, *The Praeparative* and

My Spirit, citing from the latter the passage given above (pages 151/2), and drawing special attention to its two concluding lines. Regarding this he says: 'I am much mistaken if the theory of non-existence of independent matter, which is the essence of Berkeley's system, is not to be found in this poem. The thought that the whole exterior universe is not really a thing apart from and independent of man's consciousness of it, but something which exists only as it is perceived, is undeniably found in *My Spirit*.'

The reader who has followed our exposition in the earlier parts of this chapter can be in no doubt that, to find a philosophy similar to Traherne's, he must look for it in Reid and not in Berkeley. Reid himself rightly placed Berkeley amongst the representatives of the 'ideal system' of thought. For Berkeley's philosophy represents an effort of the onlooker-consciousness, unable as it was to arrive at certainty regarding the objective existence of a material world outside itself, to secure recognition for an objective Self behind the flux of mental phenomena. Berkeley hoped to do this by supposing that the world, including God, consists of nothing but 'idea'-creating minds, operating like the human mind as man himself perceives it. His world picture, based (as is well known) entirely on optical experiences, is the perfect example of a philosophy contrived by the one-eyed, colour-blind world spectator.

We shall understand what in Traherne's descriptions reminded Dobell of Berkeley, if we take into account the connection of the soul with the body at the time when, according to Traherne, it still enjoys the untroubled perception of the true, the light-filled, Ideas of things.

In this condition the soul has only a dim and undifferentiated awareness of its connection with a spatially limited body ('I was within a house I knew not, newly clothed with skin') and it certainly knows nothing at all of the body as an instrument, through which the will can be exercised in an earthly-spatial way ('My body being dead, my limbs unknown'). Instead of this, the soul experiences itself simply as a supersensible sense-organ and as such united with the far spaces of the universe ('Before I skilled to prize those living stars, mine eyes.... Then was my soul my only All to me, a living endless eye, scarce bounded with the sky').

At the time when the soul has experiences of the kind described by Traherne, it is in a condition in which, as yet, no active contact has been established between itself and the physical matter of the body and thereby with gravity. Hence there is truth in the picture which Traherne thus sketches from actual memory. The same cannot be said of Berkeley's world-picture. The fact that both resemble each other in certain features need not surprise us, seeing that Berkeley's picture is, in its own way, a pure 'eye-picture' of the world. As such, however, it is an illusion – for it is intended for a state of man for which it is not suited, namely for adult man going upright on the earth, directing his deeds within its material realm, and in this way fashioning his own destiny.

Indeed, compared with Berkeley's eye-picture of the world, that of Reid is in every respect a 'limb-picture'. For where he seeks for the origin of our naive assurance that a real material world exists, there he reverts – guided by his common sense – to the experiences available to the soul through the fact that the limbs of the body meet with the resistant matter of the world. And whenever he turns to the various senses in his search, it is always the will-activity of the soul within the sense he is investigating – and so the limb-nature within it – to which he first turns his attention. Because, unlike Berkeley, he takes into account the experiences undergone by the soul when it leaves behind its primal condition, Reid does not fall into illusion, but discovers a fundamental truth concerning the nature of the world-picture experienced by man in his adult age. This, in turn, enables him to discover the nature of man's world-picture in early childhood and to recognise the importance of recovering it in later life as a foundation for a true philosophy.

Assuredly, the philosopher who discovered that we must become as little children again if we would be philosophers, is the one to whom we may relate Traherne, but not Berkeley. And if we wish to speak of Traherne, as Dobell tried to do, we speak correctly only if we call him a 'Reidean before Reid was born'.

* * * * *

A little more than a hundred years after Thomas Traherne taught his fellow-men 'from experience' that there is an original condition of man's soul, before it is yet able to prize 'those living stars, mine eyes', in which it is endowed with the faculty to see 'the true (fair) Ideas of all things', Goethe was led to the realisation that he had achieved the possibility of 'seeing Ideas with the very eyes'. Although he was himself not aware of it, the conception of the Idea was at this moment restored through him to its true and original Platonic significance.

The present chapter has shown us how this conception of the Idea is bound up with the view that is held of the relationship between human nature in early childhood and human nature in later life. We have seen that, when Plato introduced the term Idea as an expression for spiritual entities having a real and independent existence, men were still in possession of some recollection of their own pre-earthly existence. We then found Traherne saying from his recollections that in the original form of man's consciousness his soul is endowed with the faculty of seeing 'true' Ideas, and we found Reid on similar grounds fighting the significance which the term 'idea' had assumed under his predecessors. By their side we see Goethe as one in whom the faculty of seeing Ideas appears for the first time in adult man as a result of a systematic training of observation and thought.

In this way Goethe was taken along a path which, as we saw earlier, leads a man to become again, in some definite sense, a little child. Hence, he bore in himself a picture of infant man which we have seen to be a prerequisite for conceiving the Idea in the sense of the Platonic conception. This is shown by the following passages from Goethe's autobiography, *Truth and Fiction*.

In that part of his life story where Goethe concludes the report of the first period of his childhood (Book II), he writes:

'Who is able to speak worthily of the fullness of childhood? We cannot behold the little creatures which flit about before us otherwise than with delight, nay, with admiration; for they generally promise more than they perform and it seems that nature, among the other roguish tricks that she plays us, here also especially designs to make sport of us. The first organs she bestows upon children coming into the world, are adapted to the nearest immediate condition of the creature, which, unassuming and artless, makes use of them in the readiest way for its present purposes. The child, considered in and for itself, with its equals, and in relations suited to its powers, seems so intelligent and rational, and at the same time so easy, cheerful and clever, that one can hardly wish it further cultivation. If children grew up according to early indications, we should have nothing but geniuses.'[13]

We find further evidence in Goethe's account of an event in his seventh year, which shows how deeply his soul was filled at that time with the knowledge of its kinship with the realm from which nature herself receives its existence. This knowledge led him to approach the 'great God of Nature' through an act of ritual conceived by himself. The boy took a four-sectioned music stand and arranged on it all kinds of natural specimens, minerals and the like, until the whole formed a kind of pyramidal altar. On the top of this pyramid he placed some fumigating candles, the burning of which was to represent the 'upward yearning of the soul for its God'. In order to give nature herself an active part in the ritual, he contrived to kindle the candles by focusing upon them through a magnifying-glass the light of the rising sun. Before this symbol of the unity of the soul with the divine in nature the boy then paid his devotions.

'Unity of the soul with the divine in nature' — that was what lived vividly as a conviction in the seven-year-old boy, impelling him to act as 'nature's priest' (Wordsworth). The same impulse, in a metamorphosed form, impelled the adult to go out in quest of an understanding of nature which, as Traherne put it, was to bring back through highest reason what once had been his by way of primeval intuition. And in striving for exact sensorial fantasy he fulfilled what Reid demanded of a man who aims at being a true philosopher.

Chapter VIII

DYNAMICS VERSUS KINETICS

At the end of Chapter V, which served to introduce Goethe's method by following his morphological studies, we were able to make two statements which have a particular bearing on the physical sphere of nature and are therefore of special importance for our further studies. Through comparing certain experiences of our sense of warmth with thermometrical measurement, we found proof of the truth of Goethe's assertion that 'the senses do not deceive, but the judgment deceives' (page 107). Thus a way opened up for appealing, with scientific justification, to pure sense-experiences outside the precincts of one-eyed colour-blind perception, in order to gain true knowledge of nature. Further, we could use Hooke's case for realising how to proceed in the sphere of nature's inorganic actions in order to see there, also, Ideas 'with our very eyes'. We found that in order to recognise the relationship between human thought and external object, we must heed, not the finished object, but its coming into being. At the same time this furnished us with an insight into the different relationships between Idea and Object in the organic and inorganic realms of nature.

The purpose of the present chapter is to show that the two basic principles of Goethe's mode of research — confidence in the language of the senses, and the possibility of recognising in the phenomena themselves their relevant idea — were already active at the very birth of modern science. Galileo's discovery of the law of 'Free Fall', and of the 'Parallelogram of Forces' will bear witness to this. Through our way of discussing these two and how they came to be found, two further points will become clear which we shall need for our later observations.

One is the concept of force that will cease to be a mere auxiliary concept, which it is of necessity for the spectator-mind (page 22). As soon as one sets out on a path towards redeeming the concept of force from its auxiliary character by basing it on the actual experience of force, the term 'Dynamics' receives its proper meaning and then stands in contrast to mere Kinetics, which is concerned solely with the observation of motion without reference to force. It is to this difference which the title of the present chapter means to point.

The other point which will become clear as a result of this, concerns a question in modern science which recent thinkers have either tried to answer metaphysically (Jeans and others), or have dismissed as scientifically meaningless (Mach and his followers.) It is the question about the relationship between the mathematical faculties of the human mind and the mathematical order of the universe, or, briefly, between 'Geometry and Experience'.[1]

* * * * *

Ever since Galileo is reputed to have carried out his observations at the leaning tower of Pisa it has been known that all bodies require the same time for falling from the same height, or, as this was expressed in classical mechanics, that the acceleration of freely falling bodies is the same, irrespective of their mass.[2] In order to demonstrate this law in pure form, we must have recourse to a fairly long evacuated glass tube with a small feather and a small piece of lead enclosed in it. With the tube held vertically, they lie together at the bottom. By quickly reversing the tube we allow the two objects to fall simultaneously down its length: both are seen to reach the bottom at the same moment.

It is true that in outer nature, because of air resistance and other external influences, this process can never take place in its pure form. Thus on one occasion in school, when the experiment was demonstrated during a physics lesson, a pupil was prompted to ask, 'Then why is it called a law of *nature*?' Here was the voice of the Hans Andersen child calling attention to a simple fact: not, this time, that people were pretending to see something that was not there, but that people were using a thought without realising what it implied. We shall find the true answer to the problem thus raised by considering what must have gone on in Galileo's mind to lead him to this discovery.

It would be unjust to Galileo to say that by good fortune he lacked sufficiently precise methods of observation to show how his ideal law could be upset by incidental factors, so that he naively regarded the actual event as taking place in its ideal form. His writings show that he was well aware of the existence of these factors. On the other hand, the usual conclusion, that he inferred the law from the observed occurrence by a process of abstraction, is equally wrong, for there is nothing to suggest that he went about it in this way. The question rather is: what was it that impelled him ever to undertake observations of this kind? He must have had an inward conviction that such a law existed as an active agent in outer nature; he was on the look-out for it because the idea of it was already present in his mind. When making his observations he saw this idea 'with his very eyes', quite unconcerned with any outer disturbances that might prevent the process from taking place in its ideal form. When we come to our second example, we shall see even more clearly that this picture of what happened is correct.

When Galileo set out to measure the rate of acceleration of falling bodies, he saw that the speed of a freely falling mass was too great for him to be able to measure it; hence he had the bold idea of measuring the movement of a ball rolling down an inclined plane. He argued that since the cause of the motion was the same, the 'law' governing it must also be the same. For the difference concerns only the actual speed of the object, not the relative increase of the speed during corresponding intervals of time. Obviously, it was the expectation of the identity of the Idea working in altered circumstances – to use Goethe's language – that prompted Galileo to think and act as he did. Seen in this light, the phenomena of the free fall and of the movement down an inclined plane appear to stand in a relationship with one another for which later, in the field of organic nature, Goethe found the concept of Metamorphosis. It was this concept which enabled Galileo, still without realising it consciously, to carry out what is taken to be the first true experiment in the history of mankind.

* * * * *

We now turn to Galileo's discovery of the so-called theorem of the Parallelogram of Forces. This states that two forces of different quantity and direction, when they apply at the same point, act together in the manner of a single force whose quantity and direction may be represented by the diagonal of a parallelogram whose sides express in extent and direction the first two forces. Thus in Fig. 3, R exercises upon P the same effect as F_1 and F_2 together.

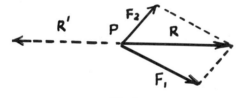

Fig. 3

Expressed in another way, a force of this quantity working in the reverse direction (R ') will establish an equilibrium with the other two forces. In technical practice, as is well known, this theorem is used for countless calculations, in both statics and dynamics, and indeed more frequently not in the form given here, but in the converse manner, when a single known force is resolved into two component forces. (Distribution of a pressure along frameworks, of air pressure along moving surfaces, etc.)

Now, there is a striking resemblance between this theorem of Galileo and another which as such is one of pure mathematics.

This is the theorem of the Parallelogram of Movements. Fig. 4 represents it diagrammatically. When a point moves with a certain speed in the direction indicated by the arrow *a*, so that in a certain time it passes from P to A, and when it is moved simultaneously with a second speed in the direction indicated by *b*, through which alone it would pass to B in the same time, its actual movement is indicated by *c*, the diagonal in the parallelogram formed by *a* and *b*. An example of the way in which this theorem is practically applied is the well-known case of a rower who sets

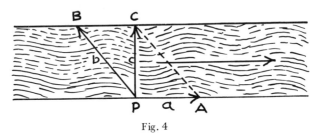

Fig. 4

out from P in order to cross at right angles a river indicated by the parallel lines. He has to counteract the motion of the water of the river flowing to the right by steering obliquely left towards B in order to arrive finally at C.

It is essential to observe that the content of this theorem does not need the confirmation of any outer experience for its discovery, or to establish its truth. Even though the recognition of the fact which it expresses may have first come to men through practical observation, yet the content of this theorem can be discovered and proved by purely logical means. In this respect it resembles any purely geometrical statement such as, that the sum of the angles of a triangle is two right angles (180°). Even though this too may have first been learnt through outer observation, yet it remains true that for the discovery of the fact expressed by it — valid for all plane triangles — no outer experience is needed. In both cases we find ourselves in the domain of pure geometric conceptions (length and direction of straight lines, movement of a point along these), whose reciprocal relationships are ordered by

the laws of pure geometric logic. So in the theorem of the Parallelogram of Movements we have a strictly geometrical theorem, whose
content is in the narrowest sense kinematic. In fact, it is the
basic theorem of kinematics.

There is, indeed, a noteworthy mathematical conformity
between both these theorems: movements and forces appear to
obey the same rule of geometrical addition and subtraction. Now
it is true that, ever since the onset of the phase in modern science
characterised by the need for a critical examination of its conceptual foundations, scientists are no longer of the opinion – as
it was held right into the nineteenth century – that the parallelogram of forces could be derived by pure logic from the parallelogram
of movements and that therefore the whole science of Dynamics
can be thus reduced to pure Kinetics. Yet, no scientific step has
become possible beyond this merely negative statement. This is
because the spectator-consciousness is inherently unable to conceive
the nature of force. As a telling symptom of this we quoted
in our first chapter Newton's first law, showing it to contain
nothing beyond the statement already used by Newton himself
for defining the concept, force. In order to attain to an autonomous conception of force we must carry our observation across
the border of the spectator-consciousness. As we shall see, this will
lead us to a true insight into the ideal relationship between the
two theorems.

* * * * *

Let us remember how Common Sense prompted Thomas
Reid, when faced with Hume's seemingly convincing conclusion
that man was not provided with a self as an enduring bearer of his
fleeting mental pictures, to observe that human language told a
different story, for it had coined the word 'I' to express man's
experience of his own self long before he started to philosophise.
Similarly, the fact that all languages possess a word for 'force'
must be taken by us as a sign that man has always had a concrete
experience of force as a reality, and that only when his conscious-

ness awoke to the onlooker-condition did he become uncertain about the existence of force as an objective reality. The source of this experience, however, will not be found so long as we keep to the communications conveyed by the senses which relate us to the external world, but only by turning to our own innermost being — indeed, to those regions of our psycho-physical organisation which are usually withdrawn from waking consciousness. For it is in the realm of our own will that we gain experience of the real existence of force whenever we set our will in action to move an outer physical object — our body itself already representing such an object. Still, this experience can be reinforced by experimenting with some outer physical object. Take a fairly heavy object into your hand, stretch out your arm lightly and move it slowly up and down, watching intently the sensation this operation rouses in you. It is thus that one can bring to awareness how force, in the form of one's own will, meets with force exerted by an outer mass.

In this way man has always known of the existence of force. And when he speaks of force in the realm of outer sense-perception, he does so on grounds of his intuitive participation in the observed event. Any other way of speaking about force, as we shall see later, leads to illusion.

This is the path we must follow, if we are to get at the origin of our knowledge of the behaviour of forces, as it comes to expression in the law of the parallelogram of forces. Our procedure, therefore, will have to be as follows.

We shall enlist two other persons, with whom we shall try to discover by means of our respective experiences of force the law under which three forces applying at a common point may hold themselves in equilibrium. Our first step will consist in grasping each other by the hand and in applying various efforts of our wills to draw one another in different directions, seeing to it that we do this in such a way that the three joined hands remain undisturbed at the same place. By this means we can get as far as to establish that, for each direction and strength of pull by two of the three persons, there is needed on the part of the third a definite direction and effort to hold the others in equilibrium.

This, however, is all that can be learnt in this way. No possibility arises at this stage of our investigation of establishing any exact quantitative comparison. For the forces which we have brought forth (and this is valid for forces in general, no matter of what kind they are) represent pure intensities, outwardly neither visible nor directly measurable. We can certainly tell whether we are intensifying or diminishing the application of our will, but a numerical comparison between different exertions of will is not possible.

In order to make such a comparison, a further step is necessary. We must convey our effort to some pointer-instrument — for instance, a spiral spring which will respond to an exerted pressure or pull by a change in its spatial extension. (Principle of the spring balance.) In this way, by making use of a certain property of matter — elasticity — the purely intensive quantities of the forces which we exert become extensibly visible and can be presented geometrically. We shall therefore continue our investigation with the aid of three spring balances, which we hook together at one end while exposing them to the three pulls at the other.

To mark the results of our repeated pulls of varying intensities and directions, we draw on the floor three chalk lines outward from the point underneath the common point of the three instruments, each in the direction taken up by one of the three persons. Along these lines we mark the extensions corresponding to those of the springs of the instruments.

By way of this procedure we shall arrive at a sequence of figures such as is shown in Fig. 5.

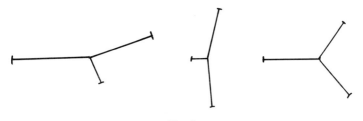

Fig. 5

This is all we can discover empirically regarding the mutual relationships of three forces engaging at a point.

Neither does this group of figures reveal directly that in each one of these trios of lines there resides a definite and identical geometrical order; nor is there anything in the realm of our logic that would lead us to expect the existence of such an order — let alone of one analogous to the parallelogram of movements. This statement is valid irrespective of whether we proceed as we have done here, for the sake of removing certain fallacious ideas, or whether we use, right from the start, a measuring instrument.

What then was it, we must now ask, if it was not logical reasoning, that enabled Galileo to find the law of the parallelogram of forces, and thus to lay the foundation for the entire edifice of modern exact science? It is known that when he had made the discovery he wrote to a friend (Lizetti): *'La natura è scritta in lingua matematica!'* ('Nature is recorded in the language of mathematics.') These words reveal his surprise when he realised the implication of his discovery. Still, he must have intuitively expected it. For there must have been something to make him believe that a use of geometrical lengths to symbolise the measured magnitudes of forces would yield some valid result. Since there is nothing, as we have seen, to prompt the mind to deduce from the ideal-geometrical parallelogram of movements a corresponding order in the dynamic realm of nature: what created this belief in Galileo? And what was it that helped him to recognise a common geometrical order in those trios of lines? Finally, since there is no logical reason for it, what are we told by the very fact that nature, at least on a certain level, exhibits rules of action which correspond to the rules of logic immanent in the human mind?

To find the answer to these questions we must revert to certain facts connected with man's psycho-physical make-up of which the considerations of Chapter II have already made us aware.

Let us, therefore, transpose ourselves once more into the condition of the child who is still entirely volition, and thus experiences himself as one with the world. Let us consider, from the point of view of this condition, the process of lifting the body into the vertical position and the acquisition of the faculty of maintaining it in this position; and let us ask what the soul, though with no consciousness of itself, experiences in all this. It is the child's will which wrestles in this act with the dynamic structure of external space, and what his will experiences is accompanied by corresponding perceptions through the sense of movement and other related bodily senses. In this way the parallelogram of forces becomes an inner experience of our organism at the beginning of our earthly life. What we thus carry in the body's will-region in the form of *experienced geometry* — this, together with the freeing and crystallising of part of our will-substance into our conceptual capacity, is transformed into our faculty of forming geometrical concepts, and among them the concept of the parallelogram of movements.

From our account it follows that no question as to the relationship between the two theorems could have arisen if man had been able to remember throughout life his experiences in early childhood. So long as he had such a memory, therefore, no question existed for him concerning the nature of force, because in the working of outer forces he saw a manifestation of will-endowed beings, just as in himself he experienced force as a manifestation of his own will-endowed being. We have seen that this form of memory had to fade away to enable man to find himself as a self-conscious personality between birth and death. As such a personality, Galileo was able to think out the parallelogram of movements, but he was unable to comprehend the origin of his faculty of mathematical thinking, or of his intuitive knowledge of the mathematical behaviour of nature in that realm of hers where she sets physical forces into action. Hence he must have been led to his discovery in the following way.

Deep below in Galileo's soul there lived, as it does in every human being, the intuitive knowledge, acquired in early childhood, that part of nature's order is recordable in the conceptual language of mathematics. In order that this intuition should rise sufficiently far into his conscious mind to guide him, as it

did, in his observations, the veil of oblivion which otherwise
separates our waking consciousness from the experiences of
earliest childhood must have been momentarily lightened. Yet,
with the veil immediately darkening again, onlooker-thinking
became subject, in the course of time, to the conviction that in
order to recognise mathematics as a means of describing nature,
it was in need of nothing more than was accessible to it on the
near side of the veil. Still, Galileo's discovery would not have
been possible unless he had in a sense become — although without
realising it — a little child again.

Thus the event that gave science its first foundations is an
occurrence in man himself of precisely the same character as the
one we have learnt to regard as necessary for building science's
new foundations. The only difference is that we are called upon
to turn into a deliberate and consciously handled method something which once in the past happened *to* man without his noticing it
at the time, and without rightly comprehending it later on.

* * * * *

Because of the way in which we have treated in this chapter
Galileo's two basic discoveries, their content appears in a light
that enables us to apply to them yet another Goethean concept.
This is the concept of the ur-phenomenon.

We found, in Goethe's own words, the ur-phenomenon characterised as 'an instance worth a thousand, bearing all within itself'
(page 123). It is, among all possible phenomena in a particular
sphere, the one through which the Idea manifests in purest form.
When discussing Reid we also found him expressing himself on
the significance of the laws of nature in such a way that we recognised in his words the concept of the ur-phenomenon (page 136).
It was given to Galileo to recognise in the fields of gravitation and
the operation of mechanical forces the ur-phenomenal value of the
observed phenomena. In this way he found the 'law' of free fall
and the 'law' of the parallelogram-relation of three forces acting at
a common point.

Our considerations, however, also throw light back on Goethe's achievements. For now they appear as the consistent continuation of Galileo's. This prompted Rudolf Steiner, in various books and lectures, to speak of Goethe as the 'Galileo of the organic sciences'. This verdict, indeed, cannot be reversed in the sense that in Galileo we may see a Goethe of the inorganic sciences. For in order to see how it is that Goethe carries further Galileo's attitude towards the Idea in the world of the senses, we need an understanding of Galileo which we can gain only by following Goethe's methods. It is Goethe, as the Galileo of the organic sciences, who enables us to interpret, as it were, Galileo to himself.

Chapter IX

PRO LEVITATE

At the present time the human mind is in danger of confusing the realm of dynamic events, into which modern atomic research has penetrated, with the world of the spirit; that is, the world whence nature is endowed with intelligent design, and, which manifests in man in conscious form as his reason. Therefore, if a science of nature aspiring to a spiritual understanding of the universe — such as Goethe founded and others have conceived more or less dimly — is to be of significance in our time, it must be carried forward to the point where matter is understood as an instrument for the spirit's intelligent, form-creating activity. To show the way towards this goal will be the subject of the present and the ensuing chapters. Before embarking upon it, however, the following general observation is necessary.

PRELIMINARY REMARK

Right at the outset of this book we pointed out that a science which deserves the name must have as its characteristic that it is grounded in activities of the human mind which take place in the full light of waking consciousness. We saw how of necessity this resulted in man enlisting for his researches only that which can be obtained by one-eyed, colour-blind perception. On the other hand, we saw how in the minds of the men working in this way a longing arose which induced them to penetrate just into those realms of nature which lie outside the boundaries of this sphere of perception. Happenings in the ultra-realm can, indeed, cause perceptions within the spectator-boundaries, but they are secondary perceptions. If we notice motion, e.g. as a result of the action of electrical forces, these motions are indeed accessible to the spectator-consciousness, but they are not electricity itself. This holds good in principle for all we designate with the name of 'force'.

Spectator-thinking, when it grew conscious of this fact, was compelled to distinguish carefully between concepts pertaining to immediate experiences, and others that have reference to things of which one can have knowledge only by way of mediate experience. The former, we saw, can only be kinematic concepts; the latter had to be regarded as auxiliary concepts. (See page 22.) To look out for the 'reality' covered by the auxiliary concepts is, for a thinking of this kind, an idle, indeed a philosophically illicit, undertaking.

On the grounds of a science working in the sense of Goethe, this fact receives full recognition, but through this science a road opens up towards attaining to immediate experiences also outside the boundaries of the spectator-consciousness which are not less objective than those inside these boundaries, and thereby to the possibility of investing certain concepts with the character of 'existence'-concepts (ontological concepts) which hitherto ranked only as auxiliary concepts. In the previous chapter we were able to apply this already to the concept of force. In the following pages other concepts will receive similar treatment. Through previous discussions we have in any case provided the necessary premises to allow the scientifically trained reader to follow us further without feeling compelled to raise unwarranted objections against our conceptual procedure. With the further progress of our discussion these premises, as the attentive reader will notice, will find increasing confirmation.

ALERTNESS *contra* INERTNESS

The picture of the world which came into being through the form of science founded by Galileo and Newton was essentially a mechanistic one. We may take as characteristic of this picture the statement by which, in textbooks of this phase of physics, the possible causation of physical movement has been defined in this or similar form: 'Any change in the state of movement of a

portion of matter is the result of the action on it of another
portion of matter.' In this statement we encounter the peculiarity
of the spectator-mind which — as already noted — allows it to
take account only of spatially extended objects, which can naturally
exist in space only in a side-by-side way. Changes in the state of
movement of spatially extended entities could for this reason be
ascribed only to the working of entities of a similar kind, which
naturally must be situated outside one another.

In this respect no real change was introduced into the picture
of the world, when, at the beginning of this century, physical
research was compelled to stop using mechanical models to
explain natural occurrences, because in the ultra-region into which
it had penetrated happenings were being registered which resisted
all attempts at mechanical explanation. Since then, this form of
explanation has been replaced by pure mathematical description —
as in the theory of relativity and the quantum theory — which
does not claim to explain the actual nature of the objects of
observation. Hence a scientist who speaks of 'portions of matter',
as in the above statement, does not now claim to know what it
is that thus comes to his notice. Yet, even in this new phase the
scientific mind has remained in the spectator-relationship to the
phenomenal world. Hence it continues to know only of relations
between movements which occur in a spatially separated way. By
using the concepts of Cause and Effect, we can express this by
saying that cause and effect stand, as before, in a spatially external
relationship to each other. We assume the right, therefore, to
describe this form of causal nexus as 'mechanical causation'
although there is no longer a mechanical model to explain the
happenings, and although no concept of a causal nexus enters
into the mathematical description. In this sense the present-day
picture of the physical world still is — though not crudely mechanical — yet in a deeper sense mechanistic.

Now, our study of the plant, in the manner first shown by
Goethe, has, in fact, confronted us already with truly non-mechanical causes of events in the physical-material sphere. For the
cause that makes plants germinate, grow, assume form, and pass

through successive stages of metamorphosis is not to be found spatially outside the created effects. Cause and effect differ here essentially in kind. We found Ruskin speaking of such causes plainly in terms of 'spirit' and 'form'. In this respect our own body is again a particularly instructive object of study. For here mechanical and non-mechanical causation can be seen working side by side in closest conjunction. Let us therefore ask what happens when we move, say, one of our limbs or a part of it.

The movement of any part of our body is always effected in some way by the movement of the corresponding part of the skeleton. This in turn is set in motion by certain lengthenings and contractions of the appropriate part of the muscular system. Now the way in which the muscles cause the bones to move falls clearly under the category of mechanical causation. Certain portions of matter are caused to move by the movement of adjacent portions of matter. The picture changes when we look for the cause to which the muscles owe their movements. For the motion of the muscles is not the effect of any cause external to them, but is effected by the purely spiritual energy of our volition working directly into the physical substance of the muscles. What scientific measuring instruments have been able to register in the form of physical, chemical, electrical, etc., changes of the muscular substance is itself an effect of this interaction.

A science which aspires at an understanding of how *spirit* moves, forms, and transforms matter, must be prepared to acknowledge the existence of such physical effects of non-physical causes. For this type of causation it thus needs a term analogous to the term 'mechanical'. Here the word 'magical' suggests itself as a suitable one. The fact that this word has gathered all sorts of doubtful associations must not hinder us from adopting it into the terminology of a science which aspires to understand the working of the supersensible in the world of the senses. The falling into disrepute of this word is characteristic of the onlooker-age. The way in which we suggest it should be used is in accord with its true and original meaning, the syllable 'mag' signifying power or might (Sanskrit *maha*, Greek *megas*, Latin *magnus*,

English *might, much,* also *master*). Henceforth we shall distinguish between 'mechanical' and 'magical' causation, the latter being a characteristic of the majority of happenings in the human, animal and plant organisms.

* * * * *

Our next step in building up a truly dynamic picture of matter must be to try to obtain a direct experience of the condition of matter when it is under the sway of magical causation. This can be brought to our immediate experience in the following way. (The reader, even if he is already familiar with this experiment, is again asked to carry it out for himself.)

Take a position close to a smooth wall, so that one arm and hand, which are left hanging down alongside the body, are pressed over their entire length between body and wall. Try now to move the arm upward, pressing it against the wall as if you wanted to shift the latter. Apply all possible effort to this attempt, and maintain the effort for about one minute. Then step away quickly from the wall by more than the length of the arm, while keeping the arm hanging down by the side of the body in a state of complete relaxation. Provided all conditions are properly fulfilled, the arm will be found rising *by itself* in accordance with the aim of the earlier effort, until it reaches the horizontal. If the arm is then lowered again and left to itself, it will at once rise again, though not quite so high as before. This can be repeated several times until the last vestige of the automatic movement has faded away.

The reader will not find it difficult to supplement this observation with others of a similar kind. Besides bringing to our direct experience the effect of magical causation, the observation is significant because the sensation which appears in the arm brings to our notice the fact that there is yet another state of matter besides that of inertness (inertia) which up to now has been regarded by scientific thought as the essential characteristic of physical matter. Let us denote this other state by the term 'alertness'. In the above experiment it becomes particularly noticeable as the after-effect of the magical operation of the will in the muscular matter of the arm.

We can characterise the difference between the states of inertness and alertness more closely by means of the following consideration, which will also bring out a further aspect of the peculiarity of magical causation.

Newton's first law is frequently called the 'law of inertia'. If we take this theorem as what it really is, namely just another formulation of Newton's definition of force (page 23) — indeed the only kind of force that Newton had in mind — then it tells us: *Where matter under the influence of some force appears to be in the state of inertness, the operating force is of the mechanical kind.* Now, this theorem is followed in Newton's *Principia* by a second theorem which, indeed, requires a different verdict from the former. It states that the quantity of the change of the state of movement (acceleration) is proportional to the applied force and inversely proportional to mass. In symbols: $a = F/M$. In principle, this is known to everyone through practical experience. The greater the force I use to set a loaded wheelbarrow in motion, the shorter the time I need to give it a certain speed, and the heavier the load of the barrow the smaller the acceleration which I bring about by the same effort. The fact that the three relevant magnitudes — force, mass, and acceleration — are related quantitatively in a way that allows mathematical expression is again a knowledge to be gained empirically, as in the case of the parallelogram of forces. In this instance, too, we are confronted with an ur-phenomenon of mechanics.

Now it is important for us to recognise just how far the above example is valid for bringing to our experience the relationship of force in *general* to its effect. We found earlier that we know of 'force' through experiences in our own volitional system. This is true also with regard to external, mechanically working forces. But our own will is a force that works magically in our own body. Consequently different persons need a quite different effort of will in order to apply the same acceleration to the same mass.

What is accomplished by one person with a trifling exertion, requires the greatest strain from another. In its own way this is revealed both to our inner experience and to outer observation by the experiment with the rising arm. In fact, a certain effort is even required to prevent the arm from moving! Thus the statement that the change of the state of movement of some mass is a direct measurement of the quantity of the force causing that change, is valid only where we have to do with the effect of purely mechanical forces. However, the question as to the particular nature of the force responsible for some observable event outside ourselves can never be answered by a mere onlooking observation.

* * * * *

A method which again and again proves helpful in one's attempts to get beyond certain current scientific conceptions is to call to mind how these conceptions first came into being. To know the Whence of a road often helps to determine the Whither. This means that in our endeavour to find a modern way of overcoming the conception of matter developed and held by science in the age of the onlooker-consciousness, we shall be helped by noticing how this conception first arose historically. Of momentous significance in this respect is the discovery of the gaseous state of matter by the Flemish physician and experimenter, Joh. Baptist van Helmont (1577-1644). The fact that the existence of this state of ponderable matter was quite unknown up to such a relatively recent date has been completely forgotten today. Moreover, it is so remote from current notions that anyone who now calls attention to van Helmont's discovery is quite likely to be met with incredulity. As a result, there is no account of the event that puts it in its true setting. In what follows pains are taken to present the facts in the form in which one comes to know them through van Helmont's own account, given in his *Ortus Medicinae*.

For reasons which need not be described here, van Helmont studied with particular interest the various modifications in which carbon is capable of occurring in nature — among them

carbon's combustion product, carbon dioxide. It was his observations of carbon dioxide which made him aware of a condition
of matter whose properties caused him the greatest surprise. For
he found it to be, at the same time, 'much finer than vapour and
much denser than air'. It appeared to him as a complete 'paradox',
because it seemed to unite in itself two contradictory qualities,
one appertaining to the realm of 'uncreated things', the other to
the realm of 'created things'. Unable to rank it with either 'vapour'
or 'air' (we shall see presently what these terms meant in van
Helmont's terminology), he found himself in need of a special
word to distinguish this new state from the other known states,
both below and above it. Since he could not expect any existing
language to possess a suitable word, he felt he must create one.
He therefore took, and changed slightly, a word signifying a
particular cosmic condition which seemed to be imaged in the
new condition he had just discovered. The word was *chaos*.
By shortening it a little, he derived from it the new word *gas*.
His own words explaining this choice are: 'Halitum illum G A S
vocavi non longe a Chaos veterum secretum.' ('I have called this
mist Gas, owing to its resemblance to the Chaos of the ancients.')[1]

Van Helmont's account brings us face to face with a number
of riddles. Certainly, there is nothing strange to us in his describing
carbon dioxide gas as being 'finer than vapour and denser than air';
but why did he call this a 'paradox'? What prevented him from
ranking it side by side with air? As to air itself, why should he
describe it as belonging to the realm of the 'uncreated things'?
What reason was there for giving 'vapour' the rank of a particular
condition of matter? And last but not least, what was the ancient
conception of Chaos which led van Helmont to choose this name
as an archetype for the new word he needed?

To appreciate van Helmont's astonishment and his further
procedure, we must first call to mind the meaning which, in
accordance with the prevailing tradition, he attached to the term
Air. For van Helmont, Air was one of the four 'Elements',
E A R T H, W A T E R, A I R, and F I R E. Of these, the first two were
held to constitute the realm of the 'created things', the other two

that of the 'uncreated things'. A brief study of the old doctrine of the Four Elements is necessary at this point in order to understand the meaning of these concepts.

* * * * *

The first systematic teaching about the four elementary constituents of nature, as they were experienced by man of old, was given by Empedocles in the fifth century B.C. It was elaborated by Aristotle. In this form it was handed down and served to guide natural observation through more than a thousand years up to the time of van Helmont. From our earlier descriptions of the changes in man's consciousness it is clear that the four terms, 'earth', 'water', 'air', 'fire', must have meant something different in former times. So 'water' did not signify merely the physical substance which modern chemistry defines by the formula H_2O; nor was 'air' the mixture of gases characteristic of the earth's atmosphere. Man in those days, on account of his particular relationship with nature, was impressed in the first place by the various dynamic conditions, four in number, which he found prevailing both in his natural surroundings and in his own organism. With his elementary concepts he tried to express, therefore, the four basic conditions which he thus experienced. He saw physical substances as being carried up and down between these conditions.

At first sight some relationship seems to exist between the concept 'element' in this older sense and the modern view of the different stages of material aggregation, solid, liquid, aeriform. There is, however, nothing in this modern view that would correspond to the element Fire. For heat in the sense of physical science is an immaterial energy which creates certain conditions in the three material states, but from these three to heat there is no transition corresponding to the transitions between themselves. Heat, therefore, does not rank as a fourth condition by the side of the solid, liquid and aeriform states, in the way that Fire ranks in the older conception by the side of Earth, Water and Air.

If we were to use the old terms for designating the three states of aggregation plus heat, as we know them today, we should say that there is a border-line dividing Fire from the three lower elements. Such a border-line existed in the older conception of the elements as well. Only its position was seen to be elsewhere — between Earth and Water on the one hand, Air and Fire on the other. This was expressed by saying that the elements below this line constituted the realm of the 'created things', those above it that of the 'uncreated things'. In order to understand how this is meant, we must take a closer view of the doctrine of the four elements.

The complete picture of the four elements comprises, in addition to these elements themselves, four elementary qualities, designated as 'Cold' and 'Warm', 'Dry' and 'Moist'. Just as in modern matter-bound thinking, water is thought of as a combination of hydrogen and oxygen, the four elements were experienced in those earlier days as a combination of each two of the four elementary qualities. Fig. 6 shows the complete picture of the four elements that arises in this way.

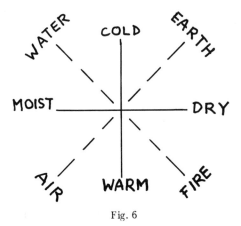

Fig. 6

In this diagram the element Earth appears as a combination of the qualities Dry and Cold; Water of Cold and Moist; Air of Moist and Warm; Fire of Warm and Dry. As a result, Earth and Fire, besides representing opposite poles, are also neighbours in the diagram. Here we encounter a picture characteristic of all earlier ways of looking at the world: the members of a system of phenomena, when ranked in due order of succession, were seen to turn back on themselves circle-wise — or more precisely, in view of their intrinsic linear progression, spiral-wise.

In the present context we need to concern ourselves only with two of the four elementary qualities, 'Cold' and 'Warm', leaving the two others for later discussion.

The terms 'cold' and 'warm' must be understood to have expressed certain qualitative experiences in which there was no separation between what is purely physical and what is purely spiritual. Expressions such as 'a cold heart', 'a warm heart', to 'show someone the cold shoulder', etc., still witness to this way of experiencing the two polar qualities, cold and warm. Quite generally we can say that, wherever man experienced some process of contraction, whether physical or non-physical, he designated it by the term 'cold', and where he experienced expansion, he called it 'warm'. In this sense he felt contractedness to be the predominant characteristic of Earth and Water, expansiveness that of Air and Fire.

With the help of these qualitative concepts we are now in a position to determine more clearly still the difference between the old and the modern conceptions: in particular the difference between the aeriform condition of matter, as we conceive of it today, and the element Air. Contractedness manifests as material density, or the specific weight of a particular substance. We know that this characteristic of matter diminishes gradually with its transition from the solid to the liquid and aeriform states. We know also that this last state is characterised by a high degree of expansiveness, which is also the outstanding property of heat. Thus there is reason to describe also from the modern point of view the solid and liquid states as essentially 'cold', and the aeriform state as 'warm'. But aeriform matter still has density and weight, and this means that matter in this state combines the two opposing qualities. Contrary to this, Air, as the second highest element in the old sense, is characterised by the quality, warm alone. Thus, when man of old spoke of 'air', he had in mind some-thing entirely free from material density and weight.

By comparing in this way the older and newer conceptions of 'air', we come to realise that ancient man must have had a conception of gravity essentially different from ours. If we take gravity in the modern scientist's sense, as a 'descriptive law of behaviour' then this behaviour is designated in the older doctrine by the quality 'cold'. If, however, we look within the system of modern science for a law of behaviour that would correspond to the quality 'warm', we do so in vain. We shall come back to this question later on.

In close connection with the polar nature of the two pairs of elements, resulting from their being determined either by 'cold' or by 'warm', there stands their differentiation into one realm of created, another of uncreated, things. To understand what these terms imply, we must turn to the ancient concept, Chaos, borrowed by Van Helmont.

Today we take the word Chaos to mean a condition of mere absence of order, mostly resulting from a destruction of existing forms, whether by nature or by the action of man. In its original sense the word meant the exact opposite. When in ancient times people spoke of Chaos, they meant the womb of all being, the exalted realm of uncreated things, where indeed forms such as are evident to the eye in the created world are not to be found, but in place of them are the archetypes of all visible forms, as though nurtured in a spiritual seed-condition. It is the state which in the Biblical narration of the creation of the world is described as 'without form and void'.

From this Chaos all the four elements are born, one by one, with the two upper ones retaining Chaos's essential characteristic in that they are 'without form' and tend to be omnipresent, whilst the two lower ones constitute a realm in which things appear in more or less clearly outlined space-bound forms. This is what the terms 'uncreated' and 'created' imply.

How strictly these two realms were distinguished can be seen by the occurrence of the concept 'vapour'. When with the

increasing interest in the realm of created things – characteristic
of the spectator consciousness which, in view of our earlier description of it, we recognise as being itself a 'created thing' – the
need arose for progressive differentiation within this realm, the
simple division of it into 'earth' and 'water' was no longer felt to
be satisfactory. After all, above the liquid state of matter there
was another state, less dense than water and yet presenting itself
through more or less clearly distinguishable space-bound objects,
such as the mists arising from and spreading over ponds and
meadows, and the clouds hovering in the sky. For this state of
matter the term 'vapour' had become customary, and it was used
by van Helmont in this sense. By its very properties, Vapour
belonged to the realm of the created things, whereas Air did not.
It was the intermediary positon of the newly discovered state of
matter between Vapour and Air, which caused van Helmont to
call it a paradox. For by its ponderability it belonged undoubtedly
to the created world, whereas by its formlessness it had to be
placed, at the same time, in the uncreated world and thereby
appeared to have some kinship with Chaos. It is this latter fact
which van Helmont tried to bring to expression by coining the
term, Gas.

* * * * *

Since it could not have been the gaseous state of matter in
the form discovered by van Helmont, what particular condition
of nature was it to which the ancients pointed when using the
term Air? Let us see how the scriptures of past human cultures
speak of air.

In all older languages, the words used to designate the element
bound up with breathing, or the act of breathing, served at the
same time to express the relationship of man to the Divine, or
even the Divine itself. One need think only of the words *Brahma*
and *Atma* of the ancient Indians, the *Pneuma* of the Greeks, the
Spiritus of the Romans. The Hebrews expressed the same idea
when they said that Jehovah had breathed the breath of life into

man and that man in this way became a living soul.

What lies behind all these words is the feeling familiar to man in those times, that breathing was not only a means of keeping the body alive, but that a spiritual essence streamed in with the breath. So long as this condition prevailed, people could expect that by changing their manner of breathing they had a means of bringing the soul into stronger relationship with spiritual Powers, as is attempted in Eastern Yoga.

Remembering the picture of man's spiritual-physical evolution which we have gained from earlier chapters, we are not astonished to find how different this early experience of the breathing process was from our own. Yet, together with the recognition of this difference there arises another question. Even if we admit that man of old was so organised that the experience of his own breathing process was an overwhelmingly spiritual one, it was, after all, the gaseous substance of the earth's atmosphere which he inhaled, and exhaled again in a transformed condition. What then was it that prevented men – apparently right up to the time of van Helmont – from gaining the slightest inkling of the materiality of this substance? To find an answer to this question, let us resort once more to our method of observing things genetically, combined with the principle of not considering parts without considering the whole to which they organically belong.

In modern science the earth is regarded as a mineral body whereon the manifold forms of nature appear as mere additions, arising more or less by chance; one can very well imagine them absent without this having any essential influence on the earth's status in the universe. The truth is quite different. For the earth, with everything that exists on it, forms a single whole, just as each separate organism is in its own way a whole.

This shows that we have no right to imagine the earth without men, and to suppose that its cosmic conditions of being would then remain unaltered – any more than we can imagine a human being deprived of some essential organ and remaining human. Mankind, and all the other kingdoms of nature, are bound up organically with the earth from the start of its existence. Moreover, just as the highest plants, seen with Goethe's eyes, manifest in the most complete manner the spiritual archetypes of the whole vegetable kingdom — i.e. the Ideas determining its evolutionary course — so we must see coming to the fore in man an archetype which, from the very beginning, has been at work behind all natural evolution as its active Idea. The evolutionary changes which we observe in the earth and in man are in fact a *single* process, working through a variety of manifested forms.

From this conception of the parallel evolution of earth and man light falls also on the historic event represented by van Helmont's discovery. Besides being a symptom of a revolution in man's way of *experiencing* the atmosphere, it speaks to us of some corresponding change in the spiritual-physical condition of the atmosphere itself. It was then that men not only came to *think* differently about air, but *breathe* an air that actually was different. To find out what kind of change this was, let us turn once more to man's own organism and see what it has to say concerning the condition under which matter is capable of being influenced by mechanical and magical causation respectively, in the sense already described.

What is it in the nature of the bones that makes them accessible to mechanical causation only, and what is it in the muscles that allows our will to rouse them magically? Bones and muscles stand in a definite genetic relationship to each other, the bones being, in relation to the muscles, a late product of organic development. This holds good equally for everything which in the body of living nature takes the form of mineralised deposits or coverings. Every kind of organism consists in its early stages entirely of living substance; in the course of time a part of the organism separates off and passes over into a more or less mineralised condition. Seen in this light, the distinction between bones and muscles is that the bones have evolved out of a condition in which the muscles persist, though to a gradually waning degree, through-out the lifetime of the body. The substance of the muscles, remaining more or less 'young', stands at the opposite pole from the 'aged' substance of the bones. Hence it depends on the 'age' of a piece of matter whether it responds to magical or mechanical causation.

Let us state here at once, that this temporal distinction has an essential bearing on our understanding of evolutionary processes in general. For if mineral matter is a late product of evolution — and nothing in nature indicates the contrary — then to explain the origins of the world (as scientific theories have always done) with the aid of events similar in character to those which now occur in the mineral realm, means explaining them against nature's own evidence. To find pictures of past conditions of the earth in present-day nature, we must look in the regions where matter, because it is still 'youthful', is played through by the magical working of purposefully active spiritual forces. Thus, instead of seeing in them the chance results of blind volcanic and similar forces, we must recognise in the formation and layout of land and sea an outcome of events more closely resembling those which occur during the embryonic development of a living organism.

The fact that Goethe thought of the earth's evolution in this way is shown by the geological dispute between Faust and Mephistopheles with which we have dealt in Chapter IV.

What, then, does van Helmont's discovery of the gaseous state of matter tell us, if we regard it in the light of our newly acquired insight into the trend of evolution both within and without man? When, in the course of its growing older, mankind had reached the stage which is expressed by the emergence of the spectator-consciousness — consciousness, that is, based on a nervous system which has grown more or less independent of the life forces of the organism — the outer elements had, in their way, arrived at such a state that man began to inhale an air whose spiritual-physical constitution corresponded exactly to that of his nervous system: on either side, Spirit and Matter, in accordance with the necessities of cosmic evolution, had lost their primeval union.

* * * * *

Our extension of the concept of evolution to the very elements of nature, whether these are of material or non-material kind, and our recognition of this evolution as leading in general from a more alert to a more inert condition, at once opens the possibility of including in our scientific world-picture certain facts which have hitherto resisted any inclusion. We mean those manifold events of 'miraculous' nature, of which the scriptures and the oral traditions of old are full. What is modern man to make of them?

The doubts which have arisen concerning events of this kind have their roots on the one hand in the apparent absence of such occurrences in our day, on the other in the fact that the laws of nature derived by science from the present condition of the world seem to rule them out. In the light of the concept of the world's 'ageing' which we have tried to develop here, not only do the relevant reports become plausible, but it also becomes understandable why, if such events have taken place in the past, they fail to do so in our own time.

To illustrate this, let us take a few instances which are symptomatic of the higher degree of youthfulness which was characteristic in former times in particular of the element of Fire.

The role which Fire was capable of playing in man's life at a time when even this element, in itself the most youthful of all, was more susceptible to magic interference than of late, is shown by the manifold fire-rites of old. In those days, when no easy means of fire-lighting were available, it was usual for the needs of daily life to keep a fire burning all the time and to kindle other fires from it. Only in cases of necessity was a new fire lit, and then the only way was by the tedious rubbing together of two pieces of dry wood.

Then both the maintenance of fires, and the deliberate kindling of a new fire, played quite a special role in the ceremonial ordering of human society. Historically, much the best known is the Roman usage in the Temple of Vesta. On the one hand, the unintentional extinction of the fire was regarded as a national calamity and as the gravest possible transgression on the part of the consecrated priestess charged with maintaining the fire. On the other hand, it was thought essential for this 'everlasting' fire to be newly kindled once a year. This took place with a special ritual at the beginning of the Roman year (1st March).

The conception behind such a ritual of fire-kindling will become clear if we compare it with certain other fire-rites which were practised in the northern parts of Europe, especially in the British Isles, until far on in the Christian era. For example, if sickness broke out among the cattle, a widespread practice was to extinguish all the hearth-fires in the district and then to kindle with certain rites a new fire, from which all the local people lit their own fires once more. Heavy penalties were prescribed for anyone who failed to extinguish his own fire — a failure usually indicated by the non-manifestation of the expected healing influence. In Anglo-Saxon speaking countries, fires of this kind were known as 'needfires'.

The spiritual significance of these fires cannot be expressed better than by the meaning of the very term 'needfire'. This word does not derive, as was formerly believed, from the word 'need', meaning a 'fire kindled in a state of need', but, as recent etymological research has shown, from a root which appears in the German word *nieten* — to clinch or rivet. 'Needfire' therefore means nothing less than a fire which was kindled for 'clinching' anew the bond between earthly life and the primal spiritual order at times when for one reason or another there was a call for this.

This explanation of the 'needfire' throws light also on the Roman custom of re-kindling annually the sacred fire in the Temple of Vesta. For the Romans this was a means of reaffirming year by year the connection of the nation with its spiritual leadership; accordingly, they chose the time when the sun in its yearly course restores — 're-clinches' — the union of the world-spirit with earthly nature, for the rebirth of the fire which throughout the rest of the year was carefully guarded against extinction.

Just as men saw in this fire-kindling a way of bringing humanity into active relation with spiritual powers, so on the other hand were these powers held to use the fire element in outer nature for the purpose of making themselves actively known to mankind. Hence we find in the records of all ancient peoples a unanimous

recognition of lightning and thunder on the one hand, and volcanic phenomena on the other, as means to which the Deity
resorts for intervening in human destiny. A well-known example
is the account in the Bible of the meeting of Moses with God on
Mount Sinai. As occurrence in the early history of the Hebrews it
gives evidence that even in historical times the fire element of the
earth was sufficiently 'young' to serve the higher spiritual powers
as an instrument for the direct expression of their interference in
the affairs of man. Something similar speaks through the Greek
experience of the thunderer Zeus, casting his lightnings.

LEVITY *contra* GRAVITY

The foregoing considerations have led to a picture of matter in
which matter no longer figures as always and absolutely inert.
We have found a way of bringing to our immediate observation
matter in the state of diminished inertness, or, as we proposed to
say, of alertness. This enables us now to go into the question of
the other property hitherto deemed to be absolutely connected
with matter, that of weight or gravity. Just as we found inertness
to have its counterpart in alertness, so we shall now find, in
addition to gravity, another force which is the exact opposite of
it, and to which we therefore can give no better name than 'levity'.
Let us emphasise, once more, however, that what we are here
setting out to investigate must not be confused with the hypothetical 'antigravity', surmised by the nuclear physicist. As the
introductory words to this chapter pointed out, the purpose of
our investigations is precisely to make accessible for scientific
cognition that realm of the world which is the very opposite to
the one explored by modern physics.

*   *   *   *   *

Many a conception which is taken for granted by modern
man, and is therefore assumed to have been always obvious,
was in fact established quite deliberately at a definite historical
moment. We have seen how this applies to our knowledge of the

gaseous state of matter; it applies also to the idea of the uniqueness of gravity. About half a century after van Helmont's discovery a treatise called *Contra Levitatem* was published in Florence by the *Accademia del Cimento*. It declares that a science firmly based on observation has no right to speak of Levity as something claiming equal rank with, and opposite to, Gravity.

This declaration was in accord with the state into which human consciousness had entered at that time. For a consciousness which is itself of the quality 'cold', because it is based on the contracting forces of the body, is naturally not in a position to take into consideration its very opposite. Therefore, to speak of a force of levity as one felt able to speak of gravity was indeed without meaning.

Just as there was historical necessity in this banishing of levity from science at the beginning of the age of the spectator-consciousness, so was there historical necessity in a renewed awareness of it arising when the time came for man to overcome the limitations of his spectator-relationship to the world. We find this in Goethe's impulse to search for the action of polarities in nature. As we shall see later, it comes to its clearest expression in Goethe's optical conceptions.

Another witness to this fact is Ruskin, through a remark which bears in more than one sense on our present subject. It occurs in his essay, *The Storm-Cloud of the Nineteenth Century*. In its context it is meant to warn the reader against treating science, which Ruskin praises as a fact-finding instrument, as an interpreter of natural facts. Ruskin takes Newton's conception of gravity as the all-moving cause of the universe, and turns against it in the following words:

'Take the very top and centre of scientific explanation by the greatest of its masters: Newton explained to you — or at least was once supposed to explain, why an apple fell; but he never thought of explaining the exact correlative but infinitely more difficult question, how the apple got up there.' [2]

This remark shows Ruskin once again as a true reader in nature's book. Looking with childlike openness and intensity of participation into the world of the senses, he allows nature's phenomena to impress themselves upon his mind without giving any preconceived preference to one kind or another. This enables him not to be led by the phenomenon of falling bodies to overlook the polarically opposite phenomenon of the upward movement of physical matter in the living plant. Ruskin's remark points directly to the new world-conception which must be striven for today — the conception in which: (1) death is recognised as a secondary form of existence preceded by life; (2) levity is given its rightful place as a force polar to gravity, and because life is bound up with it as death is with gravity, it is recognised as being of more ancient rank than gravity.

* * * * *

In proceeding now to a study of levity we shall not start, as might be expected, with plants or other living forms. We are not yet equipped to understand the part played by levity in bringing about the processes of life; we shall come to this later. For our present purpose we shall look at certain macrotelluric events — events in which large areas of the earth are engaged — taking our examples from meteorology on the one hand and from seismic (volcanic) processes on the other.

In pursuing this course we follow a method which belongs to the fundamentals of a Goetheanistic science. A few words about this method may not be out of place.

When we strive to read the book of nature as a script of the spirit we find ourselves drawn repeatedly towards two realms of natural phenomena. They are widely different in character, but studied together they render legible much that refuses to be deciphered in either realm alone. These realms are, on the one hand, the inner being of man, and, on the other, the phenomena of macrotelluric and cosmic character. The fruitfulness of linking together these two will become clear if we reflect on the following.

The field of the inner life of man allows us, as nothing else does, to penetrate it with our own intuitive experience. For we ourselves are always in some sense the cause of the events that take place there. In order to make observations in this region, however, we need to bring about a certain awakening in a part of our being which — so long as we rely on the purely natural forces of our body — remains sunk in more or less profound unconsciousness.

If this realm of events is more intimately related than any other to our intuitive experience, it has also the characteristic of remaining closed to any research by external means. Much of what lies beyond the scope of external observation, however, reveals itself all the more clearly in the realms where nature is active on the widest scale. Certainly, we must school ourselves to read aright the phenomena which come to light in those realms. And once more we must look to the way of introspection, previously mentioned, for aid in investing our gaze with the necessary intuitive force. If we succeed in this, then the heavens will become for us a text wherein secrets of human nature, hidden from mere introspection, can be read; while at the same time the introspective way enables us to experience things which we cannot uncover simply by observing the outer universe.

Apart from these methodological considerations, there is a further reason for our choice. Among the instances mentioned earlier in this chapter as symptoms of a greater 'youthfulness' prevailing in nature, and particularly in the element Fire, at a comparatively recent date, were the manifestations of the Divine-Spiritual World to man reported in the Bible as the event on Mount Sinai. There, thunder and lightning from above and volcanic action from below form the setting for the intercourse of Jehovah with Moses. Today the function of these types of phenomena, though metamorphosed by the altered conditions of the earth, is not essentially different. Here, more than in any other sphere of her activities, nature manifests that side of her which we are seeking to penetrate with understanding.

* * * * *

Let us start with an observation known to the present writer from a visit to the *Solfatara*, a volcanic region near Naples.

The *Solfatara* itself is a trough surrounded by hilly mounds; its smooth, saucepan-like bottom, covered with whitish pumice-sand, is pitted with craters containing violently boiling and fuming mud — the so-called *fango*, famous for its healing properties. All around sulphurous fumes issue from crevices in the rocks, and in one special place the *Solfatara* reveals its subterranean activity by the emergence of fine, many-coloured sand, which oozes up like boiling liquid from the depths below. The whole region gives the impression of being in a state of labile balance. How true this is becomes apparent if one drops pieces of burning paper here and there on the ground: immediately a cloud of smoke and steam rises. The effect is even more intense if a burning torch is moved about over one of the boiling *fango* holes. Then the deep answers instantly with an extraordinary intensification of the boiling process. The hot mud seems to be thrown into violent turmoil, emitting thick clouds of steam, which soon entirely envelop the spectator near the edge.

The scientific mind is at first inclined to see in this phenomenon the mechanical effect of reduced air-pressure, due to the higher temperature above the surface of the boiling mud, though doubts are raised by the unusual intensity of the reaction. The feeling that the physical explanation is inadequate is strengthened when the vapours have thinned out and one is surprised to see that every crack and cranny in the *Solfatara*, right up to the top of the trough, show signs of increased activity. Certainly, this cannot be accounted for by a cause-and-effect nexus of the kind found in the realm of mechanical causation, where an effect is propagated from point to point and the total effect is the sum of a number of partial effects. It looks rather as if the impulse applied in one spot had called for a major impulse which was now acting on the *Solfatara* as a whole.

As observers who are trying to understand natural phenomena by recognising their significance as letters in nature's script, we must look now for other phenomena which can be joined with this one to form the relevant 'word' we have set out to decipher.

All scientific theories concerning the causes of seismic occurrences, both volcanic and tectonic, have been conceived as if the
spatial motion of mineral matter were the only happening that
had to be accounted for. No wonder that none of these theories
has proved really satisfactory even to mechanistically orientated
thinking. Actually there are phenomena of a quite different
kind connected with the earth's seismic activities, and these need
to be taken into equal account.

There is, for instance, the fact that animals often show a
premonition of volcanic or tectonic disturbances. They become
restive and hide, or, if domestic, seek the protection of man.
Apparently, they react in this way to changes in nature which
precede the mechanical events by which man registers the seismic
occurrence.

Another such phenomenon is the so-called earthquake-sky,
which the present writer has had several occasions to witness. It
consists of a peculiar, almost terrifying, intense discoloration
of the sky, and, to those acquainted with it, is a sure sign of an
imminent or actual earthquake somewhere in the corresponding
region of the earth. To the same category belong the mighty
thunderstorms which in some parts of the world are known to
occur in conjunction with earthquakes. Phenomena of this kind
teach us that the change in the earth's condition which results
in a violent movement of her crust, involves a region of her organism far greater than the subterranean layers where the cause
of the purely mechanical events is usually believed to reside.

That man himself is not excluded from experiencing directly
the super-spatial nature of seismic disturbances is shown by an
event in Goethe's life, reported by his secretary Eckermann, who
himself learnt the story from an old man who had been Goethe's
valet at the time.[3]

This is what the old man, whom Eckermann met by accident
one day near Weimar, told him: 'Once Goethe rang in the middle
of the night and when I entered his room I found he had rolled
his iron bed to the window and was lying there, gazing at the
heavens. "Have you seen nothing in the sky?" asked he, and when

I answered "No", he begged me to run across to the sentry and inquire of the man on duty if he had seen nothing. He had not noticed anything and when I returned I found the master still in the same position, gazing at the sky. "Listen," he said, "this is an important moment; there is now an earthquake or one is just going to take place." Then he made me sit down on the bed and showed me by what signs he knew this.' When asked about the weather conditions, the old man said: 'It was very cloudy, very still and sultry.' To believe implicitly in Goethe was for him a matter of course, 'for things always happened as he said they would'. When next day Goethe related his observations at Court, the women tittered: 'Goethe is dreaming dreams' ('*Goethe schwärmt*'), but the Duke and the other men present believed him. A few weeks later the news reached Weimar that on that night (5th April 1783) part of Messina had been destroyed by an earthquake.

There is no record by Goethe himself of the nature of the phenomenon perceived by him during that night, except for a brief remark in a letter to Mme de Stein, written the following day, in which he claims to have seen a 'northern light in the south-east' the extraordinary character of which made him fear that an earthquake had taken place somewhere. The valet's report makes us inclined to think that there had been no outwardly perceptible phenomenon at all, but that what Goethe believed he was seeing with his bodily eyes was the projection of a purely supersensible, but not for that reason any less objective, experience.

In a picture of the seismic activities of the earth which is to comprise phenomena of this kind, the volcanic or tectonic effects cannot be attributed to purely local causes. For why, then, should the whole meteorological sphere be involved, and why should living beings react in the way described? Clearly, we must look for the origin of the total disturbance not in the interior of the earth but in the expanse of surrounding space. Indeed, the very phenomenon of the *Solfatara*, if seen in this light, can reveal to us that at least the volcanic movements of the earth's crust are not caused by pressure from within, but by suction from without — that is, by an exceptional action of levity.

We recall the fact that the whole *Solfatara* phenomenon had its origin in a flame being swayed over one of the *fango* holes. Although it remains true that the suction arising from the diminished air pressure over the hole cannot account for the intense increase of ebullition in the hole itself, not to speak of the participation of the entire region in this increase, there is the fact that the whole event starts with a suctional effect. As we shall see in the next chapter, any local production of heat interferes with the gravity conditions at that spot by shifting the balance to the side of levity. That the response in a place like the *Solfatara* is what we have seen it to be, is the result of an extraordinary lability of the equilibrium between gravity and levity, a characteristic appertaining to the earth's volcanism in general.

For the people living near the *Solfatara* it is indeed common knowledge that there are times when this lability is so great that the slightest local disturbance of the kind we have described can provoke destructive eruptions of great masses of subterranean mud. (At such times access to the *Solfatara* is prohibited.) We shall understand such an eruption rightly if we picture it as the counter-pole of an avalanche. The latter may be brought about by a fragment of matter on a snow-covered mountain, perhaps a little stone, breaking loose and in its descent bringing ever-accumulating masses of snow down with it. The levity-process polar to this demonstration of gravity is the production of a mightily growing 'negative avalanche' by comparatively weak local suction, caused by a small flame.

* * * * *

Among the concepts formed during the past phase of science, there is one that will retain its validity because it has been gained through a genuine reading of the relevant phenomena. This is the concept of the *force-field*, which we owe to the genius of Faraday.

There are dynamic effects which arise through a direct contact between the body acting as a cause and the body bearing the effect. But there are also effects where the interacting bodies are at a greater or smaller distance from each other. Examples of 'action at a distance' — as it was called — are afforded by gravity, electricity, etc. Newton himself, to whom his followers wrongly ascribed the idea of 'action at a distance', was troubled by the question of how to account for this kind of action, and he therefore refused to conceive of gravity as a property of physical bodies as such, exerted on one another across empty space. He tried, rather, to think of an agent spread throughout space as the actual bearer of the cause which impelled physical masses towards one another. This idea, however, was too vague to help in solving the problem. For the time being scientific thinking resigned itself to the unsatisfactory conception of action at a distance.

This state of affairs was brought to an end by Faraday's realistic mind. When contemplating the effect of one electrically charged body on another, he dropped altogether the idea that they 'attracted' or 'repelled' each other, but took it for granted that the effect was caused directly at the spot of its occurrence. In other words, through the presence in space of a charged body, the entire surroundings of that body assume a changed dynamic condition. This, Faraday called the 'field-of-force'. Thus, if two bodies are set in motion by one or both being electrically charged, it is the electric field filling the space around them which acts upon each body wherever it is. Applied to the earth's gravitational effects, this conception leads to a picture of the Earth as the bearer of a gravitational field, situated within the globe, and extending thence in all directions through space, across and beyond the earth's body. Every point in space, both inside and outside the earth, is characterised by a definite intensity of this field, the so-called gravitational potential. This is subject to variations due to the presence of other physical masses, which carry their own fields of gravity. What happens between such masses and that of the earth, as well as mutually between such masses themselves, is brought about by the particular conditions in space resulting from the interpenetrations of the various fields.

It is essential to realise that the gravitational and electrical fields dealt with by physical science — however much they differ otherwise — have this one characteristic in common, that they have a centre where the field is at its highest intensity, diminishing as the distance from the centre increases. Motion in such a field naturally takes place from regions of lower to those of higher intensity. This accounts for the tendency of physical masses to arrive at the shortest possible distance between them.

It was natural for the modern mind to picture a dynamic condition of the kind just described, that is, one in which the centre and source, as it were, is a point round which the dynamic condition spreads with steadily diminishing strength as the distance from the point grows. For such is the condition of man's head-bound consciousness. The locus from which modern man watches the world is a point within the field of this consciousness, and the intensity with which the world acts on it diminishes with increasing spatial distance from this point. This is the reason why levity was banished from scientific inquiry, and why, when the field-concept was created by the genius of Faraday, it did not occur to anyone that with it the way was opened to comprehend field-types other than the centric one characteristic of gravity and kindred forces. To make use of the field concept in this other way is one of the tasks we have to undertake if we are to attain to a spiritual understanding of nature.

To develop a picture of the type of field represented by levity, let us recall certain results from our discussion of volcanism. The volcanic phenomenon, when taken in its wider implications, made us realise that the upward movement of physical masses, in itself part of the total phenomenon, is due to a dynamic cause which we had to describe, in contrast to centrifugally working pressure, as peripherally working suction, this suction, however, being something different from suction caused mechanically. Whereas the latter, being the result of the difference of pressure in adjacent parts of space, acts from one point in space to another, suction caused by levity extends uniformly, as we have seen, over the entire area in question.

It is in this sense that we may speak of the seismic movements of the earth as being caused by suction acting from without. In the same sense we may say that the upward movement of the saps in the plant (to which Ruskin pointed as being responsible for the apple appearing at the top of the tree) and with it the entire growth-phenomenon in the plant world, is due to peripheral suction.

Considerations of this kind lead one to a picture in which the earth is seen to be surrounded and penetrated by a field of force which is in every respect the polar opposite of the earth's gravitational field. As the latter has its greatest intensity at its centre, which is identical with the centre of the earth's globe, so has the levitational field its greatest intensity at its circumference, which is somewhere in the width of the universe.

As the gravity-field decreases in strength with increasing distance from the centre of the field, that is, in the outward direction, so does the levity-field decrease in strength with increasing distance from its periphery, or in the inward direction. In both fields the direction of movement is from regions of lower to those of higher intensity. This is why things 'fall' under the influence of gravity and 'rise' under the influence of levity.[4]

* * * * *

Our further considerations will gradually extend our acquaintance with the nature of levity and its characteristic type of field. In the end we shall also be able to answer the natural question: what is it that causes levity and gravity, although they are polar opposites, to interact at all in the way we have seen they do?

Let us once more recollect that in this chapter, which was to lead us to the recognition of levity, we began by observing the existence of dynamic effects of a non-mechanical (magical) nature. We have now come to know levity as a force which, although capable of producing physical effects, shows by the very fact of the totally different relationship of these effects to space that it is itself of a non-physical nature.

Chapter X

SPACE AND COUNTER-SPACE

With the introduction of the peripheral type of force-field which appertains to levity as the usual central one does to gravity, we are compelled to revise our conception of space. For in a space of the kind we are accustomed to conceive, that is, the three-dimensional, Euclidean space, the existence of such a field with its characteristic of *increasing* in strength in the *outward* direction is a paradox.

As we shall see, the solution of this problem does not require, at least in its initial stages, anything alien to present-day mathematical thinking. For in modern mathematics, thought-forms are already present which make it possible to develop a space-concept adequate to levity.

In the following pages an attempt will be made to introduce the reader to the relevant geometrical concepts by means of the method of 'inward recreating', first developed by Goethe in regard to outer natural phenomena, which we have been practising already in various ways. While the road thus pursued is our own, we shall draw on the achievements of other workers in this field who first started to re-orientate mathematical thinking along the lines indicated by Rudolf Steiner. In particular, this chapter could not have been written without G. Adams's essay, *Physical and Ethereal Spaces*,[1] and the help the author has received from him personally.

* * * * *

Before we embark upon our actual task it will be well to outline briefly where modern scientific thinking has already been led by its own needs with regard to the conception of space.

One of the reasons why the world-picture developed by Einstein in his Theory of Relativity deserves to be acknowledged as a step forward, in comparison with the picture drawn by classical physics, lies in the fact that the old conception of three-dimensional space as a kind of 'cosmic container', extending in all directions into infinity and filled, as it were, with the content of the physical universe, is replaced by a conception in which the structure of space results from the laws interrelating this content.

Along his own line of reasoning however, Einstein, arrived at a space picture which though mathematically consistent, is incomprehensible by the human mind. For nothing exists in our mind that could enable us to experience as a reality a space-time continuum of four dimensions which has what mathematicians call 'curvature'.

The reason why Einstein's endeavours led to an outcome of this kind is that he pursued to its limits the onlooker's kinematic world-picture. In this way all events in the universe were reduced to mere happenings of movement, all on equal footing. Such happenings in their entirety can therefore be conceived of only as relative movements; and they cannot be pictured otherwise than after the model of the gravity-conditioned movements observable on earth. The first of these two conditions led Einstein to the 'special' form of his Theory, the second to its 'general' form. The theory's peculiar complexity with which, to quote A.N. Whitehead, it 'outruns common sense', is a consequence of the fact that the onlooker is trying here to use gravity-bound thought for comprehending universal happenings of which the true causes are non-gravitational. A thinking that has learnt to acknowledge the existence of levity must indeed pursue precisely the opposite direction. Instead of freezing time down into a spatial dimension, in order to make it fit into a world ruled by nothing but gravity, we must develop a conception of space sufficiently fluid to let true time have its place therein. We shall see how such a procedure will lead to a space-concept thoroughly conceivable by human common sense, provided we are prepared to overcome the onlooker-standpoint in mathematics also.

Einstein owed the possibility of establishing his space-picture to a certain achievement of mathematical thinking in modern times. Because a peculiar characteristic of the onlooker-consciousness is to have no real communication with the external world, man's thinking gained a degree of freedom which did not exist in former ages. In consequence, mathematicians were enabled in the course of the nineteenth century to conceive the most varied space-systems which were mathematically consistent and yet lacked all relation to external existence. A considerable number of space-systems have thus become established, among them the system that enabled Einstein to derive his space-time concept. Some of them have been more or less fully worked out, while in certain instances all that has been done is to show that they are mathematically conceivable. Among these, however, there is one which in all its characteristics is polarically opposite to the Euclidean system, and is destined for this reason to become the space-system of levity. It is symptomatic of the remoteness from reality of mathematical thinking in the onlooker-age that precisely this system has so far received no special attention.

* * * * *

For the purpose of this book it is not necessary to expound in detail why modern mathematical thinking has been led to look for thought-forms other than those of classical geometry. It is enough to remark that for quite a long time there had been an awareness of the fact that the consistency of Euclid's definitions and proofs fails as soon as one has no longer to do with finite geometrical entities, but with figures which extend into infinity, as for instance when the properties of parallel straight lines come into question. For the concept of infinity was foreign to classical geometrical thinking. Problems of the kind which had defeated Euclidean thinking became soluble directly human thinking was able to handle the concept of infinity.

We shall now indicate some of the lines of geometrical thought which follow from this.

* * * * *

Let us consider a straight line extending without limits in either direction. Projective geometry is able to state that a point moving along this line in one direction will eventually return from the other. Consequently, an unlimited straight line has only one point at infinity. Seen as a whole, it is an entity returning into itself.

A simple consideration can convince us of this. Imagine two straight lines *a* and *b* intersecting at P (Fig. 7). Let *a* be fixed and let *b* rotate uniformly about a point C, not coincident with P, in the direction indicated by the arrow. As a result of the rotation of *b*, P moves along the line *a*, a few positions being shown in the figure. There is one position of *b*, namely when it is parallel to *a*, for which it is impossible to find a point P in finite space. The point has reached infinity. The slightest further rotation of *b*, however, will bring P back from the other side.

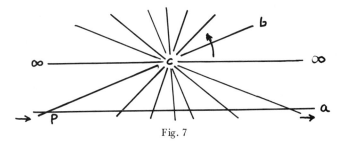

Fig. 7

We find here two forms of movement linked together – the rotational movement of a line (*b*) on a point (C), and the progressive movement of a point (P) along a line (*a*). The first movement is continuous, and observable throughout within finite space. Therefore the second movement must be continuous as well, even though it partly escapes our observation. Hence, when P disappears into infinity on one side of our own point of observation, it is at the same time in infinity on the other side.

It is clear that, in order to become familiar with this aspect of geometry, one must grow together in inward activity with the *happening* which is contained in the above description. This in itself suggests that the space-concept obtained in this way will be so flexible as to inflict no injury on the intrinsic character of time. The foregoing description is, in fact, meant to serve as a mental exercise in the sense of imparting fluidity to our geometrical thinking.

The following exercise will help us towards further clarity concerning the nature of geometrical infinity.

We imagine ourselves in the centre of a sphere which we allow to expand uniformly on all sides. Whilst the inner wall of this sphere withdraws from us into ever greater distances, it grows flatter and flatter until, on reaching infinite distance, it turns into a plane. We thus find ourselves surrounded everywhere by a surface which, in the strict mathematical sense, is a plane, and is yet one and the same surface on all sides. This leads us to the conception of the plane at infinity as a self-contained entity although it expands infinitely in all directions.

This property of a plane at infinity, however, is really a property of any plane. To realise this, we must widen our conception of infinity by freeing it from a certain one-sidedness still connected with it. This we do by transferring ourselves into the infinite plane and envisaging, not the plane from the point, but the point from the plane. This operation, however, implies something which is not obvious to a mind accustomed to the ordinary ways of mathematical reasoning. It therefore requires special explanation.

In the sense of Euclidean geometry, a plane is the sum-total of innumerable single points. To take up a position in a plane, therefore, means to imagine oneself at one point of the plane, with the latter extending around in all directions to infinity. Hence the journey from any point in space to a plane is along a straight line from one point to another. In the case of the plane being at infinity, it would be a journey along a radius of the infinitely large sphere from its centre to a point at its circumference.

In projective geometry the operation is of a different character. Just as we arrive at the infinitely large sphere by letting a finite sphere grow, so must we consider any finite sphere as having grown from a sphere with infinitely small extension; that is, from a point. To travel from the point to the infinitely distant plane in the sense of projective geometry, therefore, means that we have first to identify ourselves with the point and 'become' the plane by a process of uniform expansion in all directions.

As a result of this we do not arrive at one point in the plane, with the latter extending round us on all sides, but we are present in the plane as a whole everywhere. No point in it can be characterised as having any distance, whether finite or infinite, from us.

Now it is clear that we can establish ideally such a relationship with regard to *any* plane in space. The particular act of transformation we have here chosen was meant only as a help in our first endeavour to change over from the central relationship to space, familiar to our gravity-bound consciousness, to the peripheral one which corresponds with levity. Any such plane can then be given the character of a plane at infinity by relating it to a point infinitely far away from it (i.e. from us).

Once we have freed ourselves from the one-sided point-to-plane orientation, we feel at once stimulated to supplement the process of expansion, gone through above, by the polarically opposite one, and to examine where we are led by letting the plane, now conceived as an indivisible whole, contract until it has become the point at infinity. Obviously, this leads us again across the stage of the finite sphere, which, however, is now of a quite different quality compared with the sphere in the former case. By properly picturing this difference we shall gain a first idea of the space which corresponds to levity just as the space spreading from point to plane corresponds to gravity.

Let us imagine two finite spheres, each of which we have caused to come about in one of these two ways. Let us further imagine that in both cases the region between the two stages, the initial one and the sphere, is occupied by some substance. In the first instance we shall find the sphere filled with the substance from the centre to its inner wall; in the second instance we shall find the substance occupying the region between the plane and the sphere's outer wall. Fig. 8 represents both instances, the left-hand figure symbolising the sphere as bearing the substance internally, the right-hand figure showing it as bearing the substance externally.

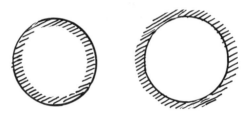

Fig. 8

To speak in this way, however, is to speak inaccurately. For once we start to conceive geometrical entities in their dual aspect, the terms 'internal' and 'external' lose their usual fixed meanings. Indeed, we think rightly only if we conceive, in the second instance, the whole region between the plane and the sphere as the sphere's interior, and the region between the sphere and the point as its exterior. We thus come to differentiate between spheres which are bent outwardly by being centred on a point, and spheres which are bent inwardly by being 'centred' on a plane. So also the quality of the point and the plane differs basically in the two instances.

We already see here how, by re-creating inwardly the different mutual relationships of the mathematical archetypes, we arrive at two polarically opposite space-concepts which correspond exactly to the two opposite field-types, the central one of gravity and the peripheral one of levity. Both spaces have in common the polarity of point and plane, the point standing for utmost contraction, the plane for utmost expansion.

By pursuing further the reversibility of the relation between point and plane, we arrive at the following picture of the qualitative difference between the two opposite space-systems.

Regarded in the Euclidean way, the point, and it alone, is an indivisible geometrical entity. Compared with it, the line is an assemblage of infinitely many points, and the plane one of infinitely many lines or points. Now, it has already become clear that from the polarically opposite aspect the plane is one and indivisible. Consequently, both line and point assume the character of composite entities. As regards the polar aspects of the relationship between point and line, we can picture them by studying Fig. 7 once again.

Let us first think of the line a in the Euclidean sense, as given by two of the points P. Then all other possible points P belong equally to this line. They are said to 'lie in' the line. The line thus appears as a manifold of points. On the other hand, we can think of the point C as the intersecting point of two lines b. From the projective-geometrical aspect, these two, as well as all other lines passing through C, 'belong' to this point, or — as we can also say here with full justification — they 'lie in' C. Thus the point appears as a manifold of lines.

There are corresponding aspects for plane and line. Just as two points determine a line, so do two planes determine a line, namely their line of intersection. These planes, and also all the infinitely many planes which pass through this line, 'belong' to it — in fact, they lie in it — just as in the Euclidean sense there are infinitely many points which belong to a line and so lie in it.

The line thus appears here as a manifold of planes. We need only continue this argument to realise that from the polar-Euclidean aspect the point appears as a manifold of planes, just as from the Euclidean aspect the plane represents a manifold of points.

This leads us to the conclusion that in polar-Euclidean space the theorem that the whole is always greater than its parts ceases to be valid. For here the unit-entities are the largest, and the more parts there are that go to make up an entity, the smaller it is. This is indeed the case everywhere in outer nature, where levity is at work.

In view of the duality of the relation between point and plane, we feel prompted to look for the polar supplement to the act, described above, by which a point is transported from a sphere's centre to its circumference. Then we had to picture a point disconnecting itself, as it were from our position at the central point, and moving away from us in a radial direction until it reaches the sphere's surface from within. Correspondingly, we have now to imagine a plane disconnecting itself from the mother-plane and moving away from us radially until it reaches the sphere's surface from without, where it then forms a tangential plane. Fig. 9 shows both processes. The small circle in the left-

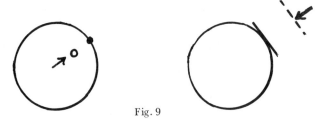

Fig. 9

hand diagram and the dotted line in the right-hand diagram symbolise some intermediary position of point and plane respectively. (The reader familiar with geometry will be reminded of the relation between 'pole' and 'polar'.)

What we have carried out here for a single direction, we can also imagine taking place in all directions simultaneously. The picture thus arises, on the one hand, of infinitely many points disconnecting themselves from the original point and moving away from it uniformly until they have reached a definite distance. There they form together the surface of a sphere. To make the sphere come into being in this way corresponds to its usual Euclidean definition as the 'locus of all points with an equal distance from a given point'. From the peripheral aspect, on the other hand, we shall find infinitely many planes disconnecting themselves from the original plane and uniformly moving away from it until they come to a standstill at some definite distance. There they form together the tangential planes of a sphere by enveloping it. Fig. 10 shows both cases.

We arrive at a further conception of the possible qualitative difference between geometrical entities which look externally identical — in our case the two spheres — by imagining that we obtain the sphere by letting a single point, or a single plane, move successively to the places of all other points, or planes, which represent the end-points of the sphere's radii, or its tangential planes. The first we actually carry out when drawing the circle with a pair of compasses.

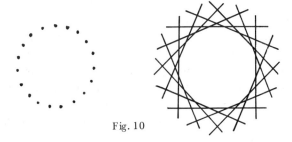

Fig. 10

Let us imagine that we have to carry out both movements with our own limbs. Then, in the first instance, we shall have to stretch out one arm and one of our fingers, say, the index, and to swing the arm in all directions while doing the same with the other arm in the opposite direction. In the second instance, we shall have to use the palms of our hands, moving them over the surface in all directions. Our experience of the two procedures may be described, in the first instance, as a 'pointing out', of the sphere; in the second instance, as a 'modelling' of it. As we shall see later, both activities correspond to real dynamic happenings in various fields of nature.

Let us now imagine that the discrete points and planes forming the sphere in one way or the other are endowed with a tendency to become one. There is no other way for the points to achieve this except by moving radially towards the sphere's centre. The sphere thereby contracts. The planes, on the other hand, can achieve this only by soaring away, as it were, from the centre to an ever-greater distance while remaining each parallel to itself. The sphere thereby expands.

Purely geometrical considerations thus lead us to the dynamic of systole and diastole which we first encountered when pursuing Goethe's way of studying the plant, and later found to be a characteristic of gravity and levity respectively. How much the geometrical conception represents outer reality becomes clear if we remember that it is a characteristic of centrally orientated force-fields to call forth effects working from point to point, whereas effects from peripherally orientated fields, as the *Solfatara* phenomenon immediately taught us, manifest in a planar way.

Here it becomes also particularly clear why the suctional effect brought about by levity must not be confused with mechanical suction, caused by a partial vacuum, the latter remaining a point-to-point effect. Where levity sucks, we have to do always with planar action, and with the plane of action, as indicated above, not as an assembly of points but as an indivisible whole. Direct experience of this can again be obtained through the experiment with the rising arm.

It will be one of the tasks of the new science to learn to conceive natural happenings in this way.

* * * * *

In the last part of our discussion we took pains to rid our terminology of a certain one-sidedness which it derives from the fact that ordinary consciousness is bound up with Euclidean space conditions. A similar treatment, as applied before to the concepts 'external' and 'internal', is now required for the concept 'infinity', or 'at infinity'. When we say that Euclidean space is characterised by being bounded up by a plane which, relatively to any point in it, is a plane at infinity, and that polar-Euclidean space is bounded up by a point which, relatively to all planes, is a point at infinity, we are using a form of expression which is truly justified only in the first instance: that is in a spatial system which results from rigid point-to-point relations. For a consciousness which experiences itself 'somewhere', and everything outside itself as 'elsewhere', as the gravity-bound consciousness of today does, the identification of the concepts of unattainability and of unlimited distance represent some actual experience. This is different for a consciousness for which the Euclidean aspect of the plane as an entity extending limitlessly in all directions is not valid, because such a consciousness experiences the plane as a closed and indivisible entity with itself omnipresent in it. To speak here of 'infinite distance' as implying unattainability ceases to have meaning.

To create a terminology which is equally valid for both spatial systems, we need first of all a qualitative expression, free from any reference to distance, for the relation between the point and the plane at infinity. Let us remember that this plane represents, in relation to the point, the extreme form of a sphere. As such it surrounds the point — as does any other sphere — on all sides. But whereas all other spheres comprise always only some *part* of the world spreading round the point, the plane at infinity, seen as such a sphere, comprises the *entirety* of this world. This suggests the expression, *all-embracing plane*, as a suitable term for this plane. A similar consideration leads us to the term, *all-relating point*, for the exceptional point in relation to the plane.

With the help of these purely qualitative concepts we can now describe the two space-structures as follows. We remember that in purely projective space, which is characterised by the pure point-plane polarity, no plane or point has preference over any other plane or point. From this primeval space-concept we arrive at Euclidean space by defining the point as the indivisible entity, while ascribing to one special plane, the plane at infinity, the quality of being all-embracing. Since, in relation to this plane as a sphere, any point in space can become the centre, no point has preference over any other. Thus there is one exceptional plane, but no exceptional point. In the outer world this is the characteristic of all gravity-bound physical bodies, in that each of them has a centre of gravity of its own, while all of them are related to the plane at infinity as their common all-embracing plane. Such is, indeed, the signature of the earth's mineral kingdom.

Conditions are different on the polar-Euclidean side. A thinking which proceeds by way of mere analogy will take it for granted that, just as in Euclidean space there are countless points, all of equal value, and one exceptional plane, so in polar-Euclidean space there must be countless planes of equal value and one exceptional point. This, however, is not so. For in life-imbued physical organisms nature shows us that levity is capable of forming separate, spatially bounded fields, each of them belonging to one such organism. Moreover, since the organisms are subject to growth and decay, there is a continuous appearance and disappearance of these levity-fields. Each of them has as its fountainhead one or several planes, which, from the Euclidean view-point, are situated at some finite distances from where their material effects come to pass. From these planes, for instance, the activities issue which our earlier considerations have taught us to ascribe to the spiritual type of the plant (Chapter V). In relation to these planes, the plant's eyes, node, etc., represent the corresponding all-relating points.[2]

Besides the fact that the property of being all-relating or all-embracing is no longer bound up with any exceptional distance, we observe that the manifoldness of all-embracing planes has as its counterpart not one all-relating point, but many. Further, in the place of one steady Euclidean space — one and the same for all physical bodies — we find here a continuous arising and vanishing of many individual polar-Euclidean spaces.

As we emphasised at the end of the last chapter, levity is not merely negative gravity with, apart from their opposite character, basically similar properties, but, as source of magical causation, it represents a force with actual non-physical properties. We now see this coming to geometrical expression in the fact that levitational space, apart from representing a structural opposite to gravitational space, possesses additional characteristics which are alien to the latter. The true relationship of levity and gravity, therefore, offers an example of what was indicated at the beginning of this chapter — namely that, if our mathematical thinking is to be truly realistic, it must, besides satisfying the order of mathematical logic, keep in line with nature's immanent order.

By following this rule we have been able to obtain a conception of space which, like Einstein's, goes beyond that of classical physics, and yet stands in full contrast to his. For the determinedness of Euclidean space, which has been fully preserved in Einstein's space system with even time made subject to it, is replaced here by a space which, being itself a product of time, shares time's intrinsic fluidity.

* * * * *

When we set out earlier in this book (Chapter VIII) to discover the source of Galilio's intuition, by which he had been enabled to find the theorem of the parallelogram of forces, we were led to certain experiences through which all men go in early childhood by erecting their body and learning to walk. We were thereby led to realise that man's general capacity for thinking mathematically is the outcome of early experiences of this kind. It is evident that geometrical concepts arising in man's mind in this way must be those of Euclidean geometry. For they are acquired by the will's struggle with gravity.

In a similar way we can now seek to find the source of our capacity to form polar-Euclidean concepts. As we were formerly led to experiences of man's early life on earth, so we are now led to his embryonic and even pre-embryonic existence.

Before man's supersensible part enters into a physical body there is no means of conveying to it experiences other than those of levity, and this condition prevails right through embryonic development. For while the body floats in the mother's foetal fluid it is virtually exempt from the influence of the earth's field of gravity.

History has given us a source of information from these early periods of man's existence in Traherne's recollections of the time when his soul was still in the state of cosmic consciousness. Among his descriptions we may therefore expect to find a picture of levity-space which will confirm through immediate experience what we have arrived at along the lines of realistic mathematical reasoning. Among poems quoted earlier, his *The Praeparative* and *My Spirit* do indeed convey this picture in the clearest possible way. The following are relevant passages from these two poems.

In the first we read:

> 'Then was my Soul my only All to me,
>   A living endless Ey,
>   Scarce bounded with the Sky
> Whose Power, and Act, and Essence was to see:
>   I was an inward Sphere of Light,
> Or an interminable Orb of Sight,
>   Exceeding that which makes the Days . . .'

In the second poem the same experience is expressed in richer detail. There he says of his own soul that it —

> '. . . being Simple, like the Deity,
>   In its own Centre is a Sphere,
>   Not limited but everywhere.
> It acts not from a Centre to
>   Its Object, as remote;
>   But present is, where it doth go
> To view the Being it doth note . . .
>
> A strange extended Orb of Joy
>   Proceeding from within,
> Which did on ev'ry side display
> Its force; and being nigh of Kin
>   To God, did ev'ry way
> Dilate its Self ev'n *instantaneously*,

Yet an Indivisible Centre stay,
In it surrounding all Eternity.
'Twas not a Sphere;
Yet did appear
One infinite: 'Twas somewhat everywhere.'

Observe the distinct description of how the relation between circumference and centre is inverted by the former becoming itself an 'indivisible centre'. In a space of this kind there is no Here and There, as in Euclidean space, for the consciousness is always and immediately at one with the whole space. Motion is thus quite different from what it is in Euclidean space. Traherne himself italicised the word 'instantaneous', so important did he find this fact. (The quality of instantaneousness — equal from the physical point of view to a velocity of the value ∞ will occupy us more closely as a characteristic of the realm of levity when we come to discuss the apparent velocity of light in connection with our optical studies.)

By thus realising the source in man of the polar-Euclidean thought-forms, we see the discovery of projective geometry in a new light. For it now assumes the significance of yet another historical symptom of the modern re-awakening of man's capacity to remember his pre-natal existence. Accordingly, the application of projective-geometrical thinking to the investigation of nature, as indicated here, means calling up forces in us which, in Thomas Reid's sense, we have brought with us into the world. In this case, also, the new science complies with his postulate that 'we must become as little children, if we will be philosophers'.

Chapter XI

PHYSICAL SUBSTANCES
AS PART OF NATURE'S ALPHABET

In our introductory description of Levity we chose the process of combustion to exemplify the peculiar relationship which man once had to the element of Fire because he still experienced this element as a manifestation of Levity. The picture of the process of combustion as conceived by man in different historical ages is indeed symptomatic of his experience of nature in general, including his particular conception of physical matter. We may therefore expect that the new picture of combustion which we can learn to form through a re-acquired acknowledgment of Levity will help us towards our goal of attaining a dynamic conception of matter.

* * * * *

So long as man continued to regard heat as a manifestation of the element Fire, thus reckoning it among the 'uncreated' things, he experienced, as we have already noted, the liberation of heat from 'created' matter as a very special, even a holy, act. Today, most people instinctively associate combustion with very different feelings by first of all thinking of the air (oxygen) that is needed for combining with the burning substances. Even the layman, when asked to describe the process, often finds it hard to express the obvious fact – the only one he directly observes – that, in burning, heat is set free from its bondage to the material substances. This shows to what extent even the scientifically untrained consciousness in our time turns instinctively to the tangible or weighable side of nature, so that some effort is required to confess simply to what the eye and the other senses perceive.

During the first hundred years after the establishment of the *Contra-Levitatem* maxim, man's situation was in a certain sense the opposite of this. Then, people were struggling hard to get away from the old concept which saw in combustion nothing but the liberation of a super-terrestrial element from earthly fetters. This struggle found expression in a theory of heat which at that time greatly occupied scientific thinking. It is the so-called phlogiston theory, which was first proposed by the chemist Stahl (1660-1734).

This theory reveals the great uncertainty into which man's thinking about the world of the senses had arrived at that time. Clinging to the ideas inherited from antiquity, man's consciousness was already so far restricted to the forming of pure matter-bound concepts that he was tempted to conceive heat as a material element. To this heat-substance the name 'phlogiston' was given. At the same time, under the *Contra-Levitatem* maxim, it was impossible to conceive of substance except as ponderable substance. This led to the conviction that whenever heat appears as a result of some treatment of matter (combustion or friction), the material substance subject to this treatment must lose weight.

The experiments of Lavoisier (1743-94), which he undertook following Priestley's discovery of the role of oxygen in combustion, put an end to this theory. These experiments are rightly regarded as the actual beginning of modern chemistry. In Lavoisier we find an observer of nature who was predominantly interested in what the scales could tell about changes in substances. It was from this aspect that he investigated the process of oxidation. What had already been observed by a few others, though without being taken seriously, he found confirmed — that, contrary to the phlogiston theory, matter does not lose weight through oxidation but gains weight. Further experiments proved beyond doubt that in all chemical reactions the total weight of the components remained constant. However much the substance resulting from the chemical reaction of others might differ from these, its weight always proved to be the same as their total weight. What else could be concluded from the apparent unchangeability of weight throughout all the chemical happenings in nature than that the ponderable world content was of eternal duration?

Together with the overcoming of the fallacy that heat is a ponderable substance (full certainty was indeed established only some time later through the investigations of Davy and Rumford into heat generated by friction) – human thinking was led into a one-sided conception of combustion which was the polar opposite of the one held earlier.

The observation that weight remained constant during chemical transformations led to the new concept of the chemical element as a state of physical matter which 'neither results from a combination of other physical substances nor is resolvable into such'. With the discovery of this condition, naturally the conviction arose that man's searching mind had reached 'rock-bottom'. This conviction, however, was shaken when, with the discovery of radium, an element became known whose property it is to disintegrate into two other elements, helium and lead. Although this did not force science to abandon the element-concept altogether, it became necessary to find a new definition for it.

This definition was established by Professor W. Ostwald at the beginning of the present century, when he stated that the chemical element represents a condition of physical matter in which 'any chemical change results in an increase of weight'. In this way, the chemical concept of the element achieved a meaning which had actually been implicit in it from its first conception; it was a true child of the *Contra-Levitatem* maxim.

In what follows we shall discuss a few chemical elements from a point of view which results from regarding as an essential characteristic how each of them behaves while its ponderable and imponderable parts are being separated. Compared with what one is used to in modern physical and chemical research, our observations will again be quite simple. Yet they will be important, *inter alia*, in enabling us to extend our concept of polarity in a way which will prove essential for the new understanding of nature.

* * * * *

It is a characteristic of all substances of organic origin that, even when life itself has withdrawn from them, or when they have been removed from the organic processes that gave rise to their existence, they are informed with levity in a dormant state. For they are all combustible. The actual bearer of combustibility in them is always the element *carbon*. This element, therefore, will be one of the objects of our discussion. The property of combustibility, however, is not limited to substances of strictly organic origin. There are purely mineral and mineral-like substances that are quite equally combustible. In them, too, levity is present as internal heat. Among the substances of this kind we will choose *sulphur* and *phosphorus*. This choice, together with that of carbon is determined by the fact that all three have distinctive relationships to the process of combustion. It is characteristic of sulphur to occur in nature in the levity-containing ('reduced') state; it always tends to reach that state and to remain in it. Phosphorus, on the contrary, tends towards the levity-free (oxidised) state. Hence it never occurs naturally in a pure form, as sulphur does. In comparison with these two, carbon holds the middle position, as we shall see, in various ways. Through having these properties, and through the manifold roles they are thereby enabled to play in nature, the three elements represent, each in its own way, an ur-phenomenal instance: that is, an instance 'worth a thousand, bearing all within itself'. Together they reveal themselves as letters in a particular 'word' of nature.

* * * * *

Before entering on a discussion of these three elements, we will try to picture, taking carbon as our example, the chemical element in general, as it appears to a mode of observation free from *Contra-Levitatem* preconceptions.

In every chemical process, heat either appears or disappears.

In chemical parlance this is called the 'reaction heat' of the process. How much heat is freed or bound in a particular instance depends on the substance involved. As is generally known, this fact plays a decisive part in many technical applications. Compared with the usual formula expressing the oxidisation of carbon to carbon dioxide:

$$C + 2O = CO_2$$

the complete formula, therefore, reads:

$$C + 2O = CO_2 + n \text{ calories}$$
(In the case of carbon n = 98,000)

So far modern science goes in complying with this fact. But a qualitative mode of investigation is compelled to draw yet other conclusions from it. For, if we write 'C' for combustible carbon in the same way as 'O' for non-combustible oxygen, we are keeping certain facts veiled and thus producing an illusion. What we ordinarily call carbon, reckoning it among the chemical elements, is in fact already a kind of compound – a compound of carbon and heat. We never get hold of carbon in its physical condition except in combinations with either heat or oxygen (or other chemical elements). That which is identically the same in each instance, appearing in one form in combination with heat (levity), or in the other form (as in our example) combined with oxygen, is never found in a physical-material condition. *Yet it is something behind all the physical appearances of carbon which alone deserves to be designated as 'elementary carbon'.*

In order to get this new picture as clear as possible, let us change for once the usual chemical notation by writing the chemical symbol, where it is to represent the elementary condition, thus: ⊡.

Let us further choose the letter L to designate the levity-ingredients of the substance in the reduced state. Then ⊡ L would designate what we usually write as C. Correspondingly, the oxidised state would have to be written as ⊡ O. If we want to indicate the faculty of carbon for assuming either condition, we can write: C_O^L.

Although we have used the faculty of the combustibility of a substance, and thereby the faculty of appearing in both the reduced and the oxidised states for describing the conception of the truly elementary condition, this conception is not valid only for substances of this kind; it applies in general to all chemical elements. It is only our line of reasoning that has to change. Take oxygen as another instance. In its physical-material condition — that is, as an externally perceptible gas — oxygen is already a 'compound with itself'. Chemical science expresses this fact by writing it as O_2. In atomistic parlance, oxygen is called a bi-atomic gas, the O_2-state being called the 'molecular' state, and the — physically never appearing — O-state, the 'atomic' state. When oxygen is chemically active by being engaged in some process of chemical transformation, one is justified in regarding it as being in the pure 'atomic' — i.e. the actually elementary — condition, and then one speaks of it being *'in statu nascendi'*, i.e. in a state of coming into being. This is a truly appropriate description, but not in the sense in which it has been interpreted scientifically, as meaning a state of material emergence from a compound in which it was present materially. The true reference is to that 'something', which, in the case of carbon, we found to lie behind all carbon-appearances.

Nature is always consistent, and we are therefore justified in saying that what we have thus identified as the real elementary state of a chemical substance applies equally to any chemical element, although there are some, such as the so-called monoatomic gases, which seem not to fit into this picture. Still, it is significant that the element which starts off the entire order of the elements, namely hydrogen, is at the same time bi-atomic and combustible, and therefore combines both characteristics used here for developing the general concept.

As was said before, the 'something' which remains identical through all its appearances has in itself no material properties. In Goethe's (and Traherne's) sense it is a pure IDEA. As such, it has a much wider range of action than is evident only in the cases where its presence can be established quantitatively. When we come to discuss in particular the three elements chosen for special observation, we shall see this quite clearly. We shall then feel prompted to speak of the 'functional' state of the element in question.

The primary state of any element is its functional, or — as we can also say — its ideal state. Every element has its corresponding Idea. This leads us to yet another thought. Viewed in the Goethean way, the various elements of the mineral kingdom correspond to the 'types' of the plant kingdom, which bring about the different species. These types we have learnt to recognise in their turn as metamorphoses of one all-comprising Idea — the *ur-plant*. Hence we may ask whether there exists also a purely ideal (functional) *ur-matter* whose offspring, as it were, we meet as the order of the chemical elements. The answer is, yes. So far as possible within the framework of this book, the ensuing chapter will give a more distinct picture of this fact.

* * * * *

Against the background thus outlined, let us now discuss the three aforenamed elements: sulphur, phosphorus, carbon.

For the chemist who thinks along purely quantitative lines, sulphur and phosphorus are both 'elements' in the sense of Ostwald's definition, quoted earlier; but how different are the dynamic conditions latent in them! This is vividly illustrated by the contrasting ways of storing them in a laboratory. For maintaining sulphur in its elementary, combustible state, no special arrangements are necessary. It lies quietly in its container, chemically tension-less. Not so phosphorus, which has to be kept under water in order to prevent oxygen from getting at it. For just as the reduced state is natural for sulphur, so is the oxidised state for phosphorus, the combination with 'L' being congenial to the former and foreign to the latter. This difference between the two elements determines all their chemical reactions.

To object here that the different reactions of the two substances are due only to the difference of their respective temperatures of ignition and that above these temperatures the difference will more or less disappear (all combustible substances at a sufficiently high temperature becoming more or less similar to phosphorus), would not meet the argument. For what matters here is just how the particular substance behaves at that level of temperature on which the earth unfolds her normal planetary activity. To ignore this would be to violate one of the principles we have adopted from Goethe, which is never to derive fundamental concepts of nature from observations obtained under artificial conditions.

Fig. 11

Sulphur and phosphorus are thus seen to represent two polarically opposite tendencies with regard to the levity-gravity coherence which breaks up when combustion occurs. In the case of sulphur, the ponderable and imponderable entities appear to cling together; in the case of phosphorus, they seem to be anxious to part. These two different tendencies — which are characteristic of many other substances and represent a basic factor in the chemical happenings of the earth — are in their own way a pair of opposites. Since each of them represents in itself a relationship between two poles of a polarity — gravity and levity — so in their mutual relationship they represent a 'polarity of polarities'. In Fig. 11 an attempt has been made to represent this fact by a symbolic diagram.

In this figure the shaded part represents the imponderable, the black part the ponderable entity. In the left-hand symbol both are shown in a relationship corresponding to the one characteristic of sulphur; in the right-hand figure the relationship is characteristic of phosphorus.

Here we have an instance of a kind of polarity which belongs to the fundamentals of nature as much as does the levity-gravity polarity itself. Wherever two poles of a polarity meet, they have the possibility of interacting in two ways which in themselves are again polarically opposite. This shows that we have to distinguish in nature between two kinds of polarities which we may aptly term as *polarities of the first order*, and, arising from them, *polarities of the second order*, or *primary* and *secondary* polarities. Our further studies will bring up various other instances of this kind, and will show that part of the epistemological trouble in which science finds itself today results from the fact that the scientific mind, unable to distinguish between the two kinds of polarity, has been led to a fatal confusion of both. For this reason they will be discussed here at once.

* * * * *

In actual fact, the distinction between the two orders of polarity has been implicit in the descriptions given in this book right from the start. Remember, in this respect, how the picture of the threefold psycho-physical structure of man, which has proved a master-key for unlocking the most varied scientific problems, was first built up. There, 'body' and 'soul' represented a polarity which is obviously one of the first order. By our observation of the human organism, in relation both to the different functions of the soul and to the different main organic systems, we further recognised the fact that the ways in which body and soul are interrelated are polarically opposite in the region of the brain and nerves and in the region of the metabolic processes, which again results in two polarically opposite activities of the soul, mental on the one hand, and volitional on the other. In what we called the pole of consciousness and the pole of life we therefore have a clear polarity of the second order. For at either pole we find functions of both soul and body at work, but co-ordinated in a polarically opposite way. Among the polarities of the second order which we shall encounter later on we shall indeed find some having a more direct, and others a less direct, connection with the polarity represented by man himself.

Remembering that our first occasion to concern ourselves overtly with the concept of polarity was in connection with the four elements, we may now ask whether the old doctrine did not embrace some conception of secondary polarity as well as of primary polarity, and if so, whether this might not prove as helpful in clarifying our own conception as was the primary polarity cold-warm. This is indeed so.

In Chapter IX we pointed out that in the original view of the four elements they were regarded as springing from four primal qualities, Cold, Warm, Dry, and Moist. We have so far discussed only the first two; it is now time to consider the others. They, too, regain their significance in a science seeking for a truly dynamic picture of the universe: As will be seen, the first two, as a pair of opposites, represent a primary polarity, the other two a secondary polarity.

To understand more clearly what is meant by 'dry' and 'moist' in their elementary sense, we must give these qualities the same sort of examination that we gave the two others.

It lies in the nature of things that we instinctively associate these qualities with the solid and liquid states of matter respectively. This certainly agrees with the diagram given earlier, where the elements Earth and Water are distinguished precisely by their connection with these two characteristics. Yet, in addition to this, the qualities dry and moist are found to be characteristic also of Fire and Air respectively, though with the difference that they are linked not with the quality cold, as in the case of the lower elements, but with the quality warm. So we see that the concepts Dry and Moist, as they lived in the old picturing of them, mean a good deal more than we understand by them today.

That these two respective attributes do not belong exclusively to the solid and the liquid states of matter can be seen at once by observing the different reactions of certain liquids to a solid surface which they touch. One need only recall the difference between water and quicksilver. If water runs over a surface it leaves a trail; quicksilver does not. Water clings to the side of a vessel; again, quicksilver does not. A well-known consequence of this difference is that in a narrow tube the surface of the liquid − the so-called meniscus − stands higher at the circumference than at the centre in the case of water; with quicksilver it is just the reverse. In the sense of the two qualities, dry and moist, water is a 'moist' liquid; quicksilver a 'dry' one. On the other hand, the quality of moistness in a solid substance appears in the adhesive power of glue.

Let us now see what the two pairs of qualities, cold-warm and dry-moist, tell us about the nature of the four elements when we let them speak to us in their various combinations.

The element Fire reveals its attributes of warm and dry in a behaviour which combines a tendency to dynamic expansion with a disinclination to enter into a lasting combination with the other elements. Correspondingly, the behaviour of the element Earth unites a tendency to contraction with an inclination to fall out of conjunction with the other elements. Thus the attribute, dry, belongs equally to pure flame and sheer dust, though for opposite reasons. Distinct from both these elements are the middle elements Water and Air; with them the attribute, moist, comes to expression in their tendency both to interpenetrate mutually and to absorb their neighbours − the liquid element absorbing solid matter and the aeriform element taking up heat. What distinguishes them is that water has a 'cold' nature, from which it gains its density; while air has a 'warm' nature, to which it owes its tendency to expand.

In the most general sense, the quality 'moist' applies wherever two different entities are drawn into some kind of intimate relationship with one another; 'dry' applies where the relationship is of a more external kind: in the extreme case, that of a mere spatial side-by-side existence. This gives to this pair of qualities the character of a secondary polarity, for they describe relationships of two already existing entities or conditions which, as in the case of the four elements, stand themselves in a polar relationship.

The elementary qualities 'dry' and 'moist' thus appear to have the characteristics of relative qualities. By comparison, as the following consideration will show, the qualities 'cold' and 'warm' have absolute properties.

We remember that by 'cold' and 'warm', in their elementary meaning, we must understand neither mere experiences of our sense of warmth, nor purely externally measured degrees of temperature. For both these represent level-differences — either directly experienced or measured — and the cancellation of these differences: in other words, mutual relations between two conditions. The quality 'warm' differs by representing a form of absolute cosmic dynamic, Levity; in the same way 'cold' represents an absolute cosmic dynamic, Gravity. Hence, these two elementary qualities form a primary polarity.

Henceforth we shall repeatedly encounter the contrast of 'dry' and 'moist' as a characteristic of the different secondary polarities which nature manifests in her various fields of action. The manifestations of these polarities, however, will at first sight seem to differ basically from the form in which we have now traced their, as it were, *ur*-representative in the cross of the Elements. For in all future instances we shall find the two qualities 'dry' and 'moist' as characteristics of the mode of interaction between the poles of the primary polarity, levity-gravity — i.e., 'warm' and 'cold' — whereas in the cross of the Elements they turn up seemingly independent from the latter two, even entering into

various combinations with them. Nevertheless, the cross of the
Elements can also be seen under the aspect which will henceforth
be the essential one for us. We need only think of Earth and Fire
on the one hand, and of Water and Air on the other, as being combined in a common dynamic. Then we find the two compound
elements, Fire-Earth and Water-Air, both made up of the qualities
Cold and Warm, yet with the difference that in the first instance
they are interrelated in a 'dry' manner, and in the second instance
in a 'moist'.

* * * * *

The behaviour of sulphur and phosphorus in the process of
combustion has led us to the concept of polarities of the second
order, and we have now recognised the second pair of qualities
in the cross of the Elements as representing this polarity. Now, the
way in which the ponderable and the imponderable parts are
related in sulphur is precisely the 'moist' way and correspondingly
in phosphorus the 'dry' one. The same is true of the poles of man's
organisation, the nervous system being 'dry', the metabolic system
'moist'. The same antithesis is shown in the psychological functions
connected with these bodily systems. For on the one hand there is
the 'dry' onlooker-relationship of the purely brain-bound intellect,
which apprehends only a picture of the world, never its essence.
On the other hand, there is the 'moist' intermingling of the will-
force with the actual forces of the world. And again, in full agreement with this, we find sulphur predominant in those protein
substances which serve the body's metabolism, while phosphorus
is a characteristic ingredient of the nerves and bones.

In particular the plant reveals clearly the functional significance of phosphorus as the bearer of the quality 'dry'. For its
healthy growth the plant needs the quality 'dry' in two places:
at the root, where it unites with the element earth, and in the
flower, where it opens itself to the fire element. Root and flower
as distinct from the middle parts of the plant are both 'dry'
formations. In a still higher degree this applies to the seed, which

must separate itself from the mother plant to produce a separate new organism. All these are functions in the plant which require phosphorus for their healthy performance.

The following may serve as an example of how this kind of examination of substances from the functional point of view throws light on their potential remedial value. We remember how in the beginning we recognised the sleeping condition as one in which the nervous system is pervaded by building-up metabolic processes, or, as we are now in a position to say, one in which it exchanges its otherwise more 'dry' state for a more 'moist' one. Disturbances in the change-over between these two states can indeed be cured by suitable applications of sulphur and phosphorus respectively. Another instance calling for a corresponding application of one or the other occurs when in the naturally 'dry' skeleton the opposite quality comes to the fore (rickets), or where the polarically opposite condition appears in the normally 'moist' metabolic region (concretions of various kinds). This may suffice as an indication of how the study of the functional qualities of such substances can lead to rational therapeutic applications of them, instead of depending merely on trial and error.

* * * * *

To complete the functional picture of sulphur and phosphorus, provided so far by their behaviour in the laboratory and in the interior of living organisms, let us look to the macrotelluric sphere for phenomena which reveal their participation in the life of the earth as a whole. Here, sulphur points unmistakably to the earth's volcanism. It is a fact that wherever mineral sulphur occurs in the earth, there we find a site of former or present volcanic activity. Similarly, there is no such volcanic site where sulphur is not present in one form or other. Hence the name *Solfatara* for the fumarole described earlier (Chapter IX).

One of the characteristics of the volcanic regions of the earth is the healing effect of substances found there. Fango-mud, for instance, which has also been mentioned before, is a much-used remedy against rheumatism. This is typical of functional sulphur. We may truly characterise the earth's volcanism as being qualitatively sulphurous. It is the sulphur-function coming to expression through a higher degree of 'moistness' in the relationship between gravity and levity which distinguishes volcanic regions from the rest of the otherwise 'dry' earth's crust.

Let us now look for the macrotelluric process which, in the sense of a secondary polarity, represents the dynamic opposite of the earth's volcanic activity. This we find in the phenomenon of snow-formation. The coming into being of snow is dynamically as much 'phosphorus', as volcanism is dynamically 'sulphur'. Let us visualise this process in its peculiar dynamic course. We find, to begin with, water in the state of atmospheric vapour. At this stage of the water-substance, the influence of the terrestrial field of gravity is comparatively weak. Directly out of this floating condition congeal a great number of single snow-crystals, all of which bear most precise and often astoundingly complicated forms. Plate III shows a variety of such forms; these are of particular interest to us, also because of the striking example they afford of nature's way of working through metamorphosis. Now, obeying the trend of gravity, more and more of these crystals unite in their descent and gradually form flakes of varying size. The nearer they come to earth, the closer they fall, until at last on the ground they form an unbroken, more or less spherical, cover.

Imagine a snow-covered field glistening in the sun on a clear, quiet winter's day. As far as we can see, there is no sign of life, no movement. Here water, which is normally fluid and, in its liquid state, serves the ever-changing life-processes, covers the earth in the form of millions of separate crystals shaped with mathematical exactitude, each of which breaks and reflects in a million rays the light from the sun. A contrast, indeed, between this quiet emergence of forms from levity into gravity, and the form-denying volcanism surging up out of gravity into levity, as shown by the ever-restless activity of the *Solfatara*. As we found volcanism to be a macrotelluric manifestation of functional

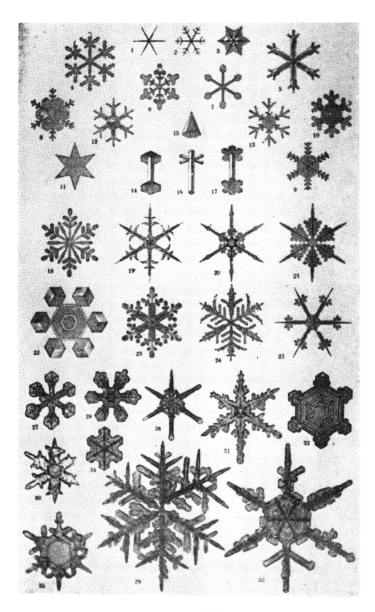

PLATE III

Snow-crystals

sulphur, we find in the process of snow-formation a corresponding manifestation of functional phosphorus.

In the formation of snow, nature shown us *in statu agendi* a process which we otherwise meet in the earth only in its finished results, crystallisation. We may, therefore, rightly look upon snow-formation as an ur-phenomenon in this sphere of nature's activities. As such it allows us to learn something concerning the origin in general of the crystalline realm of the earth; and, vice versa, our insight into the 'becoming' of this realm will enable us to see more clearly the universal function of which phosphorus is the main representative among the physical substances of the earth.

It has puzzled many an observer that crystals occur in the earth with directions of their main axes entirely independent of the direction of the earthly pull of gravity. This riddle is solved by the phenomenon of snow-formation, provided we allow it to speak to us as an ur-phenomenon. For it then tells us that matter must be in a state of transition from lightness into heaviness if it is to appear in crystalline form. The crystals in the earth, therefore, must have originated at a time when the relation between levity and gravity on the earth was different from what it is today.

The same language is spoken by the property of transparency which is so predominant among crystals. One of the fundamental characteristics of heavy solid matter is to resist light — in other words, to be opaque. Exposed to heat, however, physical substance loses this feature to the extent that at the border of its ponderability all matter becomes pervious to light. Now, in the transparent crystal, matter retains this kinship to light even in its solid state.

A corresponding message comes from the peculiar colouring of crystals. These colours are known to result from quantitatively small metallic ingredients in the particular mineral. They mostly differ entirely from those of the corresponding metallic salts, where the same metal is the basis of the chemical compound; some of these salts are even colourless. On the other hand, metals are known to give the flame a particular colour if they are vaporised in such a flame, and in many instances these colours coincide with those of crystals coloured by the same metal. Read as a letter in nature's script, this fact tells us that precious stones with their flame-like colours are characterised by having kept something of the nature that was theirs before they coalesced into ponderable existence. In fact, they are 'frozen flames'.

It is this fact, known from ancient intuitive experience, which prompted man of old to attribute particular spiritual significance to the various precious stones of the earth and to use them correspondingly in his rituals.

Crystallisation, seen thus in its cosmic aspect, shows a dynamic orientation which is polarically opposite to that of the earth's seismic activities. Just as in the latter we observe levity taking hold of ponderable matter and moving it in a direction opposite to the pull of gravity, so in crystallisation we see imponderable matter passing over from levity into gravity. And just as we found in volcanism and related processes a field of activity of 'functional sulphur', so we found in snow-formation and related processes a field of activity of 'functional phosphorus'. Both fields are characterised by an interaction between gravity and levity, this interaction being of opposite nature in each of them. Here, again, sulphur and phosphorus appear as bearers of a polarity of the second order which springs from the two polarically opposite ways of interaction between the poles of the polarity of the first order: levity-gravity.

* * * * *

As in man there is a third system, mediating between the two polar systems of his organism, so between sulphur and phosphorus there is a third element which holds a middle place between them and is the bearer of a corresponding function. This element is carbon.

To see this we need only take into consideration carbon's relationship to oxidation and reduction respectively. As it is natural for sulphur to tend towards the reduced state, and for phosphorus to tend towards the oxidised state, so it is in the nature of carbon to be related to both states and therefore to oscillate between them. By its readiness to change over from the oxidised to the combustible state, it can serve the plant in the assimilation of light, while by its readiness to make the reverse change it serves man and animal in the breathing process. We breathe in oxygen from the air; the oxygen circulates through the blood stream and passes out again in conjunction with carbon, as carbon dioxide, when we exhale. In the process whereby the plants reduce the carbon dioxide exhaled by man and animal, while the latter again absorb with their food the carbon produced in the form of organic matter by the plant, we see carbon moving to and fro between the two opposite conditions.

Within the plant itself, too, carbon acts as functionary of the alternation between oxidation and reduction. During the first half of the year, when vegetation is unfolding, there is a great reduction process of oxidised carbon, while in the second half of the year, when the withering process prevails, a great deal of the previously reduced carbon passes into the oxidised condition. As this is connected with exhaling and inhaling of oxygen through carbon, carbon can be regarded as having the function of the lung-organ of the earth. Logically enough, we find carbon playing the same role in the middle part of the threefold human organism.

Another indication of the midway position of carbon is its ability to combine as readily with hydrogen as with oxygen, and, in these polar combinations, even to combine with itself. In this latter form it provides the basis of the innumerable organic substances in nature, and serves as the 'building stones' of the body-substances of living organisms. Among these, the carbohydrates produced by the plants show clearly the double function of carbon in the way it alternates between the states of starch and sugar.

When the plant absorbs through its leaves carbonic acid from the air and condenses it into the multiple grains of starch with their peculiar structure characteristic for each plant species, we have a biological event which corresponds to the formation of snow in the meteorological realm. Here we see carbon at work in a manner functionally akin to that of phosphorus. Sugar, on the other hand, has its place in the saps of the plants which rise through the stems and carry up with them the mineral substances of the earth. Here we find carbon acting in a way akin to the function of sulphur.

Fig. 12

This twofold nature of carbon makes itself noticeable down to the very mineral sphere of the earth. There we find it in the fact that carbon occurs both in the form of the diamond, the hardest of all mineral substances, and in the form of the softest, graphite. In the diamond's brilliant transparency, and in the dense blackness of graphite, carbon reveals its twofold relation to light.

In Fig. 12 an attempt has been made to represent diagram-matically the function of Carbon in a way corresponding to the previous representation of the functions of Sulphur and Phos-phorus.

* * * * *

Our investigation has led us from the modes of action of

sulphur, phosphorus and carbon in their physical-material condition to a picture of these modes of action as certain universal
functions, so that we were able eventually to speak simply of
'functional sulphur', etc. In this way we have taken a step towards
the goal of the present part of our considerations – the gaining
of a dynamic conception of matter which will allow us to recognise
matter as an instrument of the spirit's ideal-creative activity. For,
in all these cases, what we can see and touch as space-bound
matter turns out to be a mode of appearance of certain universal
functions which we encounter also otherwise in nature in manifold
metamorphoses. In the sense of the genetic conception which we
have repeatedly applied, the physical state of the substances
discussed above must be conceived as a terminal state of the
cosmic functions they represent. In this way we arrive at an
altogether new conception of the chemical element in general,
free from *Contra-Levitatem* restrictions. For what is true for
these particular chemical elements holds good equally for all
other elements, and thereby also for their various compounds,
which in their own ways turn out to be appearances of correspondingly combined functions. Let us take from nature's basic
substances a few to exemplify this.

In the sense of present-day chemistry, water as a physical
substance is 'composed' of physical hydrogen and physical oxygen.
In contrast to this kind of interpretation, we will try to gain a
functional picture of water and then see how the functional
properties of hydrogen and oxygen fit into it.

We remember the peculiar nature of 'Water' as one of the
four Elements, where it appears as the bearer of the qualities
Cold and Moist. Although Water in this sense comprises everything on earth that has the property of being liquid, we may
recognise physical-material water as an ur-phenomenal appearance
of the corresponding Element. Water, it is true, is present on earth
also in solid form as ice, and as vapour (in the air), but its intrinsic
functions are to *dissolve* and to *mediate*, and these it can exert
only in the liquid state. Consequently, if through outer influence
– heat or cold – it changes over into one of the adjacent states,

it presses back into its native condition. We see this, on the one hand, as the phenomenon of cloud formation, so characteristic of our atmosphere, whereby the water always returns as rain to the earth. On the other hand, there is the peculiar 'anomaly' of the spatial behaviour of water in the course of its cooling towards the freezing point. Water has its greatest density at +4°C. It contracts down to this point, as all other substances do, but below this point it expands again until the freezing point is reached. Ice is thus specifically lighter than liquid water, and therefore floats on its mother substance. In nature's household this has the result that the waters of the earth never solidify completely. For under a closed cover of ice the temperature of water does not fall below +4°C (it always freezes from the top downwards), and this guarantees the continuation of life within the water. On the other hand, when ice is exposed to sufficient pressure, it melts without requiring heat, and this again has the effect that the glaciers of the earth are always liquid underneath and so are in constant motion. In this way water maintains even in the solid state its capacity for flowing. If we gaze into nature with eyes trained in Goethe's way of contemplating polarities, we recognise in the accumulating clouds and in the floating ice polarically co-ordinated phenomena.

We now turn to the properties and functions of hydrogen and oxygen. The former we find active where organic entities decay, and so where forms shaped by life dissolve. The function of hydrogen is to de-individualise, or, as we can also say, to chaoticise. Everything it gets hold of it carries from 'Earth' via 'Water' and 'Air' to 'Fire', and thereby towards 'Chaos' (Chapter IX). Oxygen does just the opposite. By replacing, in the course of oxidisation, the levity content of the oxidisable substance, it carries the latter towards the mineral state, or more deeply into it. Oxygen is the true generator of ashes, and thereby carries substances towards the element 'Earth'. It is not a matter of chance that precisely the process of oxidisation enabled Lavoisier to establish the fact that substances do not lose weight when they combine chemically.

These tendencies of hydrogen and oxygen come impressively to the fore under certain extreme conditions. Both elements then exhibit well-known properties which, in comparison with those of other substances, could be called 'anomalous', but which, when read as characters of a script, represent a 'manifest mystery.'

Generally, if a gas is made to expand suddenly, its temperature falls. According to physical laws this cannot be otherwise, for the gas, in order to expand, requires heat. Not so hydrogen; quick expansion makes its temperature rise. In this way, as the lightest chemical element, it shows its capacity for releasing levity in a process by which, normally, levity is absorbed. In our next chapter we shall come to a more detailed picture of this process itself; at the moment it suffices to take into account this special property of hydrogen.

We now ask — what is the polarically opposite process to which we should have to expose oxygen in order to let the corresponding polar property come to the fore? Obviously, this must be the driving of oxygen into the liquid and finally into the solid state — by means of high pressure and low temperature. If our reasoning is correct — or, as Goethe would say, if it is 'natural' — we may ex - pect that in this state oxygen will exhibit a 'surplus' of gravity, just as hydrogen in the opposite state exhibits a 'surplus' of levity. The fact is that oxygen in the solid state exhibits magnetic properties!

Returning now to the picture of the macrotelluric behaviour of water, we find ourselves in a position to 'read' the following:

What the substance of water manifests in the phenomenon of accumulating clouds and expanding ice, both of which it needs to fulfil its role as the mediator-substance in nature, this we see appearing in oxygen in the state of extreme contraction as its intrinsic magnetic property, and in hydrogen in the state of extreme expansion as its power to generate heat. Yet, to say that water owes its capacity for thermal action, shortly before it freezes, to hydrogen being physically contained in it, and its corresponding polar capacity to the physical presence of oxygen in it, would not be in line with the mode of reasoning here practised. Water in itself is an 'Idea' whose peculiarity it is to combine in itself two polar functions similarly to what carbon does in relationship to sulphur and phosphorus. If the two functions, co-operatively allied in water, assume separate material existence, they appear as hydrogen and oxygen respectively.

What we have thus learnt by contemplating these various

instances, we can express in a general form by saying: *Nature's physical substances are congealed cosmic functions.*

* * * * *

As a further example of this concept of matter, we will discuss two more substances which also represent two basic functions in nature. In former times, when terms were used solely to denote qualitative properties people spoke simply of 'flint' and 'chalk' to distinguish two large groups of rocks with fundamentally different origins and properties. Analytical chemistry has recognised flint as the bearer of the element *silicon*, and chalk as the bearer of *calcium*. We will take only such instances of them as seem necessary for our purpose.

The function of these two elements comes to an ur-phenomenal expression in two kinds of unicellular organism. Both belong to the species of *amoeba*, but with the peculiarity that the cell produces a kind of case or outer skeleton, one calcareous, the other siliceous. Notwithstanding the extreme variety of forms of these shells in both groups, each group is marked by quite consistent features. In zoology, siliceous amoebae are called *radiolaria*, from their raylike formations, and the calcareous ones, *foraminifera*, from certain apertures in their shells. German zoological nomenclature speaks of 'ray-animalcules' (*Strahlentierchen*) and 'chamber-animalcules' (*Kammertierchen*); the latter term is more appropriate than the usual Latin name, because these shells consist, in fact, of a smaller or larger number of chambers (whose apertures serve as outlets for the animal's pseudopodes). In Plate IV, the left-hand picture shows the siliceous shell of radiolarian; the right-hand, the calcareous shell of a foraminifer. Both are microscope drawings from Haeckel's great work, *Art-Forms of Nature*.[1]

In view of such forms one is inclined to speak of two 'gestures' of nature; the gestures which we, as humans, carry out when we either stretch out our arms and spread our fingers while lifting our head with wide-open eyes, or when we contract our whole body, while lowering our head and dropping our eyelids. These are, in fact, precisely the functions exerted by silicon and calcium

Types of skeletons of the species Radiolaria

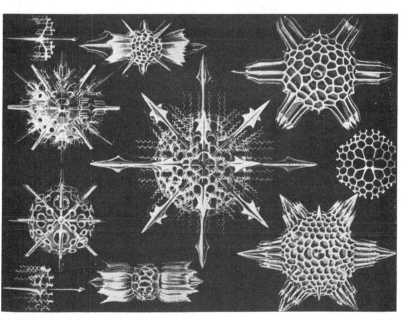

PLATE IV

Types of shells of the species Foraminifera

in our organism. Silicon is at work wherever the organism opens itself to the outer world: in the raylike spread of hair, in the skin permeable to air and light, and especially in the eyes, whose lens (not for nothing called the 'crystalline lens') actually consists of fibres which in their cross-section have the same hexagonal shape that is found in rocks based on silica — i.e. rock-crystal and its relatives. Calcium in the human organism, however, is always used inwardly for the formation of bones, both in the skull encasing the central nervous organ and in the bones supporting trunk and limbs from within. Moreover, the blood requires calcium in order to coagulate — a process which in its own way represents the aforementioned 'gesture' of this element.

Turning from man once more to outer nature, we find the same contrast between shell-fish with their compact calcareous cases, inhabiting the darkness of the sea, and the birds with their silicic plumage, built from innumerable delicate rays, inhabiting the light-pervaded air. In one group of the animal kingdom, comprising the so-called jointed animals (arthropods), both features are found, with the crab-like animals at one pole, the insects at the other. The reader may form for himself a vivid picture of a chalk-encased crayfish, preferably crawling backwards, and then of a light- and air-pervaded butterfly with its eyes composed of thousands of hexagonal, silicic facets, and he will recognise what we have described as nature's two opposite gestures. The same dynamic contrast, but this time in terms of structure, has been at work in the formation of the two basic mountain-formations, one consisting of primeval rock, the other of limestone. In the plant kingdom the same contrast comes to expression in yet another way — among the trees, for instance, in oak and birch, or in such plants as cactus on the one hand and mare's tail on the other.

We might expect that this kind of knowledge of the functional values of substances will have a medical application. This is indeed so in the art of therapy based on modern spiritual science. In yet another direction such knowledge leads to a rational use of both substances for the treatment of the soil in agriculture and horticulture. This indeed forms part of the methods of so-called

Bio-Dynamic farming and gardening, also based on spiritual science.

In concluding this part of our discussion certain cross-connections between sulphur and calcium on the one hand, and phosphorus and silicon on the other, may be mentioned. Where the fire-encasing sulphur occurs, we find it in contact with calciferous rock (limestone). The modern optical industry came to birth when the kinship between silicon and phosphorus was discovered, and thereby the possibility of endowing glass, which is normally based on silicon, with certain optical properties through substituting phosphorus for silicon to a greater or lesser extent.

Just as water takes the middle position between hydrogen and oxygen, and carbon between sulphur and phosphorus, so is there a mediating substance between flint and chalk. Outside on the earth this is clay, with aluminium as its basic element. This brief indication will be enough for our present purpose.

* * * * *

As once before, in the case of the four elements, our method of observation leads to a functional picture of nature which was known to man in earlier times in a more or less instinctive way. If in what follows we examine more closely concepts of this kind in forms familiar to certain medieval seekers for a deeper understanding of nature, this again is not done out of mere historical interest, but because of the help we shall gain in building up a conceptual language for the new functional conception of nature.

The medieval seekers for knowledge whom we have in mind were the alchemists. This is not the place to enter into a full examination of the meaning and value of alchemy in its original legitimate sense (which must not be confused with activities that later on paraded under the same name). Only this we will say — that genuine alchemy owes its origin to an impulse which, at a time when the onlooker-consciousness first arose, led to the foundation of a school for the development of an intuitive relationship of the soul with the world of the senses. This was to enable man to resist the effects of the division which evolution was about to set up in his soul life — the division which was to give him, on the one hand, an abstract experience of his own self, divorced from the outer world, and on the other, a mere onlooker's experience of that outer world. As a result of these endeavours, concepts were formed which in their literal meaning seemed to apply merely to outwardly perceptible substances, while in truth they stood for the spiritual functions represented by those substances, both within and outside the human organism.

Thus the alchemist who used these concepts thought of them first as referring to his own soul, and to the inner organic processes corresponding to the various activities of his soul. Older alchemical writings, therefore, can be understood only if prescriptions which seem to signify certain chemical manipulations are read as instructions for certain exercises of the soul, or as advices for the redirection of corresponding processes in the body. This applies precisely to the triad of alchemical concepts, *Salt, Mercury,* and *Sulphur,* which now require our special attention.

When speaking of Salt, the alchemist meant the regulated formative activity of his thinking, based on the salt-forming process in his nervous system. When he spoke of Mercury he meant the quickly changing emotional life of the soul and the corresponding activities of the rhythmic processes of the body. Lastly, Sulphur meant the will activities of his soul and the corresponding metabolic processes of the body. Only through studying these functions within himself, and through re-establishing the harmony between them which had been theirs in the beginning, and from which, he felt, man had deviated in the course of time, did the alchemist hope to come to an understanding of their counterparts in the external cosmos. Therefore, if an alchemist gave directions, say, for a certain treatment of Sulphur, Mercury and Salt, with the assertion that by carrying out these directions properly, one would obtain Aurum (gold), he really spoke of a method for directing the thinking, feeling and willing activities of the soul in such a way as to gain true Wisdom.[2]

These brief indications may suffice to show that, in fact, the alchemist's Sulphur corresponds with what we mean by 'functional sulphur'; his Salt with our 'functional phosphorus'; and his Mercury with our 'functional carbon'. In this sense we shall henceforth use this alchemical terminology for describing corresponding phenomena and processes in nature.

* * * * *

As in previous instances, the extension of our observation of natural phenomena practised in this chapter has given opportunity to add some further basic concepts of the new natural science to those developed before, among them the concept of the polarity of the second order. As was said before, this concept has special value as a guide through certain orders of natural phenomena. By using it in this way one grows aware of certain characteristic features common to all the phenomena in question. Because of their funda- mental importance for all future understanding of nature, we shall describe these features now, and for this purpose turn back once more to the geometrical considerations of the previous chapter.

In the light of what we have learnt since then, it will be clear that the geometrical polarity of point and plane represents a po- larity of the first order. What then, we are now prompted to ask, is the corresponding polarity of the second order? In other words: What are the formative elements in nature which are as representa- tive of the 'sulphurous' and the 'saline' interplay of levity and gravity as plane and point are representative of levity and gravity themselves? For a 'reading' in the world of the senses, trained in the way we have here tried to indicate, these formative elements are not difficult to detect. Natural happenings of the sulphurous type are found to present themselves always through *linear* forma- tions, those of the saline type through *spherical* formations. A few of nature's many examples may be described here. Others will be met with in the further course of our studies.

Take the contrast between volcanism and snow-formation. In volcanism we can now see the importance of the fact that the planar levitational suction on the subterranean magmatic matter does not result in an even rise of it over the entire area which is under the suctional influence — which in the *Solfatara* would involve a rise of the entire ground — but in the formation of single, spatially restricted openings, often in the form of mountainous upheavals. Some of these have been piled up by volcanic action itself, and all of them have at the summit a crateriform opening across which the eruption takes place, as though along a line. If we try to bring this fact to life in us by inwardly re-creating it, we come to realise that this spatial concentration of the levity-effect must result from the influence of the gravity-field across which the levity-action is taking place. In the living kingdoms of nature we find the same in the linear shape of the plant's stalk- and stem-formations, and of the limbs in our own body.

On the other hand, when through snow and also through rain imponderable substance enters the ponderable condition, we see it appearing in a spherical order by arranging itself parallel to the earth's surface. As a correlative in the plant kingdom we find the formation of the point-centred starch-bodies out of the surrounding air within the plane-like leaves of the plants, these leaves forming together the spherically-spread green cover of the earth. And just as the limbs show particularly clearly the linear shape as a characteristic of the sulphurous pole of the human organism, so does the head show the spherical shape most conspicuously as a characteristic of the saline pole.

The same is true for the two opposite functions of the soul. For there we find the panorama of the sense-world spreading spherically round our own head-bound consciousness and related quite individually to the centre of this consciousness, while in the volitional part of the soul we press out radially, as it were, along the limbs into the outer world, where our own deeds weave together with the deeds of other human beings in mankind's common field of destiny.

Also in the animal kingdom a corresponding polarisation can be observed. Here, however, we must realise that the animal, by having the main axis of its body in the horizontal direction, has a relationship to the gravity-levity fields of the earth different from those of both man and plant. As a result, the single animal body shows the sphere-radius polarity much less sharply. If we compare the different groups of the animal kingdom, however, we find that the animals, too, bear this polarity as a formative element. The birds represent the spherical (dry, saline) pole; the ruminants the linear (moist, sulphurous) pole. The carnivorous quadrupeds form the intermediary (mercurial) group. As ur-phenomenal types we may name among the birds the eagle, clothed in its dry, silicic plumage, hovering with far-spread wings in the heights of the atmosphere, united with the expanses of space through its far-reaching sight; among the ruminants, the cow, lying heavily on the ground of the earth, given over entirely to the immensely elaborated sulphurous process of its own digest-ion. Between them comes the lion – the most characteristic animal for the preponderance of heart-and-lung activities in the body, with all the attributes resulting from that.

Within the scope of this book it can only be intimated briefly, but should not be left unmentioned for the sake of those interested in a further pursuit of these lines of thought, that the morpho-logical mean between radius and sphere (corresponding to Mercurius in the alchemical triad) is represented by a geometrical figure known as the 'lemniscate', a particular modification of the so-called Cassinian curves.[3]

Chapter XII

THE FOURTH STATE OF MATTER

When William Crookes chose as one of the titles of his paper on the newly discovered properties of electricity, 'The Fourth State of Matter', it was to express his belief that he had found a state of matter, additional to the three known ones, which represented 'the borderland where matter and force seem to merge into one another, the shadowy realm between known and unknown' for which his soul had been longing ever since the death of his beloved brother.[1] All that has followed from his discovery, down to the transformation of matter itself into freely working energy, shows that he was right in thinking he had reached some borderland of nature. Only the country into which this borderland leads is not the one he had really been looking for.

Today, a clear insight is necessary into the fact that nature — by which we mean *physical* nature — has in fact two borders, one touching the realm of the intra-material energies which modern atomic physics has learnt to liberate, the other leading over into creative Chaos, the fountain-head of all that appears in nature as intelligent design — the actual goal of Crookes's endeavours. The previous chapter has already shown that what was denied to Crookes, we are in a position to achieve today by continuing the road first opened by Goethe. Needless to say, the results gained along this road will differ in kind from those obtained by modern physics at *its* border. As a result of our discussion of certain outstanding physical substances we were able to state quite generally that 'physical substances are congealed cosmic functions'. A concept of matter of this kind, however, necessitates a revision of the picture of the possible states of matter which scientific thinking has formed in the past through recognising the so-called three states of aggregation — solid, liquid, gaseous. We have to add a fourth state, rightly so called, which represents the upper border of nature just as electricity and kindred energies represent the lower.

From the comparison drawn in Chapter IX between the older conception of the four elementary conditions of nature and that now held of the three states of ponderable matter, we may expect that the fourth state will have something in common with heat. So far heat has been recognised by science as an agent which affects matter in the way of transforming its physical condition. What is not recognised is that heat represents the very essence underlying all material existence, out of which matter in its three ponderable states comes into being and into which it is capable of returning again.

*   *   *   *   *

Against the acknowledgment of heat as an autonomous state of matter there stands the present-day mechanistic conception of heat. Hence our first step towards the new conception must be the development of an appropriate judgment concerning the existing one.

As pointed out in Chapter V, we know of heat through the medium of a special sense, the sense of warmth, the objectivity of whose findings we then took opportunity to test. One-eyed, colour-blind observation is naturally unable to take account of these sense-messages. To this kind of observation nothing is accessible, we know, except spatial displacements of single point-like entities. Hence we find Bacon and Hooke already attributing the sensation of warmth to minute fast-moving particles of matter impinging on the skin. Some time later we find Locke taking up the same picture. We see from this how little the mechanical theory of heat owes to empirical facts. For even in Locke's time the connection between heat and mechanical action, as recognised today, was completely unknown.

It was under the coercion of a preconceived idea that both

thermal expansion and the liquefying and vaporising effects of
heat came to be attributed to an increase in the average distance
between the assumed minute particles, caused by an increase in
their rate of movement. Consequently, the liquid state was held
to differ from the solid, and similarly the gaseous from the liquid,
by the interspaces between the articles becoming relatively so
great that the forces between them became too weak to hold
them together. In this way an explanation of the properties of
the liquid and the gaseous states of matter was believed to have
been found.

Tested from a viewpoint outside the onlooker-consciousness,
this whole picture of the interaction between matter and heat
appears to run counter to the cosmic order of things in a way
typical of other spectator-theories. For each of those minute
particles, in its solidity and state of spatial separation from the
others, presents itself as an effigy of the element Earth, being
characterised in this way by the qualities 'cold' and 'old'. Yet
the workings of heat belong to the realm of Fire and therefore
have as their characteristics the qualities 'warm' and 'young'.

Once again we find occasion to admire Ruskin's unfailing
realism, which helped him to judge the kinetic theory of heat
directly it appeared in precisely the sense just pointed out. Stirred
by Tyndall's newly published treatise, *Heat: A Mode of Motion,*[2]
he at once raised, in his *Queen of the Air,* a warning against the
endeavour of contemporary science 'to simplify the various forms
of energy more and more into modes of one force, or finally
into mere motion, communicable in various states, but not des-
tructible', by declaring that he would himself 'like better in order
of thought to consider motion as a mode of heat than heat as a
mode of motion'.

* * * * *

In the course of the nineteenth century, the preconceived
mechanistic interpretation of heat received an apparent confirmation through the discovery of the constant numerical relation

between heat and mechanical work, known as the mechanical equivalent of heat. This discovery was made at about the same time by Joule in England and J.R. Mayer in Germany, although by entirely different routes. Joule, a brewer, was a man of practical bent. Trained by Dalton, the founder of the atomic theory, in experimental research, he continued Rumford's and Davy's researches which they had undertaken to prove that heat is not, as it was for a time believed to be, a ponderable substance, but an imponderable agent.[3] As a starting-point he took the heating effect of electric currents. The fact that these could be generated by turning a machine, that is, by the expenditure of mechanical energy, gave him the idea of determining the amount of work done by the machine and then comparing this with the amount of heat generated by the current. A number of ingenious experiments enabled him to determine with increasing exactitude the numerical relation between work and heat, as well as to establish the absolute constancy of the relation.

This he regarded as proof of the mechanical theory of heat, which he had taken from Rumford and Davy. What simpler explanation could there be for the constant numerical relation between work and heat than the conception that transformation of one form of energy into another was simply a transmission of motion from one object to another? From the quantitative equality of expended and generated energy was it not natural to argue the qualitative similarity of the two forms of energy, which only externally seemed different? In this way heat came to be understood as being the energy of the motion of the molecules themselves.

It was by quite a different path that the Heilbronn doctor, Mayer, arrived at his results. To escape from the narrow confines of his South German home town, he went, while still a youth, as doctor to a Dutch ship sailing to Java. When in the tropics he treated a number of sailors by blood-letting, he observed that the venous blood was much nearer in colour the paler arterial blood than was usual at home. This change in the colour he attributed to the diminished intensity of bodily combustion, due, he believed, to the higher temperature of the tropics.

Scarcely had this thought passed through his mind than it induced another — that of a universal interrelationship between all possible forms of energy. This last idea so took possession of him that during the return voyage, as he himself related, he could scarcely think of anything but how to prove the correctness of his idea and what the consequences would be for the general view of nature. From the moment of his return he devoted his life to practical research into the connection between the various manifestations of energy. It was in this way that he was led to the determination of the so-called mechanical equivalent of heat, shortly before the same discovery was made in a quite different manner by Joule.

So far as science allowed Mayer any credit for his work, this was based on the opinion that through his discovery he had provided the final vindication of the mechanical theory of heat. This judgment, however, was only piling one wrong upon another. Mayer's destiny was truly tragic. When he began to publicise his conviction of the numerical equilibrium between spent and created energy, he met with so much scepticism, even derision, that from sheer despair his mind at times became clouded. When at last toward the end of his life he received the recognition his discovery deserved (not before being dragged through a painful priority dispute which Joule forced upon him and lost), the scientists had begun to use his idea for bolstering up a hypothesis directly counter to the idea which had led him to his discovery, and for the sake of which he had accepted so much suffering. For it is in the nature of the onlooker-consciousness that it is unable to interpret numerical equality between natural phenomena save as indicating the presence of an equal number of calculable objects or of spatial movements of equal quantity. It was therefore consistent for such a consciousness to regard the discovery by Mayer of the mechanical heat-equivalent as a confirmation of the existing mechanical conception of heat.

If one considers how slender a connection there was between Mayer's observation on the sailors in Java and the idea of the quantitative equilibrium of all physical nature-forces, and if one contrasts this with the fanaticism he showed during the rest of his life in proving against all obstacles the correctness of his idea, one must feel that the origin of the thought in Mayer's mind lay elsewhere than in mere physical observations and logical deductions. Confirmation of this may be found in what Mayer himself declared to be his view concerning the actual grounds for the existence of a constant numerical association between the various manifestations of natural energy. In the picture of the physical universe which hovered before him, the transformation of one form of energy into another – such as mechanical energy into electrical, this into chemical and so on – was somewhat similar to Goethe's picture of the organic life of the earth, in which the metamorphosis of one living form into another constantly occurred. Just as Goethe saw in the ur-plant the Idea common to all plant-forms, or, in the various plant organs, the metamorphosis of one and the same ur-organ, so was Mayer convinced of the existence of an ur-force which expressed itself in varying guises in the separate energy-forms of nature. 'There is in nature', said Mayer, 'a specific dimension of immaterial constitution which preserves its value in all changes taking place among the objects observed, whereas its form of appearance alters in the most manifold ways.' For him, the arising of heat represented a *disappearance* of mechanical energy.

Mayer's conviction of the existence of an ur-force, manifesting through metamorphosis in all natural forces, led him to expect a constant numerical relation amongst these, without requiring him to deny the objective existence of qualititive differences, as these displayed themselves in the field of phenomena. He was spiritually akin to Goethe, also, in that he guarded himself strictly against substituting for the contents of our perception conveyed by nature purely hypothetical entities which, while fashioned after the world of the senses, are, in principle, imperceptible. Mayer sought after a truly empirically founded concept of force, and his method was that of reading from all the various manifestations of force which were open to sense observation. One such manifestation, capable of empirical determination, was the balance between appearing and disappearing energy.

Science treated Mayer in the same way as it treated Howard. It took from him what it wanted for its purpose without concerning itself with the epistemological principle which had led him to his discovery. Thus it was that Mayer's discovery led to most important consequences for the development of modern technical devices, whereas it was the fate of his guiding idea to be first derided, then misunderstood and finally forgotten. The consequence was that the knowledge of the numerical equilibrium between created and expended energy in the economy of nature has widened more and more the abyss separating spirit and matter in human life, instead of leading, as indeed it might have done, to a bridging of the abyss. The thought, therefore, regarding the appearing and disappearing of measurable cosmic substance, to which we are led when following Goethe's method of observing nature, stands in no sort of contradiction to what Mayer himself conceived as the relation of the various forms of energy to one another, and the maintenance of the numerical balance between them.

* * * * *

On the ground of these considerations we may now proceed, unimpeded by any kinematic theory, to making ourselves acquainted with the nature of heat through trying to *read* the relevant phenomena, first of all those shown by matter under the influence of heat. To this end we must start by developing a truly dynamic picture of the known states of matter themselves. It will be well to take first the solid state and let the others follow in turn.

As a representative of the element Earth, a solid body is characterised by the quality 'cold'. Expressed in terms of the field concept introduced in Chapter IX, this means that such a body, like the earth as a whole, is the bearer of a certain gravitational field which has its centre in the body's interior, forming its so-called centre of gravity or mass-centre. To this field the body owes its coherence and permanency of shape. Now heat is known to affect a physical body in such a way that the latter's volume increases. This phenomenon calls to mind two kindred phenomena previously discussed: that of the *Solfatara* and of the upward growth of plants. Though there are differences in detail, the event is in each case essentially the same. We observe matter moving away from its centre of gravity under a certain influence of levity. In the case of thermal expansion, we see directly the surface of the warmed-up body moving in the direction of the cosmic periphery as a result of a decreased influence of the gravitational pressure which is holding the body together.

Now this picture of thermal expansion has an immediately significant consequence for our conception of the dynamic condition of spatially-extended matter in general. Obviously, a physical body is always in some thermal state which may be regarded as higher than another, and it may therefore be regarded as being at all times thermally expanded to some extent. Hence, it is all the time under the sway of both gravitational pressure and anti-gravitational suction. In fact, we may say ideally that, if there were no field working inwards from the cosmic periphery, the entire material content of the earthly realm would be reduced by gravitation to a spaceless point; just as under the sole influence of the peripheral field of levity it would dissipate into the universe. All solid substance, therefore, owes to levity the mere fact of it being spatially extended, just as it owes to gravity its density and cohesion.

Customary thinking ought not to find this paradoxical. Observation of the nature of solid matter has led atomistic thought to conceive of a physical body as a heap of minute particles so far apart that by far the greater part of the volume occupied by the body is just 'empty' space. In the scientific picture of molecules constituting a physical body, of atoms constituting the molecules, of electrons, protons, etc., constituting the atoms, all separated by spaces far exceeding the size of the elementary particles themselves, we find reflected, in a form comprehensible to the onlooker-consciousness, the fact that matter, even in the solid state, is kept in spatial extension by a field of force relating it to the cosmic periphery.

The fact that a certain quantity of physical matter is the more closely related to levity, the more space it occupies, is clearly shown by the effect of the opposite change to the one so far considered, namely the diminution of volume through pressure. If we did not know from experience that this results in a rise in the body's temperature, we would have indeed to postulate this form out of the picture of its relationship to levity and gravity already obtained. For from this picture it follows that through compression of the body, levity is, as it were, squeezed out of it, not unlike water from a wet sponge. Whilst gravity gets a stronger hold on it, the liberated levity appears as externally observable heat, which immediately follows its own tendency of expansion into the surrounding space. If the pressure grows very high, it is possible that part of the heat may be absorbed by the body with the result that it melts without its temperature having risen to its normal melting point. In this respect conditions are particularly favourable with substances of metallic nature, because metals, even in the solid state, are really fluids. This accounts also for the well-known 'flowing' of metallic bodies which are subjected to a strong pull. In this case the volume becomes forcibly enlarged, whereby its relation to levity is enhanced, and it is again characteristic of a metal to engage some levity in the direction of a genuine liquefaction.

In this context we must remember once more the peculiarity of water in the solid state whereby it melts under pressure alone as discussed from another point of view in the previous chapter. Owing to the thermal anomaly of water, a relatively small pressure suffices to free enough levity for the ice to melt. Correspondingly, the water freezes again at once when the pressure decreases. This can be demonstrated in an impressive way with a block of ice supported at both ends and fitted round the middle with a weight-loaded loop of wire. Where the wire presses on the surface of the ice, the ice melts. Hence the wire sinks a little into the block, with the result that under its pressure the ice further inside melts. Meanwhile the water on top of the wire is released from the pressure and immediately re-solidifies. In the course of time the wire sinks ever deeper, while the water above re-freezes at once. Eventually the wire emerges from the under-surface of the block and together with the weight drops on the floor. The block is an undivided whole as before, although it has been cut through and through. We shall return to this phenomenon later in this chapter, when we will discuss it from yet another angle.

* * * * *

In order to obtain an appropriate picture of the higher states of matter, let us again follow Goethe by turning the question 'What *is* it?' into the question: 'How does it *become*?' We will therefore inquire into the dynamic change to which matter becomes subject when crossing over from the solid into the liquid, and again from the liquid into the gaseous state. We shall again keep strictly to what can be phenomenologically observed.

Regarded outwardly, liquid matter is characterised by having no form of its own. The only natural boundary of a liquid substance is its upper surface. Since this surface always lies parallel with the surface of the earth it forms part of a sphere, the centre point of which is identical with that of the gravitational centre of the earth. The passage of a portion of matter from solid to liquid thus signifies that it ceases to possess a centre of gravity of its own and is now merely obedient to the general gravity-field of the earth. We can thus speak of a transition of matter from the individual to the planetary condition. This is what heat brings about when a solid body melts.

During the process of melting, the temperature of the substance concerned is known to remain unchanged. The heat used for liquefaction has no influence on the temperature until the entire substance has grown liquid. Only then does the thermometer begin to rise again. Physics here speaks of 'sensible' heat becoming 'latent'. From the Goethean point of view we see heat passing through a metamorphosis. Whereas, previously, heat was perceptible to our sense of warmth, it now manifests as a gravity-denying property of matter.

In order to obtain an idea of the liquid state of matter corresponding to reality, we must take into account yet another of its characteristics. When the heat becomes latent, it goes even further in contradicting gravity than by robbing matter of its own point of gravity and relating it to the earth's centre of gravity. This effect is shown in the well-known urge of all liquids to evaporate. Hence we must say that even where matter in a liquid state preserves its own surface, this does not by any means represent an absolute boundary. Above the surface there proceeds a continuous transition of substance into the next higher condition through evaporation. We see here the activity of heat going beyond the mere denial of gravity to a positive affirmation of levity.

With the help of this conception of the integration of the liquid state within the polarity of gravity and levity, we are now able to draw a picture of the earth which, once obtained, answers many a question left unanswered by current scientific notions, among them the question why the earth's volcanic activity is confined to maritime regions.

Regarding the distribution of land and water on the earth's surface, we may say that to an observer in cosmic space the earth would not look at all like a solid body. Rather would it appear as a gigantic 'drop' of water, its surface interspersed with solid formations, the continents and other land masses.[4] Moreover, the evidence assembled ever since Professor A. Wegener's first researches suggests that the continents are clod-like formations which 'float' on an underlying viscous substance and are able to move (very slowly) in both the vertical and horizontal directions. The oceanic waters are in fact separated from the viscous substratum by no more than a thin layer of solid earth, a mere skin in comparision with the size of the planet. Further, this 'drop' of liquid which represents the earth is in constant communication with its environment through the perpetual evaporation from the ocean, as well as from every other body of water.

This picture of the earth shows it lying under the twofold influence of the compressive force of gravity and the sucking force of levity. Wherever land meets sea, there levity tends to prevail over gravity. It is in maritime regions, accordingly, that the inner strata of the earth succumb most readily to those sudden changes in the gravity-levity tension wherein we have recognised the origin of seismic occurrences.

* * * * *

Turning to the gaseous condition, we realise that although even here matter retains traces of a connection with terrestrial gravity, levity is now the dominant factor. There are three characteristics of the gaseous conditon which bring this out. One is the extreme readiness of gases to expand when heated; we see here how much easier than with solid substances it is for heat to overcome the influence of gravity. The second characteristic is the property of gases, peculiar to them, of expanding spontaneously, even when not heated. Here we find gaseous matter displaying a dynamic behaviour which at lower stages occurs only under the stimulus of heat. The third characteristic is shown by the fact that all gases, unlike solids or liquids, respond with the same increase of volume to a given rise of temperature, however diverse their other qualities may be. Once gases are mixed, therefore, they cannot be separated merely by raising or lowering the temperature. Here we find the unifying effect of the cosmic periphery prevailing over the differentiating effect of terrestrial gravity.

At this point we may recall Goethe's reply to the botanist, Wolff, who had ascribed the metamorphosis of plant-organs from root to blossom to a gradual stunting or atrophy of their vegetative force, whereas it was clear to Goethe that simultaneously with a physical retrogression, there is a spiritual progress in the development of the plant. The fact that all Wolff's efforts to see clearly did not save him from 'seeing past the thing' seemed to Goethe an inevitable result of Wolff's failure to associate with the eyes of the body those of the spirit.

Exactly the same thing holds good for the sequence of physical states of matter which we are considering here. Observation of this sequence with the bodily eyes alone will show nothing but a reduction of the specific gravity of the material concerned. He who is at pains to observe also with the eye of the spirit, however, is aware of a positive increase of lightness going hand in hand with a decrease of heaviness. Regarded thus, the three ponderable conditions form what Goethe would have called a 'spiritual-ladder'. As 'rungs' of such a ladder, however, they clearly point to a fourth rung — that is, a fourth state in which levity prevails entirely, with the effect that the substance no longer has any weight at all, thus taking on the nature of heat itself.

* * * * *

Our consideration of the transition of the three known states of matter into one another has enabled us to infer ideally the existence of a corresponding fourth state. In actual fact, however, such transitions seem to be observable only between the three lower stages. Still, our line of reasoning requires us to postulate the existence of an actual transition also — in either direction — between the third and fourth stages. This, therefore, is what we have now to look out for. Naturally, we are faced here with a certain difficulty. For in passing over from the third to the fourth state, matter leaves entirely the condition where it can be traced quantitatively, and beyond the boundary we are called upon to assume a standpoint (although by the very nature of things there can no longer be a 'point' on which to 'stand') in the very realm of imponderability. For this reason the conventional mode of observation, limited to 'seeing with the eye of the body', has, in gazing assiduously, been gazing 'past the thing', as Goethe put it in his comment on Wolff. The very first of the facts now to be taken into consideration will make this clear.

That ponderable substance can be carried over into a purely dynamic condition is a fact long since known, and indeed acted on, even if its true significance for a corresponding conception of matter has not been recognised. The method of treating matter we have in mind is associated with the school of medicine known as Homoeopathy, founded by the German doctor, Hahnemann. Since it has some bearing on the purpose of this book, we will deal with it, as far as necessary, here.

The word 'homoeopathy' means 'healing through like'; the basic principle is to treat disease symptoms with highly diluted substances which produce similar symptoms if ingested in normal quantity. Experience has in fact shown that the physiological effect of a substance taken from external nature is reversed when the substance is highly diluted.

The method of diluting, or 'potentising', is as follows:

A given volume of the material to be diluted is dissolved in nine times its volume of distilled water. The degree of dilution thus arrived at is 1 : 10, usually symbolised as 1x. A tenth part of this solution is again mixed with nine times its bulk of water. The degree of dilution is now 1 : 100, or 2x. This process is continued as far as is found necessary for a given purpose. Insoluble substances can be dealt with in the same manner by first grinding them together with corresponding quantities of a neutral powder, generally sugar of milk. After a certain number of stages the powder can be dissolved in water; the solution may then be diluted further in the manner described. Here we have to do with transfer of the quality of a substance, itself insoluble, to the dissolving medium, and then with the further treatment of the latter as if it were the original bearer of the quality concerned.[5]

This fact alone shows that potentisation leads into a realm of material effects at variance with the ordinary scientific conception of matter. Moreover, we can carry the dilutions as far as we please without destroying the capacity of the substance to produce physiological reactions. On the contrary, as soon as its orginal capacity is reduced to a minimum by dilution, further dilution gives it the power to cause actually stronger reactions, of a different and usually opposite kind. This second capacity rises through stages to a variable maximum as dilution proceeds.

A simple calculation shows — if we accept the ordinary scientific view as to the size of a molecule — that not a single molecule of the original substance will remain in the solution after a certain degree of dilution has been reached. Yet the biological and other reactions continue long after this, and are even enhanced.

What this potentising process shows is that, by repeated expansions in space, a substance can be carried beyond the ponderable conditions of matter into the realm of pure functional effect. The potentising of physical substances thus gains a significance far wider than that of its medical use.[6]

As we have seen, the dissipation (dilution) of matter within another material substance, for the purpose of potentising it, calls for certain processes of motion through which the internal cohesion of the substances is loosened. In one case this takes place through shaking, in the other through grinding, which involves friction. Seen dynamically, both these processes are essentially the same, and so is the effect. Let us therefore scrutinise the process itself. In this way we shall see more closely into the act of potentising, as well as gain some further viewpoints for our understanding of the fourth state of matter.

* * * * *

If two physical bodies with surfaces in contact are set into relative motion, there is always a tearing off of small particles, and so an interference with the body's inner cohesion. This effect manifests as a resistance against the movement: we call it *friction*, and find that heat arises from it. According to the law found by J.R. Mayer and Joule there is a definite numerical relation between the amount of work applied in overcoming the friction and the amount of heat produced. As we have said, this fact does not justify the conclusion that the mechanical energy as such is being transformed into heat, still less that heat is 'actually' mechanical movement, differing only in kind and dimension from the movement that causes it. All we are told by pure observation is that interference with the cohesion of a spatially extended mass — and so with its levity-gravity relation — entails the occurrence of heat. Viewed in this light, this event becomes another letter in the series of those already brought forward — a letter we must attempt to *read* in order to obtain a picture of heat that will be true to its own nature.

In order to find the right concepts for the processes involved in the friction of solids, it will be helpful, first of all, to envisage the corresponding facts in the liquid and gaseous realms, because they are more clearly manifest there than in the solid stage. A natural characteristic of liquids and gases is that they are easily split and can immediately reunite. We are so used to moving our own bodies through the air that generally we do not bring to consciousness the fact that by every movement of a solid body through the air the latter is actually 'cut into two'. The same is true of water. As we have seen, it belongs to the nature of liquids, and even more so of gaseous matter, as a result of their immanent heat, that no individual mass-centres can exist permanently in them. Consequently no 'cut' in them can last. In the liquid state, it is true, individual mass-centres can exist at least for a short time, because fluids break up easily into drops. This happens conspicuously when water moves quickly through air; and something similar happens within a liquid mass when it is shaken. In both cases a variable number of individual mass-centres occur, but, compared with the splitting of solid matter, they are short-lived. Yet in these cases also free heat appears, a fact easily shown — e.g., through the rise in the temperature of water under the turning of a paddle-wheel.

The phenomenon of splitting of matter being automatically cancelled is one we have met once before, when we discussed the thermal anomaly of water near its freezing point. For this is just what happens, though more slowly, when a wire sinks through a lump of ice without the ice being cut into two. To customary scientific thought it may seem strange to regard this phenomenon as standing in an inner connection with the one mentioned before. In the sense of Goethe's concept of metamorphosis, it is the sameness underlying the apparent difference which characterises these two phenomena as belonging to the same 'word' of nature. In the phenomenon thus shown by water, nature indeed gives us the possibility of observing in the realm of solid matter — and thereby more slowly — a fact otherwise reserved for the liquid and the gaseous states. The experiment with the block of ice enables us to observe heat *in statu agendi*: how through pressure heat gets 'squeezed out'; how this heat works back on the part of matter involved, lifting it up to a higher material stage; how it is in line with the nature of heat to cancel the interference in the material cohesion. Of these three facts, the first and third are directly observable in the liquid and gaseous realms. What is it that impels — or, rather, permits — us to deny the occurrence in these realms of the second heat-effect mentioned above — that is an at least temporary transition of water into the aeriform condition or of aeriform matter into pure heat as a result of their being disrupted? Nature always works with inner consistency. Therefore we may regard the phenomenon which water in the state of ice allows us to observe directly as an *image* of what takes place under the same conditions at higher stages, although the corresponding processes are not so easily observable.

Let us now turn to the friction of solids. In the first place we will deal with certain results of recent experimental research carried out with the aid of the most modern tools (electron-microscope, artificial radioactivity, etc.), because they confirm the opinion, formerly often questioned, that friction of solids invariably entails interference with the material coherence of the surface involved.[7]

Today it is known that metallic surfaces, even when they have been most highly polished, still carry asperities of the order of one ten thousandth to one hundred thousandth of a millimetre. Consequently, as with less smooth surfaces, contact first sets in where the projections of one surface meet those of the other. The smaller the area of contact, however, the higher will be the local pressure resulting from the force used to move the two solids against each other. Observation shows that at these points, while the piece of matter as a whole appears quite cool, local temperatures of 1,000° C. and more can occur. As we have here to do with metals, the two sets of contact points are welded together by the high temperature. Depending on the nature of the metals, particles of one will cross over to the other. In fact, one can never turn a screw with a screw-driver without the latter catching particles of the screw's material. Two highly polished pieces of metal *in vacuo*, whose surfaces have been freed from all impurities (films of oxide, occluded gas, etc.), cannot be moved at all against each other, for both get immediately welded together. Hence again we see heat at work in unifying separate parts. Naturally, this effect comes about only if the two solids are metals, because it is a peculiarity of the metallic nature to maintain in the solid state properties of the liquid. In all other instances, there occurs a lasting severance of particles of matter from the surface of the solid, this being the cause of the continuous wearing down of all objects of daily use.

What modern research has thus brought to light, could have been learnt long ago from quite simple facts, accessible to everyone. Only the onlooker-consciousness failed to interpret them properly. The following example may show this.

Almost everyone knows that if two pieces of flint are struck together, sparks will appear. For this reason they were used in times past for striking fire. In a similar way, sparks will appear when stone is struck with steel. This tells us that in both cases relatively high temperatures occur, though only for short moments and in very small areas. That this effect is not due only to the intensity of the impact is shown by the fact that it suffices to rub two pieces of flint more or less gently against each other in order to cause them to smell in a characteristic manner, reminding one of the smell of charred horn. Now, flint is known to consist of silica bearing certain amounts of carbon and sulphur, all of which are also characteristic ingredients of horn. In flint, however, they are all in an inorganic state, which means that a relatively high temperature is required to make them smell. For the sense of smell is known to react only to substances in the aeriform condition. This simple observation, therefore, is enough to show that the pressure exerted in ordinary friction suffices to produce very high local temperatures.

We can learn even more by taking careful notice of the functioning of the sense of smell. Among the various senses, those of taste and smell are the only ones through which our consciousness enters into direct communication with the world of matter. This is even more true of smell than of taste. In order to be tasted, a substance meets certain juices of our body — yet in that very moment the substance undergoes a chemical change. What we actually experience is the interaction between the chemical nature of the substance and our own organism. In the act of smell, however, the gaseous substance does not undergo any change, but communicates to our consciousness — i.e. to our soul — something of its own intrinsic being. Soul and Matter: what seems to be more alien to each other than these two! Yet in smelling they enter into direct intercourse. This accounts for both the good and the bad effects that smells can have on our psycho-physical organisation. The term 'essential oil' for scenting stuffs produced by plants in their flowers or leaves, handed down from the times of alchemical knowledge, speaks of the insight the medieval alchemist still had into the process of smelling and what it conveys. These volatile oils are 'essential' because they convey to man's experience something of the essential nature of the plant that produces them.

A further peculiarity of the olfactory sense is that it reacts to the presence of substances in extremely small amounts — i.e. in a state of very high dissipation in the air. Two extreme examples are, musk, one millionth of a milligram of which in 1,000 c.c. of air is enough to make it noticeable, and mercaptane, a chemically produced substance of which even the twenty-eighth part of a millionth can be distinctly smelt. In this connection we may also think of certain scented tropical woods. Objects made from them are known to keep on scenting apparently for ever without any noticeable loss of substance, although no smell can occur unless the object continually gives off some physical matter.

Obviously, we have here to do with matter at the border of its ponderable existence. If we take this together with what the process of friction has taught us, we find this whole series of phenomena consistently in line with those considered earlier in this part of our disucssion. In the case of ice subject to pressure, we found heat being set free through the temporary cancellation of the material coherence, and this heat, by melting the ice, lifting the substance to a more strongly levity-determined state. Later, the process of potentising taught us that matter can be definitely transformed into a purely dynamic condition. Lastly, friction told us the same. Looking back, we come to see why for proper potentising a thorough shaking or rubbing is indispensable. For in this way manifold acts of severance take place which enable the levity thus set free to lift some of the material to the border of its ponderable existence.

There remains the question — how does the liberation of levity through the cancellation of material coherence, so far dealt with as an empirical fact, actually come about?

We will remember that any breaking up of a physical mass results in an increase of the absolute number of single mass-centres in relation to the all-embracing periphery. It is true, that with continued dismemberment of the whole into an ever-increasing number of ever smaller parts, the total surface-area of the mass continually increases (a fact well recognised by physical science and duly made use of in many technical applications). Yet apart from this purely quantitative change, there is also a qualitative one which we must not overlook: the single surfaces become progressively more sharply curved by bending more and more closely round their respective mass-centres. As a result, they get more and more alienated from the cosmic periphery. Numerous small particles, therefore, are to a lesser degree levity-bound than is the same mass as a coherent whole. Hence the transition from one state to the other results in levity getting free, as our observations have shown in various ways.[8]

Two facts, well-known in themselves, may serve as a further illustration. If two equal masses of the same material, one entire, the other split up, are brought to the same level of temperature above that of the environment, the latter will cool down more quickly than the former. This shows that from the mass which is centred round the larger number of centres, heat can follow more easily its own tendency of expansion. The other fact consists in the increased inflammability of combustible substances when in a highly pulverised form, which can lead even to spontaneous combustion — as with iron or coal dust, for example. In the last chapter we found that combustion (oxidisation) means a 'getting dry' of the ponderable and the imponderable parts of the burning substance. Applied to the present case, this tells us again that through the increase of mass-centres the whole mass gets more strongly earth-bound, so that the connection with the fire occluded in the substance is no longer strong enough to bind the two together. The result is that severance can occur at a temperature much below the normal.

* * * * *

In the foregoing chapter, mention was made of the fallacious phlogiston theory, which regarded heat as a ponderable substance, and of how this was disproved by the experiments of Davy and Rumford. We now see that these experiments, while clearing away an old error, opened the gate for a new one — the belief that heat produced by friction is nothing but transformed mechanical energy, with no regard paid to the material change of condition brought about in the body subject to the friction. As we have seen, this heat really originates from the material substance, though in a different way from that assumed by the phlogiston theory.

From what we have learnt concerning the process of friction, a significant light falls on the history of the generation of energy by man. At the beginning of this chapter we said that nature has a nether and an upper border, and that while modern nuclear physics does its work at the nether border, we should pay attention to the behaviour of matter at the upper one. Turning our gaze into mankind's past, we find that the first means of generating and applying energy was in the making of fire by rubbing together two pieces of wood. We now realise that this implies the lifting of matter to the border of its pure-dynamic condition.

By comparison, the modern generation of heat by splitting the atomic nucleus appears as the exact counterpart of the old process, because it means a shifting of matter across nature's nether border.

* * * * *

If there are processes through which matter crosses over in the upward direction from the ponderable to the imponderable state, we may expect to find processes occurring also in the opposite direction, with matter changing over from the imponderable to the ponderable state. In fact, this is already implied in the basic concept of physical matter being congealed cosmic function which we established in our last chapter. But are there actual events of this kind, taking place, as it were, before our very eyes? It belongs to the nature of things that in studying this direction of change it is harder to pick a series of phenomena and to order them appropriately so as to let nature's action become readable through them. Obviously we must start our inquiry in the biological realm.

Here, indeed, nature offers a guiding phenomenon in the form of the process of so-called photosynthesis or assimilation in plants. It is by this means, carried out with the aid of the chlorophyll in the green leaves, that the plant builds up the living parts of its organism. The plant inhales carbon dioxide from the air, reduces it by drawing on the radiant energy of sunlight, and, by combining it with water, condenses it to sugar or further to starch. Recent physical and biological research has shown that carbon is by no means the only substance received by the plant in this way. These findings have necessitated a complete change in previously held conceptions of plant nutrition. At the same time they signify a welcome confirmation of a conception developed along the lines of intuitive judgment in the first edition of this book, before these new findings were available. Hence we can now treat the subject rather differently.[9]

The findings we have in mind have shown that, in addition to carbon, the plant absorbs from its atmospheric environment such elements as phosphorus, potassium, even metals such as zinc (oranges). These substances are not stored up entirely in the plant; a part of them is transferred — 'sacrificed', as the report significantly says — to the soil on which the plant grows. This has led to the idea of supplying the plant with certain substances required for its healthy growth, not by putting them into the soil, but by spraying them in a fine dilution over the plant's foliage. Other observations have shown that considerable amounts of various chemical elements in the form of certain isotopes constantly shower down on the earth from the outer atmosphere.[10] A thinking bound by the *Contra-Levitatem* maxim is, of course, inclined to conceive of the origin of these substances after the pattern of the transformation of atomic nuclei artificially engendered by man at nature's nether border. Along our line of observation we recognise here, capable of being physically established, the natural counter-process to the homoeopathic potentisation of matter — namely a coagulation of substance from the cosmic-functional state to ponderable existence.

There is a plant, indigenous to tropical America, which, in respect of the above, represents a model case of this counter-process. For this reason we discussed it in the first edition of this book while claiming it as an 'instance worth a thousand, bearing all within itself'. The plant is *Tillandsia usneoides*, generally known as Spanish Moss. Its peculiarity is that it grows and flourishes without taking its nutriment from the sources of physical matter on which one would expect the plant to draw. Its natural habitat is the dry bark of the virgin forest trees. Since civilisation invaded its home, it has acquired the habit of growing on telegraph wires, which has given it the popular name of 'telegraph tresses'. Chemical analysis of the ashes of this plant shows the presence of an average of 17 per cent iron, 36 per cent silicic acid, and 1.85 per cent phosphoric acid.[11] Naturally, rainwater was expected to be the source of these substances. But in these districts the rain was found to contain at most 1.65 per cent iron, 0.01 per cent silicic acid and no phosphoric acid. Since all other attempts to explain the origin of these substances failed, the plant remained a riddle for biologists. Still, in Goethe's sense it represents a 'manifest mystery'. As such we discussed it in our first edition. This situation has been changed by the investigations carried out since then, for they have established a form of plant nutrition in general of which Tillandsia represents an extreme case.

It is thus that orthodox research has confirmed the following concept which we originally developed in the light of what the life of the plant, as well as the greater cycle of nature, had already taught us.

In Chapter V we put forward Goethe's term, 'spiritual anasto-mosis', which he ⏤oined for the process of pollination by seeing in it a 'heightening' of the method according to which the veins in the plant's leaves grow — a method generally called 'anastomosis' (page 95). By analogy with this, we coined the term 'spiritual assimilation' for the foliar resorption of nutrients by the plant, using it to designate a heightened form of the process through which the plant receives carbon from the air. Here is now experi-mental proof that such spiritual assimilation exists.

The same proof has confirmed yet another aspect developed by us. As already mentioned, it has been found that the plant passes part of the substance thus received into the soil where it grows. In this connection the publication cited above makes particular mention of the so-called trace-elements. This, too, we had discussed in principle in a precisely similar sense. In what follows we therefore repeat our original statements, with only a few minor alterations.

To begin with, a brief exposition is necessary of the role of the trace-elements in general.

Modern agricultural chemistry has found of a number of chemical elements that their presence in the soil in scarcely traceable amounts is necessary in order to enable the plant to unfold healthily its latent characteristics. All sorts of deficiencies in cultivated plants have led to a recognition that the soil is impoverished of certain elements by intensive modern cultivation, and that it is to the lack of these elements that the deficiencies are due. Much work has meanwhile been done in classifying the various deficiencies and in devising ways of giving the soil chemical substitutes for what is lacking.

Let us be clear what it is that occurs when a plant exhibits any of the observed abnormalities. Expressed in a Goethean manner, these are the consequence of an insufficient direction of the organic processes in the plant body by the spiritual plant-type underlying it. That which Ruskin called 'spirit of the plant', and to which he drew attention in his aphorism 'Stand by Form against Force' (by 'form' *all* the peculiar qualities of the plant are to be understood), is unable to express itself in full measure. Now we know that, in order to unfold its activities on the physical plane, spirit requires 'young' matter — that is, matter which is either in, or has just emerged from, a purely dynamic state. Normally a definite spiritual type co-ordinates the dynamic functions present in the superphysical sphere of nature in the manner required to give the plant-organism its appropriate form. As, through the action of the type, these functions are brought down from the sphere of levity into that of gravity, they condense to the corresponding material elements and thus reach the soil in material form via the physical organism of the plant.

The pattern as usually seen is now reversed; the presence of the various elements in the soil no longer appears as the origin of one or another function in the building up of the plant-body, but quite the reverse. The functions appear now as the cause, and the soil-elements as the effect. We may thus recognise the value of the latter as *symptoms* from which we can read the existence of a healthy connection between the plant and the corresponding form-creating functions working on it from its surroundings.

With this reversal of the relationship between cause and effect it is not, however, intended to represent the commonly accepted order of things as entirely incorrect. In the realm of life, cause and effect are not so onesidedly fixed as in the realm of mechanical forces. We may therefore admit that a reverse effect of the soil-elements upon the plant does take place. And yet, it remains true that to attempt to cure deficiencies in plants by adding to the soil chemical substitutes for the trace-elements is an unbiological procedure. In the condition in which this material is offered to the plant, it is truly 'old' material. In order to be able to use it functionally, the plant has first to convey it into the 'young' condition. This indeed happens whilst the material is rising in the plant combined with the juices drawn by the plant from the soil under the influence of levity-force. Only when this has occurred are the chemical elements able to serve the plant functionally. Thus, by trying to give help to the plant in this way, we injure it at the same time. For by forcing it to perform the operation described, its general life-forces are diminished.[12] In comparison with this, spraying the foliage with the required substances in a finely dissipated form is much better suited to the plant's nature. Insight into the functional significance of the trace-elements, and into the way they get into the soil, prompts one to go still further and to look for a means of helping both plant and soil to enter into a closer relationship with the functional flux itself.[13]

The picture of the plant's nutrition thus gained is also valid — though in an altered form — for the higher organisms of nature. Man and the beast, too, need 'young material' for their nourishment, so that the type active in them — which in animals is the group-soul of the species and in man is the single individual — can express its true form and character. (We saw earlier that the will requires 'young' material in order to penetrate into the material layers of the muscles, as happens when the limbs are set in motion). In this respect, the difference between ensouled creatures and plants is that, what is harmful to plants is natural for men and animals: when taking nourishment the latter are able to bring about quickly and purposefully a transformation of matter into the purely dynamic state. Their metabolic system is designed to enable them to take alien material from outer nature and to transform it through the forces of the various digestive enzymes; in the course of this process the material passes through a condition of complete 'chaos', in order to emerge from this state in a form typical of the species.

* * * * *

In the course of our study of the nutritional process of the plant, our attention was drawn to the existence of a macrotelluric influx of matter from the functional state, in which we recognised a counterpart to the process of homoeopathic potentisation. The fact that such a flux does exist can teach us that the earth as a whole is subject to certain life-processes not unlike those of the single organic entities that live on its surface. In both cases we have to reckon with a constant to and fro motion of matter between ponderable and imponderable conditions. Knowledge of this fact enables us also to free ourselves from one of the typical misconceptions of nature to which the onlooker-mind has been exposed in the past. It concerns the atmospheric water-circuit, and, in connection with it, the nature of thunderstorms. For the explanation of the latter as an electric charge-exchange represents a characteristic confusion of the upper and nether borders of nature.

In an age following van Helmont's discovery of the gaseous state of matter and the statement of the *Contra-Levitatem* maxim, men were bound to think that the circulation of atmospheric moisture was limited to the three stages of liquid, vaporous (peculiar to the clouds, etc.) and the invisible aeriform condition. Yet the role played by clouds in the myths of early peoples shows that they were once given a quite different status, between the 'created' and 'uncreated' worlds. Our observations lead to a corresponding conception, but along the path of knowledge, guided by sense-perception, as befits our own age.

In discussing Howard's discovery of the stages of cloud-formation we found something lacking, for it was clear that the three stages of cloud proper — stratus, cumulus, and cirrus — have a symmetry which is disturbed by the addition of the fourth stage, represented by the nimbus. This showed that there was need for a fifth stage, at the top of the series, to establish a balanced polarity. We can now clear up this question of a fifth stage, as follows.

In the three actual cloud-forms, gravity and levity are more or less in equilibrium, but in the nimbus, gravity predominates, and the atmospheric vapour condenses accordingly into separate liquid bodies, the drops of rain. The polar opposite of this process must therefore be one in which cloud-vapour, under the dominating influence of levity, passes up through a transitional condition into a state of pure heat.

Such a conception by no means contradicts the findings of scientific research. For meteorology has come to know of a heat-mantle surrounding the earth's atmosphere for which various hypothetical explanations have been advanced. Naturally, none of them envisages the possibility of atmospheric substance changing into the heat-condition and back again. But if we learn to look on the chain of cloud-forms as a 'spiritual ladder', then we must expect the chain to conclude with a stage of pure heat, lying above the cirrus-sphere.[14] (Note, in this respect, the close of Goethe's poem dedicated to the cirrus-formation and the poem inspired by his sight of a waterfall in the Bernese Alps, *Gesang der Geister über den Wassern*, as indications of the fact that he was himself aware of the water-rejuvenating process in the higher reaches of the atmosphere.)

Before embarking upon a discussion of thunderstorms on the ground thus gained for a proper interpretation of the happenings in the outer reaches of the earth, let us note that science has already found it necessary to abandon the long-held explanation of thunderstorms, and to a certain extent, has even reversed it. Whereas it was formerly taken for granted — and the assumption was supposed to rest upon experimental proof — that the condensing of atmospheric vapour which accompanied lightning was the consequence of a release of electrical tension by the lightning, the view now held is that the electrical tension responsible for the occurrence of lightning is itself the effect of a sudden condensing process of atmospheric moisture.

Recent precise observations of the happenings on the one

hand in lightning, and on the other in electrical spark discharge, have shown that the energy-processes in one and the other are completely contradictory! Yet even this has not been able to shake up the conviction, embedded in modern thought, of the electrical nature of lightning.

To conclude from the presence of electric tensions in the earth's atmosphere as an accompaniment of lightning, in the way first observed by Franklin, that lightning itself is an electrical process, is to be under the same kind of illusion that led men to attribute electrical characteristics to the human soul because its activity in the body was found to be accompanied by electrical processes in the latter. The identification of lightning with the electric spark is a case of a confusion between the upper and lower boundaries of nature, characteristic of the onlooker-consciousness. As such, it has stood in the way of a real understanding both of non-electrical natural phenomena and of electricity itself.

What we observe in lightning is really an instantaneous execution of a process which runs its course continually in the atmosphere, quietly and unnoticed. It is the process by which water reverts from the imponderable to the ponderable condition, after having been converted to the former through levity set in action by the sun (as usually happens in a high degree just before a thunderstorm). We form a true picture of the course of a storm if we say that nature enables us to witness a sublime display of the sudden bringing to birth of matter in earthbound form. What falls to the ground as rain (or hail) is substantially identical with what was perceptible to the eye, a moment before, as a majestic light-phenomenon. The accompanying electrical occurrence is the appropriate counter-event at nature's lower boundary. Since the two form part of a larger whole they necessarily occur together; but the electrical occurrence must not be identified with the event in the heavens. The reason for their conjunction will become clear later, when we shall show how electrical polarity arises from the polarity between gravity and levity.

If one learns to view a thunderstorm in this way, its spiritual connection with the earth's volcanic processes becomes manifest;

there is in fact a polar relationship between them. For just as in volcanic activity heavy matter is suddenly and swiftly driven heavenwards under the influence of levity, so in a storm does light matter stream earthwards under the influence of gravity.

It is this combination of kinship and polar opposition which led people of old to regard both lightning in the heights and seismic disturbances in the depths as signs of direct intervention by higher powers in the affairs of men. A trace of this old feeling lingers in the Greek word θειον (theion), divine, which was used to denote both lightning and sulphur. Influenced by the same conception, the Romans regarded as holy a spot where lightning had struck the earth; they even fenced it off to protect it from human contact. Note in this respect also the Biblical report of the event on Mount Sinai, mentioned before, telling of an interplay of volcanic and meteorological phenomena as a sign of the direct intervention of the Godhead.

* * * * *

The considerations of the previous and the present chapter, aimed at establishing a functional conception of matter, would not fulfil their purpose in our age if we left undiscussed their relation to the usual atomistic conception of matter. The remaining part of this chapter will therefore be devoted to this question.

The history of the scientific concept of the atom is symptomatic for the problem of the spectator-consciousness. The stimulus to develop a picture of matter as made up of very small, discrete particles, the molecules, and these in turn of atoms, had come from Lavoisier's discovery that the total weight of the substances entering into chemical combination remains unchanged; furthermore that the basic substances which make up a compound react with one another only in certain set ratios of weight or in their entire multiples of these: carbon and oxygen, for instance, combining in the ratio either of 12 to 16 (CO) or of 12 to 32 (CO_2). What could have been more natural to the onlooker-mind than to represent such arithmetical facts in the picture of spatially separate, computable material entities, the atoms, of which a definite number combine in each case to form the fundamental particles, the molecules, of the various compounds? In the above instances this means one C atom with one O atom, or else one C atom with two O atoms.

As mentioned once before, modern atomism was founded by John Dalton, an experimentalist working under the instigation of Joule. He conceived it as a means of giving a simple explanation of the relevant facts, and the way in which this conception took immediate possession of the contemporary mind was typical of the period. True, the really great ones of the then young science of chemistry — such men as Berzelius and even later Canizarro — took great pains to guard themselves and their pupils against allowing the concepts of the atom and the molecule, which were originally no more than easy mental aids, to assume in their minds the roles of real physical entities. Still, this did not hinder scientific thinking from coming very soon — and for the remainder of the nineteenth century — to picture the atom as a compact material reality, a sort of 'tiny billiard-ball'. This picture was shattered by the discovery of radioactivity. Exact thinking forbids the present-day scientist even to ask about the 'reality' of the atom, let alone its nature: he is satisfied if, by assuming the atom, he manages to predict physical events correctly. In so far, and in so far only, the atom has 'reality' for him.[15] For reasons expounded at the beginning of this book (page 22), he has to consider the concept of the atom as an 'auxiliary' concept. In this way, scientific thinking seems to have returned to the attitude of Berzelius and others. But, as we shall see, this is only apparently so.

In yet another way a return to an earlier picture of the atom seems to have taken place — but again only in appearance. When we introduced in Chapter IX the concept of the force-field, we pointed to the realistic nature of Faraday's way of thinking. This realism prompted him, when Dalton's theory became known, to remonstrate immediately against it. 'As to the little solid particles' — so his biographer J.H. Gladstone reports him saying — 'I cannot form any idea of them apart from the forces, so I neither

admit nor deny them. They do not afford me the least help in
my endeavour to form an idea of a particle of matter. On the
contrary, they greatly embarrass me.' And again: 'Particles are
only centres of force; the force or forces constitute matter ....
Water is not two particles of oxygen side by side and one particle
of hydrogen next to them, but two spheres of power mutually
penetrated and the centres even coinciding.'[16] Against Dalton,
he insists that the only actual facts are the 'definite proportions',
the 'equivalents', the 'primes' (so ingeniously investigated by him),
in comparison with which the 'atom' is a mere word.[17] In so far
as there are atoms, they are nothing but force. 'Matter fills all
space, or at least all space to which gravitation extends .... Each
atom extends throughout the whole solar system, yet always
retaining its own centre of force.'

Ever since mass and energy were recognised by modern science
as two modes of occurrence of one and the same thing,
the statement that matter consists of atoms has become synonymous with the other — that atoms are centres of a special accumulation of energy. And ever since scientific thinking was compelled
to conceive of energy processes as undulatory processes, such
centres appear as loci of a wave-like 'disturbance' in a comprehensive
force-field. In this way the modern picture of the atom seems to
come quite near to that of Faraday; but only in semblance.

Earlier in this chapter we remarked that the tendency to think
atomistically appeared already in Bacon and Hooke, and thus at
a time when no empirical facts were yet known to suggest it. To
think in this way is inherent in the spectator-mind, compelled as it
is to proceed from the parts to the whole. Nothing, in this respect,
has since changed despite all the changes which the concept of
the atom itself has undergone from Dalton until today. In whatever way the atom is being represented, and however far scientists
have gone in resigning from asking about the atom's 'reality': the
unknown entities — and, today, their constitutents — continue to
be regarded as 'building stones' (or in whatever way this may be
expressed) of the physical universe.

This has carried its influence right into the epistemological endeavours of modern physicists. Whatever turns up before the experimenting observer as an event between the smallest entities is regarded as forming the foundation of the very Being and Life of the physical universe, and therefore as something from which understanding of the universe has to be developed. Among other things, the principle of Indeterminacy (uncertainty principle) is here at home, and governs the epistemological considerations (Chapter III). In this mode of thought the macroscopically observable facts and processes play the role of 'limiting cases' and are so treated mathematically. In this sense, for instance, the 'good old' Newtonian mechanics appears as a limiting case of quantum mechanics which applies to the atomic region. Laws of nature, in themselves open to be grasped by more or less simple mathematical operations, are limiting cases of the uncertainty-relations which are valid in the region of the quantum of action (Planck's Constant). Yet no question ever arises as to whether the whole relationship might perhaps be the opposite — i.e. whether the uncertainty-relations may not be limiting cases of the laws of nature?

If one declares the concept of the atom to be a mere auxiliary concept, and at the same time clings to the conviction that the Something, covered by this concept, forms the foundation of the physical universe, and is to be regarded as the determining factor for scientific epistemology, one is not really consistent. This was not the attitude of the fathers of modern chemistry. Similarly, there is no real accord between the dynamic picture of the atom held today and the one held by Faraday. His words, cited above, clearly show that his thinking was directed from outside in — i.e. from the whole to the parts. It is only in our own day that we have been enabled to recover in a new way this aspect of his conceptions.[18]

Let us remember that we found any spatially extended, coherent mass to be subject to both gravity and levity, one relating it to its interior mass-centre, the other to the cosmic periphery. Each mass, therefore, is both plane-related and point-related. Now, there is no objection to thinking — and many observations seem to speak for it — that the point-relatedness of the mass as a whole occurs in innumerable repetitions inside it. For such is the tendency of the gravitational sphere. Then everywhere there must also be the corresponding peripheral relationship. What is true of the mass as a whole, that it is congealed function, must be equally true of its 'atoms'. They need to be understood in the same way as the bulk of the mass, namely from the common cosmic periphery down to each centre. To see things in this light would enable us also to recognise the true quality of those entities with which, under the name of fundamental particles, nuclear physics is working today.

When we speak of physical substance as 'congealed cosmic function' we refer to the macroscopically recognisable quality of the particular substance. Sulphur, phosphorus, etc., are functions of the universe. They turn into physically tangible substances when they pass from the levity-realm to the point-relatedness of the gravity-realm. Hence each dynamic point within such a material body is — to use an expression from the realm of electricity — 'charged' with the substance's potential function. This picture, and this only, corresponds to the one Faraday had in mind. It leads us to a qualitative concept of the atom, radically different, indeed, from the usual one, and yet bearing the usual one within it.

Every physical substance represents a definite sum of certain qualities: its colour, hardness, specific gravity, its relation to heat, to other substances, etc., etc. By combining in other ways, these qualities make up other substances, a particular combination of qualities giving each substance its unique character. 'A-tom' means 'indivisible'. So long as sulphur exists as 'sulphur', the qualities characteristic of it are indivisibly combined with each other. In this way each chemical element is a *qualitative atom*.

Compared with this, what is the atom as known to present-day physics? Penetration of its interior has revealed it to be a most complex composition of electricity and magnetism. Now, these two — as the next chapter will show — are, each in its own way, a pure combination of gravity and levity, or, more precisely, of gravity-caught levity. Imagine the all-relating points in the interior of a physical substance divested of any distinctive quality except the particular gravity-levity relation which provides the foundation for the appearance of its particular combination of qualities in physical material form — and we are left with what the modern physicist is getting hold of at nature's nether border. It is conceivable that this residue is — in the physicist's own way of speaking — pure *structure*.

We shall need some later considerations to understand how it comes about that the various cosmic functions (quality-combinations), when appearing physically, do so in specific, mathematically determinable structures. This much, however, can be said at once: that, taking the whole of nature in view, we are faced here with a fact which we encounter elsewhere in manifold metamorphoses, such as, for example, the numerical order of the bones in the animal and human skeletons, or the numerical order of chromosomes in the cells of different living species. These constituents form part of the total combination of qualities; but, in order to isolate them, we must destroy the combination.

This is precisely what the atomic physicist does when producing from some chemical element its physical atoms and their constituents. He has, however, even gone further, for he has contrived to manufacture artificial elements (plutonium, etc.) by bringing into being new structures, and thereby temporary combinations of qualities which are alien to the existing universe.

Chapter XIII

'RADIANT MATTER'

When man in the state of world-onlooker undertook to form a dynamic picture of the nature of matter, this picture was bound to have certain limitations from the very start. We have seen that, because man's consciousness, at this stage of its evolution, was closely bound up with the force of gravity inherent in the human body, he was unable to form any conception of levity, as a force opposite to gravity. Yet, nature is built bipolarically, and polarity-concepts are therefore indispensable for developing a true understanding of her actions. This accounts for the fact that the unipolar concept of gravity had eventually to be supplemented by some kind of bipolar concept.

Now, the only sphere of nature-phenomena with a bipolar character accessible to the onlooker-consciousness was that of electricity and the kindred force, magnetism. It was thus that man in this state of consciousness was compelled to picture the foundation of the physical universe as being made up of gravity and electricity. Once scientific observation and thought are freed from the limitations of the onlooker-consciousness, both gravity and electricity appear in a new perspective, though the change is different for each of them. Gravity, while it becomes one pole of a polarity, with levity as the opposite pole, still retains its character as a fundamental force of the physical universe, the gravity-levity polarity being one of the first order. Not so electricity. For, as the following discussion will show, the electrical polarity is one of the second order; moreover, instead of constituting matter as is usually believed, electricity turns out to be in reality a product of matter. Hence the title of this chapter.[1]

When the onlooker-mind perceives entities or phenomena

which appear to be *parts*, because they stand in mutual relation and together point to a common *whole*, it is forced to conclude that the parts are the primary existence and the whole the secondary through being itself compounded of them. We have already met this fact in our last chapter when we dealt with the relationship between the organism and its cells and, by analogy, between any physical body and its supposed atomic structure. We shall encounter the same mode of judgment repeatedly in the further course of our observations and we shall have to replace it each time by the opposite. Electricity is no exception. There are the two modifications in which it occurs, so-called negative and positive electricity. Both are 'electricty' and both condition each other whereby they prove to be parts of a common whole. True, this 'whole' is of a peculiar nature, because when the parts meet they neutralise each other. To outer perception, therefore, the whole appears to be just 'nothing'. So in this case it seemed all the more obvious to attribute primary existence to the two observable electrical conditions. Hence, every non-electrical condition has been regarded as being made up of both electricities, which, because they are present in the same amounts, are just not noticed. The appearance of an electrical state, therefore, is regarded as being due to the two electricities becoming, at that particular point, spatially separated. In this way everything has been interpreted from the long-known phenomena of static electricity up to the most recently discovered internal happenings in matter. Atomistic thinking, supported by certain electrical phenomena of an atomistic character (of which we shall hear more later), led to the well-known picture of the atom as being composed of a nucleus bearing so many unit charges of positive electricity, with the same number of electrons, viewed as the elementary particles of negative electricity, surrounding it. The result of this is that electricity itself has remained unknown.

The following exposition will show that the two modes of electricity, in whatever way they may occur, do not exist, as it were, ready-made in the electrically neutral state, but that in each case they are the product of a particular interaction of levity and gravity. Thereby they provide an instance of something which is, indeed, by no means unknown to orthodox science. Just as the two modes of electricity have been held to be present as such in the electrically neutral state, so in the field of optics the spectral colours have, since Newton's day, been assumed to be present as such in so-called white light. However, as we shall point out in our next chapter, science had to abandon this view at the end of the nineteenth century. For a closer inspection of the relevant optical happenings has shown that the colours actually come into being as a result of the effect of the apparatus on the light with which it interferes. Whereas Newton and his followers were of the opinion that the apparatus serves to 'discover' the (pre-existing) colours, it has been known ever since the researches of Lord Rayleigh that in fact the apparatus 'manufactures' them.

What we intend to show is that the same is true concerning the two modes of electricity – namely, that they are not 'discovered' emerging from the non-electrical state, but that on every such occasion they are 'manufactured'.[2]

True to Goethe's method, we shall refrain from any attempt to 'explain' electricity with thoughts of our own, but will make it our task so to contemplate the phenomena that they utter their own theory, or, which is the same thing, to 'read' them after having so co-ordinated them with other phenomena of kindred nature that they become readable. To this end we must, in the first place, distinguish clearly, in Goethe's sense, between primary and derived electrical phenomena. For only those of the first kind will suit the purpose. This means that we have to by-pass what has been brought to light by more or less recent research and turn, instead, to phenomena that stand at the beginning of the great series of electrical discoveries. Hence we find our attention directed to the phenomenon, first reported by Thales and mentioned in Chapter IV, that small physical objects will move towards a piece of amber which has been rubbed with some fur or wool. We supplement this at once with the twin phenomenon, although it was discovered much later, of the tendency of two physical bodies to move away from one another under the influence of the same force.

In respect of these two phenomena we have purposely avoided speaking of 'attraction' and 'repulsion'. For these terms belong to a time when it was still believed that the seat of the cause of the respective motion was the electrically excited body itself. Ever since Faraday introduced the field-concept, it has been thought that the electrical state of a body finds expression in the surrounding space undergoing a dynamic change in the form of an electrical field-of-force. When two such fields come to interpenetrate, they act upon each other at every point in space and this action will be of the nature of pressure, if both fields are of the same kind of electricity, and of suction, if the two fields are of the opposite kind. It is this pressure or suction which is then obeyed by the material bearers of the two fields. That is how science really came to conceive it about a hundred years ago.

It is in line with the nature of electricity that the basic phenomenon through which it presents itself appeals at once via the optical sense to sense-experiences connected with our motor-system. In Chapters VIII and IX we have seen which realm of experience within ourselves we must call upon in order to develop a realistic conception of force. Electricity appears primarily as a motive force, and we shall therefore do well to approach it in the first place through our own motor-system. Instead of being satisfied with the optical image interpreted as 'attraction' and 'repulsion', e.g. of a suspended pith-ball moving towards or away from a rubbed stick of sealing-wax, let us imagine ourselves actively engaged in the process, as we did for experiencing gravity and levity. Let us start with the case of the little ball moving away from the stick of sealing-wax because both are bearers of the same electricity. The ball is set in motion by the moving stick without the latter touching it. The experience we get from the interspace between the two bodies while repeating the movement forwards and backwards several times, is as if this interspace were filled with some elastic material. In the other case, when the two bodies carry opposite electrical fields, we should enter into the experience of the suction which tends to move the ball and the stick towards each other, thus calling up in us the experience of the 'rising arm' (page 176). In both instances, naturally, the sensation remains weak. A much stronger one can be had by using magnets of a certain strength.

We thus come to realise space itself as being qualitatively changed. If to space in its usual, non-electrical condition we ascribe the density 'zero', we find the density increased above zero in one case and decreased below it in the other. From other connections we know that positive and negative density are the effects of gravity and levity respectively. Thus we come to realise at the very outset of our observations that electricity, in either of its modifications, unites in itself the properties of both gravity and levity. It is in some way both 'matter' and 'anti-matter'.

There is yet another conclusion we can already draw concerning the relationship between the two polar kinds of electricity. Since both represent a combination of the properties of levity and gravity, they represent a polarity of the second order. Their polarity, therefore, must depend on levity and gravity being interrelated in each of them in an opposite way. This is in principle not a novelty for us. We must remember our observations in Chapter X, when we first introduced the concept of the two orders of polarities. We may expect that the concepts of the two basic qualities Dry and Moist, and with them those of the two polar conditions called Salt and Sulphur, will be applicable to the electrical polarity. Our next task, therefore, will be to find out which of the two kinds of electricity represents the 'dry' (saline) pole and which of them the 'moist' (sulphurous) pole of this secondary polarity. To this end we must inspect the way in which they come into being. Here again we will turn to the first and primitive way of exciting the electrical state, through friction.

In the previous chapter we discussed at some length the happenings connected with friction, partly in view of what we now need to know of them in order to understand the origin of frictional electricity. A process of friction which gives rise to electricity as well as heat differs from the ordinary one in that the two bodies subject to it, must be of different materials. We may therefore expect that this difference is in some way responsible for the appearance of the two opposite electricities.

When the existence of two kinds of electricity was discovered in the eighteenth century, it became clear that it was not enough to ascribe the appearance of electricity to the intrinsic nature of amber, or sulphur, or any other single substance, but that the substance with which the first substance was brought into contact was equally important, and that on this second surface the opposite kind of electricity was always present. In this way it became known that both kinds of electricity always occur together, and that it depended on quite incidental circumstances which of the two impressed its presence more strongly on the observer.

Before embarking on a closer study of the substances in question, it should be mentioned that more recently certain observations have been made which seem to invalidate the line of investigation we follow here. For they have shown that even when the two sides consist of the same material, a certain kind of relative motion will bring about the electrical condition. This is the case, for instance, when dust of some suitable substance is blown on to or from the surface of an entire piece of the same material. Depending on the direction of the movement, one or other kind of electricity will appear on the surface, while the dust will bear the corresponding opposite charge. In order to realise that a phenomenon of this kind stands in no contradiction to the principle we are about to establish, we need only remember what we have learnt in the previous chapter concerning the different levity-gravity relationship of matter when in the state of a coherent mass or of dust. Add to this the fact of the entirely different states of motion on both sides — the bulk of the matter being at rest and the particles in the first instance loosened from it, in the second arrested at it — and it will be clear that what counts here, notwithstanding the identity of the material substance, on both sides, is the totally different condition of each. By taking all such factors into proper regard, we shall find also this case and others like it fitting into the general scheme. Moreover, phenomena of this kind must be recognised as of a more or less 'derived' nature, compared with those first known by man and therefore first to be considered here.

The two substances which first taught man the polar nature of electricity were *glass* and *resin*, after which the two electricities were named in the beginning. It is not difficult to recognise in them representatives of the Salt-Sulphur polarity. Indeed, glass as a mineral substance, which actually owes its specific character to the presence of silicon in it, clearly stands on the phosphoric-crystalline side, while resin, being itself a sort of 'gum', on the sulphurous-volcanic side. In fact, sulphur itself was soon found to be a particularly suitable substance for producing 'resin-electricity'.

Now the usual way of producing one kind of electricity is by rubbing resin (or sulphur, or ebonite) with wool or fur, and the other by rubbing glass with leather. At first sight, it does not seem as if the counter-substances represent the required alchemic counter-poles to resin and glass. For both hair and leather are animal products and therefore seem to be of like nature. Closer inspection, however, shows that they do obey the rule. For hair, like all horny substances, is a dead product of external secretion by the animal organism. An ur-phenomenal example of it, showing its kinship to glass-like substances is the transparent cornea of the eye, close to the crystal-lens. Leather, on the other hand, is a product of the hypodermic part of the body and, as such, belongs to those parts of the organism which are filled with blood, and, therefore, permeated with life. (Note as a characteristic of leather that it requires a special treatment, tanning, to make it as immune from decay as hair is by nature.) Hair and leather, therefore, represent in themselves a salt-sulphur polarity, and thus fulfil the corresponding function when brought together with resin or glass respectively.

What is true for the particular substances which originally led man to discover the dual nature of electricity, holds good equally for any pair of substances capable of assuming the electric state when rubbed against each other. If we examine from this point of view the series of such substances, as usually given in the textbooks on electricity, we shall always find a substance of extreme salt-character at the one end, and one of extreme sulphur-character at the other, the substances as a whole forming a gradual transition from one extreme to the other. Which kind of electricity appears on each, when submitted to friction, depends whether the counter-substance stands on its right or left in the series. It is the particular relation between the two which makes them behave in one way or the other. As an example we may mention the following order: *Hair* (cat's fur, fox's tail); *polished glass; wool; silk; frosted glass; rubber; resin; amber; sulphur.*

We observe how even the dry hair of the cat or fox stands in a Salt-Sulphur relationship to the sheep's wool which, although scoured, is more fatty, and therefore has a much stronger relation to heat. Note further the stronger Sulphur-nature of silk, which — in view of its origin from the caterpillar, feeding on the light-imbued leaves — is, as it were, materialised sunlight, in relation to the more external excretion of the hair of higher animals. Then there is the surprising fact that glass occurs twice with a different surface condition. Ignorance of the polarity-relations involved has caused instances of this kind to be regarded as 'irregularities', because — apparently without reasonable cause — such substances can become bearers now of one kind of electricity and then of the other. Observation guided by a true polarity concept shows that in these cases also the rule is not violated. In this respect, interesting information can be gained from the observations of J.W. Ritter (1776-1810), an ingenious *natural philosopher* from the circle round Goethe, but to whom, also, physical science is indebted for his discovery of the ultra-violet part of the spectrum and of galvanic polarisation. Among his writings there is a treatise on electricity, giving many generally unknown instances of frictional electricity which are in good accord with our picture and well worth investigating. According to Ritter, even black and white silk will become electrical when rubbed against each other — the black, in accordance with the rule, on the sulphuric side, the white on the saline. Similarly with the two kinds of glass: the glass with the smooth, and therefore less attackable, surface will be superior in the sense of Salt-quality to the rough, less stable surface of the other. Ritter further indicates that two crystalline substances of different hardness, such as calcite and quartz, become electrical when rubbed together, the softer playing the part of 'resin' and the harder that of 'glass'.

We will recall from the previous chapter that the generation of heat through friction or pressure is based on a change in the relation of the body involved to levity and gravity. By being split up, the mass is freed from some of the connection with levity which characterises its spatially extended, coherent state, so that levity and gravity fall apart to some extent as a primary polarity. We must expect that this process will change when the bodies subjected to friction are opposed to each other in the sense of a salt-sulphur polarity, i.e. of a secondary polarity. Instead of levity and gravity getting properly apart, both are claimed by the two bodies. The levity which would otherwise be free remains fixed to the substances, which means that it remains bound up with gravity, and this in such a way that the levity-gravity inter-connection turns out to be polarically opposite at the Sulphur-side and at the Salt-side of the process.

Two more recently discovered ways of evoking the electric condition in a piece of matter — piezo-electricity and pyro-electricity — confirm this picture. Both signify the occurrence of the electrical polarity at the two ends of an asymmetically built (hemimorphous) crystal, as a result of changing the crystal's spatial condition. In piezo-electricity the change consists in a diminution of the crystal's volume through pressure; in pyro-electricity, in an increase of the volume by raising the temperature. Apparently, the hemimorphous nature of the crystal, due to a one-sided working of the forces of crystallisation, plays the role of the material polarity of the substances used for frictional electricity. Note that the electrical state occurs both as a result of levity becoming free (through pressure) and of it becoming bound (through thermal expansion of the body).

We have reached a point in our observations where we can say that *electricity is gravity-bound levity, and therefore polarised in the sense of a secondary polarity.*

* * * * *

The conception thus gained of electrical polarity receives further elucidation through a study of the galvanic way of generating it, the next in the historical order.

Galvanism, as it became established through Volta's work, rests on certain properties of metallic substances. Compared with the substances which may be used for producing electricity through friction, the metals hold a mid-position. They are all essentially mercurial substances. In quicksilver, which for this reason was given the name 'mercury' by the alchemists, this fact comes to an ur-phenomenal expression. A characteristic of all metals is their capacity to conduct both heat and electricity. Expressed in purely phenomenological terms, this means that in their presence no differences of level and no polar opposites can persist. In their group we find also such contrasting properties as the propensity towards both the oxidised and the reduced states that has served us as a pointer towards recognising the alchemical polarity of Salt and Sulphur. It is this last characteristic which now requires our particular attention.

Metals, in their metallic state, are bearers of latent levity, which can be set free through combustion or corrosion. They differ from one another by their relative degree of eagerness to enter into and remain in the metallic — that is, the reduced — state, or to assume and keep the state of the oxide (when they form the various metallic oxides and salts). There are metals such as: gold, silver, etc., for which the reduced state is more or less natural; others, such as potassium, sodium, etc., find the oxidised state natural and can be brought into and kept in the reduced state only by artificial means. Between these extremes there are all possible degrees of transition, some metals more nearly resembling the 'noble', others more nearly the 'corrosive', metals.

We will remember that it was the different relationship of sulphur and phosphorus to reduction and oxidation which led us to envisage them as ur-phenomenal representatives of the alchemic polarity. We may therefore say that there are metals which from the alchemic point of view more nearly resemble sulphur, others more nearly phosphorus, whilst others again hold an intermediary position between the extremes. It is on these differences among the various metals that their galvanic properties are based.

Let us from this point of view contemplate the following series of chemical elements, which is a representation of the so-called electrochemical series:

Graphite, Platinum, Gold, Silver, Copper, Iron, Tin, Lead, Zinc, Aluminium, Magnesium, Sodium, Potassium.

Any two of these metals constitute an electrochemical cell. Its electromotive force is determined by the distance in the series between the metals used. Just as in the case of frictional electricity, the kind of electricity which is supplied by a certain metal depends on whether the other metal with which it is coupled stands to the right or to the left of it in the series.[3]

Let us now see what happens in a galvanic cell when the two different metals are simultaneously exposed to the chemical action of the connecting fluid. Each metal by itself would undergo oxidation with greater or less intensity, and the calorific energy hidden in it would become free in the form of heat. This process suffers a certain alteration through the presence of the second metal, which sets up an alchemic tension between the two. Instead of a proper segregation of the primary polarity, heat — dust (in this case, heat — oxide), the heat remains matter-bound and appears on the surface of the two metals in a secondarily split form as positive and negative electricity.

The similarity between this process and the frictional generation of electricity is evident.

* * * * *

We proceed now in historical order to the electrodynamic or electromagnetic way of generating electricity. When Faraday discovered it, the birth-hour of the age of electricity actually struck. True, this discovery had been preceded by that of the magnetic properties of the electric current. But as we are now discussing the various modes of generating electricity, we will keep to this subject and leave for later the question of electro-magnetism itself.

The place of the physical substances used for generating electricity through friction, or in the galvanic way, is now taken by a pure force, magnetism. As in the previous instances we began by inquiring into the nature of the relevant substances, we must start now with investigating the nature of magnetism.

Unlike electricity, magnetism was first known in the form of its natural occurrence, namely as a property of certain minerals. If we follow the same course which led us to start our study of electricity with the primitive process of generating it, we shall turn now to the basic phenomenon produced by a magnetic field already in existence. (Only when we have learnt all we can from this, shall we proceed to ask how magnetism comes into being.) Obviously, we shall find this basic phenomenon in the effect of a magnet on a heap of iron filings.

Let us, to begin with, compare a mass of solid iron with the same quantity of it in powdered form. The difference is that the powder lacks the binding force which holds the solid piece together. Now let us expose the powdered iron to the influence of a magnet. At once a certain ordering principle takes hold of the single particles. They no longer lie at random and unrelated, apart from the inconspicuous gravitational effect they exert on one another, but are drawn into a coherent whole, thus acquiring properties resembling those of an ordinary piece of solid matter.

Read thus, the phenomenon tells us that a part of space occupied by a magnetic field has qualities which are otherwise found only where a coherent solid mass is present. A magnetic piece of solid iron, therefore, differs from a non-magnetic piece by giving rise in its surroundings to dynamic conditions which would otherwise exist only in its interior. This picture of the relatedness of magnetism to solidity is confirmed by the fact that both are cancelled by heat, and increased by cold.

Seen thus, magnetism appears to rank alongside gravitation,

to which physical bodies owe their coherence, but it differs in being itself of a bipolar nature. Hence it cannot, as gravity can, be one pole of a primary polarity, with levity at the other pole. Rather may we expect it to represent, somewhat as electricity does, a polarity of the second order, with both gravity and levity partaking on either side. This is indeed show by the occurrence of effects of pressure or suction, depending on whether two fields of the same or of opposite nature meet, just as in the case of the electrical polarity. With magnetism, however, the accent does not, as with the more fugitive electricity, lie on levity, but on gravity. We shall hear more of this later. At the present stage it suffices to have found that magnetism is secondarily polarised gravity. How then is electricity generated by means of magnetism, as is done in a modern dynamo?

As polarised gravity, magnetism shares with gravity the characteristic of tending always to maintain an existent condition. In bodies subject to gravity, this tendency reveals itself as their inertia. It is the inertia inherent in magnetism which we employ when using it to generate electricity. The simplest example is when, by interrupting a 'primary current', we induce a 'secondary current' in a neighbouring circuit. By the sudden alteration of the electric condition on the primary side, the magnetic condition of the surrounding space is exposed to a sudden corresponding change. Against this the magnetic field 'puts up' a resistance by calling forth, on the secondary side, an electrical process of such direction and strength that the entire magnetic condition remains first unaltered and then, instead of changing suddenly, undergoes a gradual transformation which ideally needs an infinite time for its accomplishment (asymptotic course of the exponential curve). This principle rules every process of electromagnetic induction, whatever the cause and direction of the change of the magnetic field.

We know that electromagnetic induction takes place also when a conductor is moved across a magnetic field in such a way that, as the technical term goes, it 'cuts' the field's lines of force. Whereas the process discussed above is employed in the transformer, this latter process is used in generation of electricity by dynamo. We have seen that a magnetic field imparts to the relevant part of space qualities of density which otherwise prevail only in the interior of solid masses. We remember further that the appearance of electricity, in the two other modes of generating it, is caused by the loosening of the coherence of the material substance. A similar loosening of the coherence of the magnetic field takes place when its field-lines are cut by the movement of the conductor across it. Just as heat occurs when we move a solid object through a liquid, electricity occurs when we move a conductor across a magnetic field. In each case we interfere with an existing levity-gravity relationship.

* * * * *

We turn now to the phenomenon of electromagnetism itself, the discovery of which was the precondition for Faraday's discovery of electromagnetic induction. Our observations will throw some new light also on the phenomenon of the so-called electric current, and in this way we shall gain further insight into the nature of electricity itself.

The discovery of the phenomena we call electromagnetic depended on the possibility of producing continuous electrical processes. This arose with Volta's invention. When it became necessary to find a concept for the process which takes place in an electric conductor between the poles of a galvanic cell, the concept of the 'current', borrowed from hydrodynamics, suggested itself. Ever since then it has been the rule to speak of the existence of a current within an electric circuit; its strength or intensity is measured in terms of a unit, named in honour of Ampère. As we shall see later, this concept of the current has had a fate typical of the whole relationship of human thought to the facts concerned with electricity. Let us, at the present point, gather together the relevant phenomena by means of pure observation.

While keeping once again to the historical order of things, we shall try first to form a picture of what happens when we connect two electrically charged bodies by a conductor. We know that we rightly describe the change of the dynamic properties of the part of space, in which the two bodies are present, by saying that a certain electric field prevails in it. This field possesses different 'potentials' at its various points and so there exists a certain potential difference between the two electric charges. What then happens when a so-called 'conductor' is brought into such a field?

From the point of view of the field-concept, conductivity consists in the property of a body not to allow any change of potential along its surface. Such a surface, therefore, is always an equipotential. In the language of alchemy, conductivity is a mercurial property. In the presence of such a body, therefore, no Salt-Sulphur contrasts can obtain. In view of what we found above as the mean position of the metals in the alchemic triad, it is significant that they, precisely, should play so outstanding a role as electrical conductors.

If we keep to pure observation, the only statement we can make concerning the effect produced by the introduction of such a body into the electric field is that this field suddenly disappears. We shall see later in which direction this vanishing occurs. For the present it is sufficient to have formed the picture of the disappearance of the electrical conditon of space as a result of the presence of a body with certain mercurial properties.

Nothing else, indeed, happens when we make the process continuous by using a galvanic source of electricity. All that distinguishes a galvanic cell from the sources of electricity used before the time of Volta is its faculty of immediately re-establishing the field which prevails between its poles, whenever this field becomes extinguished by the presence of a conductor. Volta himself saw this quite correctly. In his first account of the new apparatus he describes it as 'Leyden jars with a continuously re-established charge'. Every enduring electrical process, indeed, consists in nothing but a vanishing and re-establishment of the electrical field with such rapidity that the whole process appears continuous.

Here, also, pure observation of the effect of a conductor in an electric field, tells us that its action consists in the annihilation of the field. There is no phenomenon which allows us to state that this process takes place along the axis of the conductor. If we wish to obtain a picture of the true direction, we must consider the condition of space which arises in place of the electric condition that has disappeared.

With the possibility of turning the cancellation of the electrical condition of space into a continuous process, it became possible to observe that the neutralisation of electric charges entails the appearance of heat and magnetism. Our picture of the electric and magnetic polarity enables us to understand why this must be so.

As we have seen, electricity is levity coupled in a peculiar way with gravity; it is polarised levity (accompanied by a corresponding polarisation of gravity). An electric field, therefore, always has both qualities, those of levity and of gravity. We saw a symptom of this in electrical attraction and repulsion, so called; the attraction, we found, was due to negative density, the repulsion to positive density, imparted to space by the electrical fields present there. Now we see that when, through the presence of a conductor, the electrical field round the two opposing poles vanishes, in its place two other fields, a thermal and a magnetic, appear. Clearly, one of them represents the levity-part, the other the gravity-part, of the vanished electric field. The whole process reminds one of combustion through which the ponderable and imponderable parts, combined in the combustible substance, fall apart and appear on the one hand as heat, and on the other as oxidised substance ('ash'). Yet, between these two manifestations of heat there is an essential qualitative difference.

Following the cancellation of the electric field, magnetism appears as one 'half' of the complete happening, being itself secondarily polarised gravity. We may therefore expect that its counterpart, heat, will not be pure levity either. The fact that heat occurs here coupled in some way with gravity, can indeed be read from the phenomenon itself. Unlike the levity-gravity polarity, in which one pole is peripheral and the other point-centred, both poles of the electrical polarity are point-centred; both are located in physical space, and thereby determine a definite direction within this space. It is this direction which remains a characteristic of both the magnetic and the thermal fields. The direction of the thermal field as much as that of the magnetic is determined by its having as its axis the conductor joining the poles of the antecedent electrical field. Both fields supplement each other in that the thermal radiation forms the radii which belong to the circular magnetic lines-of-force surrounding the conductor.[4]

Our picture of the process which is commonly called an electric current is now sufficiently complete to allow us to make a positive statement concerning the direction in which it takes place. Let us once more sum up: In order that this process may occur, there must be present in an electrically excited part of space a body which does not suffer the particular polarisation of space bound up with such a field. As a result, the electrical field disappears, and in place of it appear a thermal field and a magnetic field, both having as their axis the line connecting the two poles. Each of them spreads out in a direction at right-angles to this line, one cylindrically, the other radially. Obviously, therefore, it is in this direction, i.e. at right-angles to the conductor, that the transformation of the electric into the thermomagnetic condition takes place.

Here we encounter a fact we have met more than once, namely that quite primitive observations, when properly read, lead to findings for which scientific thought had to wait until they were forced on it by the progress of experimental technique — still without attaining to a uniformly valid picture of the dynamic behaviour of electricity.

We have already hinted at the fact that the concept of the electric current, first formed quite naively, has met with the typical fate of having become paradoxical with progressing scientific research. Long after it had been coined to cover phenomena which in themselves betray no movement of any kind between the electrical poles, other phenomena which do in fact show such movements became known through Crookes's observations. Just as in the case of atomism, they seemed to prove the validity of the preconceived idea of the current. Soon, however, radiant electricity showed properties which contradicted the picture of something flowing from one pole to the other. The cathode rays, for instance, were found to shoot forth into space perpendicularly from the surface of the cathode, without regard to the position of the anode. At the same time Maxwell's hydrodynamic analogy (as our historical survey has shown, page 55) led to a view of the nature of electricity by which this very analogy was put out of court. By predicting certain properties of electricity which come to the fore when its poles alternate rapidly, he seemed to bring electricity into close kinship with light. Mathematical treatment then made it necessary to regard the essential energy process as occurring, not from one pole to the other, but at right-angles to a line joining the poles (Poynting's vector). This picture, however, satisfactory though it was in the realm of high frequency, failed as a means of describing so-called direct-current processes. In spite of all this, scientific thinking (not to speak of the layman's) has not managed to discard the old concept of the current. As a result, the theory of electricity has fallen apart into several conceptual realms lying, as it were, alongside one another, each consistent in itself but lacking logical connection with the others.

The situation changes as soon as one learns to free oneself altogether from the concept of the electric current in the way shown here. This much, at any rate, we can see at once – the picture of the electromagnetic process as one that takes place in a radial direction at right-angles to the conductor, to which observations of the oscillatory processes have led, holds valid for all electrical processes.

Heretical though the abolition of the concept of the current may seem today, it is fully in line with an earlier realistic mode of thought. Surprisingly, it is Faraday again who proves to be a true forerunner and ally in this respect. As his biographer,

J.H. Gladstone, reports, Faraday was a sworn enemy of all such 'figurative concepts' as that of the electric current.[5]

The findings lead to a conclusion which contributes significantly to our understanding of electricity. When we apply electricity to practical purposes, we are in fact seldom using electricity itself, but other forces (that is, other combinations of gravity and levity) which we make effective by making electricity *disappear*. The same is true of most of the methods of measuring electricity. As a rule, the force which sets the instrument in motion is not electricity but another force (magnetism, heat, etc.,) which appears in the place of the vanishing electricity. Thus the so-called intensity of an electric current is actually the intensity with which the electricity in question disappears! In fact, electricity serves us in our machines in the same way that food serves a living organism: it gets itself digested, and what matters is the resulting secondary product.

Evidently the concept of electrical resistance, too, assumes a new interpretation in this way. The existing theory of electricity is already familiar with the concept of electrical conductance, the reciprocal of resistance. This concept turns out to be the truly realistic one, in comparison with that of resistance. For the more intensively a substance consumes electricity, the better it conducts it.

With the recognition that we have to do with electricity proper only in the case of an electric field exerting its power directly (as in the electroscope), whereas all other so-called electrical processes consist in a consumption of the electric force, it becomes possible to form an adequate picture also of the oscillating circuit, an essential implement of wireless technique. It consists in principle in a coupling of a condensor with a helix, or, expressed differently, of a capacitance with an inductance. (Fig. 13.) In this connection the term 'capacitance' denotes the power of a condensor to accumulate on its two coatings an electric charge and thereby to give rise to an electric field. By 'inductance' is meant the power of a conductor (in this case wound up spirally) to give rise to a magnetic field by annihilating the electric charge. Both together form a closed circuit in which an electric condition, once roused, will start a rhythmic process

Fig. 13

in the system as a whole. This consists in the condensor first getting discharged through the helix, and then recharging itself through the secondary electric force produced by the magnetic field in the helix, so that an electric and magnetic field arise in alternation. As always when two dynamic opposites enter into mutual relation, so in this case an oscillatory process results.

Since all man's inventions are, even if unconsciously, derived in some way from his own organism, we are not surprised to recognise in the oscillating circuit a certain replica of his own make-up, namely the two polar systems of the nerves and the metabolic organs, with the rhythmic system as a mediator. Storage (memory) and consumption (nutrition) are as much functions of the head-part and the abdominal parts of our organism as of the condensor and the helix of the oscillating circuit. In fact, even in its outer form, the condensor reminds one of the plate-like structure of the skull, and the helix of the intestinal loops. Moreover, that which goes on between the two can get disconnected from the closed system and radiate into outer space, thus furnishing a means for human intercommunication, just as in his rhythmic system man communicates through his breathing with the world around both materially and, by using his breath for speech, mentally.

* * * * *

Earlier in this chapter we left open the question as to the absolute character of the single poles of the electrical and magnetic polarity. Both could be recognised by us as polarities of the second order, related to the alchemical polarity of Salt and Sulphur. We shall have to show which of the two kinds of electricity and which of the two magnetic poles is saline in nature and which is sulphurous.

We will remember that Galvani was led to his observations by the results of Walsh's study of electric fishes. He himself clung to the view that the phenomena he observed were also due to a source of electricity within the animal bodies. Volta saw the fallacy of that. This enabled him to conceive the idea of imitating with purely inorganic substances the set-up which Galvani had come upon by accident. The paradoxical result — as he himself noticed with surprise — was that his apparatus turned out to be a close replica of the peculiar organ with which the electric fishes are endowed by nature. We must now take a closer view of this organ.

The electric organ of such a fish consists of many thousands of little piles, each made up of a very great number of plates of two different kinds, arranged in alternating layers. The two kinds differ in substance: in one case the plate is made from a material similar to that present in the nervous system of animals: in the other the resemblance is to a substance present in the muscular system, though only when the muscles are in a state of decay. In this way the two opposing systems of the animal body seem to be brought here into direct contact, repeated many thousands of times.

In the electric fishes, accordingly, sensation and will are brought into a peculiar interrelation. For as a result of the spatial fixation and the state of deterioration of its bodily foundation the animal's will-pole is related to its bodily foundation in a manner which otherwise obtains only between the nervous system and the psychological processes co-ordinated with it. These fishes have the capacity to send out force-currents which produce in other animals and in man 'concussion of the limbs', or in extreme cases paralysis and even death. When contemplated with pure observation this phenomenon tells us that in cases of minor strength, this force causes processes of a volitional character in bodies affected by it. Through stronger effects the organic system which serves the will of the creature involved passes into disuse, either for a time or for good. By describing the process in this way we realise that electricity appears here as metamorphosed animal will, which takes this peculiar form because part of the animal's volitional system is assimilated to its sensory system in an exceptional manner.

It is known today that what nature reveals so strikingly in the case of the electric fish is nothing but the manifestation of a principle at work in the bodies of all beings endowed with sensation and volition — in corporeal terms, with the duality of a nervous and a muscular system — and therefore at work also in the human body. Observation has show that the activities of these two systems in man and animal are accompanied by the occurrence of different electric potential in different parts of the body. Manifold in detail though the relevant observations are, they all confirm a definite correlation of negative electricity with the nerve-and-sense pole (sensation) and of positive electricity with the blood-and-muscle pole (volition). Negative electricity, therefore, appears to represent the Salt-pole of the polarity, and positive electricity the Sulphur-pole.

This finding is confirmed by electrical phenomena in the realm of nature most remote from man (though it was an effort to solve the enigma of man which led to the discovery of this realm). Since Crookes's observation of the behaviour of electricity in a vacuum it is common knowledge that only negative electricity appears in a free form, whereas positive electricity is always bound to matter in the form of positive ions. At the negative pole, therefore, the relationship electricity-matter is of the quality 'dry', at the positive, 'moist'. The same language is spoken by the forms in which the luminous phenomena appear at the two poles. At the anode we see radial forms; at the cathode, planar forms. Cosmic periphery and terrestrial centre stand in polar relationship to each other at the two poles in such a manner that we can say: *negative electricity is gravity-laden levity, positive electricity is levity-raised gravity.* As we shall see when discussing the nature of colour, the luminous colours at the two poles — reddish at the anode, bluish at the cathode — are also in accord with this.

* * * * *

Let us remember at this point how we first came to recognise the electrical polarity as a polarity of the second order. It was by recognising the polar nature of the substances used for friction, or in the galvanic process. If now we examine the distribution of the two kinds of electricity between the two sets of substances, it seems to contradict what we have learnt. For in both cases the 'sulphurous' substances (resin in one, the nobler metals in the other) become bearers of negative electricity; whilst the 'saline' substances (glass and the more corrosive metals) carry positive electricity. That is why at the beginning of our discussion we were careful not to draw conclusions about the absolute character of the two electricities from their distribution. Compared with our previous finding, a criss-crossing of the poles seems to have occurred. However, this is not a novelty for us. We met it in the distribution of the functions of the plant's organs of propagation, and we shall meet a further instance of it when studying the functions of the different parts of the human eye. Through criss-crossings of this kind nature seems to create safeguards against polarity-effects of the sort known as 'chain-reactions', which man has contrived to get going against nature's own order at her nether border.

* * * * *

As with the electric field, the magnetic field does not in itself reveal the absolute characters of the two kinds of magnetism. In the case of electricity it was the human organism which — in Goethe's sense — rendered manifest the mystery. As electricity points to man, so does magnetism point to the earth. For just as the earth is the bearer of a levity-field and a gravity-field, whose function it is to be the mother fields of the respective forces in all earthly occurrences, so is the earth bearer also of a magnetic field, the direction of whose axis, significantly, coincides with that of the earth's physical body. When read as a letter in nature's script this will help us, when also held side by side with kindred phenomena in this field, to attain an insight into the qualitative difference, otherwise hidden, between the two polar ways the magnetic field manifests itself.

Once the north-south direction of the earth's magnetism had become known to man, he soon learned to make use of it in the form of the compass needle. He pictured the relationship of such a piece of magnetic material to the earth's magnetism as being that between a small and a large magnet, the poles of the one being 'attracted' by the respective poles of the other. When learning to know that it requires poles of the opposite nature to bring about this effect, and once having named the end of the needle pointing northward its 'north pole', he consequently was forced to regard the earth's magnetic pole situated near the geographical north pole to be its magnetic south pole and vice versa. Consequently it became customary to refer to south magnetism as that related to the earth's northern hemisphere. Along our way of letting the phenomena speak for themselves we shall in place of this purely nominalistic terminology attain to the proper realistic one which indeed will prove just the opposite.

As the bearer of its magnetic field, the earth calls upon us to take into consideration its own polar structure as shown by the one-sided distribution and corresponding formations of its continental land masses: the majority of the solid land covers the northern hemisphere, whereas the southern hemisphere is mainly covered by water. When read in the language of the four elements this tells us that the north is predominantly 'dry', the south correspondingly 'moist'. Seen thus, the earth appears to be polarised in the way of a secondary polarity, 'saline' in the north and 'sulphuric' in the south. In so far as the earth manifests itself magnetically it is subject to the same ordering. North-magnetism therefore, is of necessity orientated *spherically*, south-magnetism *radially*.

As we saw earlier, since Faraday's formation of the *Field* concept there is no longer any justification for speaking of single poles 'attracting' or 'repelling' each other, whether they be magnetic or electric. Keeping consistently to the field concept enables us to assign the two polar manifestations of the magnetic force their proper names: 'North' to the one covering the earth's northern hemisphere and 'South' to its opposite. It is in this order, therefore, that they will appear in the scheme shown below with their appropriate symbols.

What we have thus come to see holds equally well for any magnetic field, whether bound up with naturally magnetic or artificially magnetised pieces of matter. For when seen properly as part of a whole, what makes a body magnetic is the fact that part of the mother field of the earth has been drawn into it.

The picture of the secondary polar nature of magnetism seems at first sight to be incompatible with the fact that the magnetic lines of force, unlike those of electricity, run back into themselves. In reality the latter, too, are closed lines, but via infinity. Seen thus, what is otherwise infinite becomes, in magnetism, finite. As will be seen later on, it is essential to conceive of magnetism in this way.

Earlier on in this book (Chapter IV) we came to realise as man's twofold problem the fact that not only has his Knowing outrun his Doing, resulting from a certain deviation of his innermost nature through Lucifer's influence on him in the far past, but also that with the coming into being of the age of natural science his Doing began to outrun his Knowing. This is predominantly the effect of his discovery of the usefulness of the powers of electricity and magnetism for all sorts of practical purposes, leading thereby to a civilisation that threatens to devour him. It is above all in this field, therefore, that a decisive step needs to be taken in the direction of a Knowing capable of so handling these forces that, instead of dragging us ever deeper into the country that is not ours, they can become vehicles for the life-promoting forces from out of the country that is truly ours.

In dealing with a renewed science of optics we shall come to develop an appropriate picture of the spectrum and its phenomena which will lead to a definite outlook in this direction.

* * * * *

Notwithstanding its gravitational character, electricity is an offspring of levity. This became clear enough through the initial investigations in this chapter. Equally clearly, we found magnetism to be an offspring of gravity, notwithstanding its levitational character. Both, therefore, represent once more a levity-gravity polarity. The following is an attempt to fix these facts in a concise scheme:

	Electricity	*Magnetism*	
—	Gravity-laden L E V I T Y	G R A V I T Y -laden Levity	N
+	L E V I T Y -raised Gravity	Levity-raised G R A V I T Y	S

* * * * *

Our observations have shown that the emergence of the electric state, whether it be caused by friction or galvanically, depends on matter entering into a condition in which its cohesion is loosened — or, as we also put it, on its being turned into 'dust' — and this in such a way that the escaping levity remains dust-bound. This picture of electricity now enables us to give a realistic interpretation to certain phenomena which, in the interpretation which the physicist of the past was bound to give them, have contributed much to the tightening of the net of scientific illusion.

Some sixty years after Dalton had established, purely hypothetically, the theory of the atomistic structure of matter, scientific research was led to the observation of actual atomistic phenomena in electricity. Sir J.J. Thomson found electricity appearing in gas discharge tubes in the form of discrete particles, with properties hitherto known only as appertaining to mass. What could be more natural than to assume that the method of thought developed during the past era of science was on the right course, and therefore to suppose that what had been discovered was the atom of electricity which was a constituent of all matter?

The same phenomena appear in quite a different light when we view them against the background of the picture of electricity to which our observations have led. Knowing that the appearance of electricity depends on a process of atomisation of some sort, we shall expect that where electricity becomes freely observable, it will yield phenomena of an atomistic kind. The observations of electricity in a vacuum, therefore, yield no confirmation whatsoever of the atomistic view of matter.

The insight we have gained into the nature of electricity and magnetism has led us to the realisation that with every act of setting electromagnetic energies in motion we interfere with the entire levity-gravity balance of our planet by turning part of the earth's coherent substance into cosmic 'dust'. Thus we may say that whenever we generate electricity we speed up the earth's process of cosmic ageing. Obviously this is tremendously enhanced by the creation of artificial radioactivity along the lines recently discovered, whereby it has now become possible to transmute chemical elements into one another, or even to cancel altogether their gravity-bound existence.

To see things in this light is to realise that with our having become able to rouse electricity and magnetism from their dormant state and make them work for us, a gigantic responsibility has devolved upon mankind. It was man's fate to remain unaware of this fact during the first phase of the electrification of his civilisation; to continue now in this state of unawareness would spell peril for the human race.

Chapter XIV

COLOURS AS 'DEEDS AND SUFFERINGS OF LIGHT'

'As for what I have done as a poet, I take no pride in it whatever. Excellent poets have lived at the same time as myself; poets more excellent have lived before me, and others will come after me. But that in my century I am the only person who knows the truth in the difficult science of colours — of that, I say, I am not a little proud, and here I have a consciousness of a superiority to many.'

In these words spoken to his secretary, Eckermann, in 1829, a few years before his death, Goethe gave his opinion on the significance of his scientific researches in the field of optical phenomena. He knew that the path he had opened up had led him to truths which belong to the original truths of mankind. He expressed this by remarking that his theory of colour was 'as old as the world'.

If in this book we come somewhat late to a discussion of Goethe's colour-theory, in spite of the part it played in his own scientific work, and in spite of its significance for the founding of a physics based on his method, the reasons are these. When Goethe undertook his studies in this field he had not to reckon with the forms of thought which have become customary since the development of mechanistic and above all — to put it concisely — of 'electricalistic' thinking. Before a hearing can be gained in our age for a physics of Light and Colour as conceived by Goethe, certain hindrances must first be cleared away. So a picture on the one hand of matter, and on the other of electricity, such as is given when they are studied by Goethean methods, had first to be built up; only then is the ground provided for an un-prejudiced judgment of Goethe's observations and the deductions that can be made from them today.

As Professor Heisenberg, in his lecture quoted earlier (Chapter I), rightly remarks, Goethe strove directly with Newton only in the realms of colour-theory and optics. Nevertheless his campaign was not merely against Newton's *opinions* in this field. He was guided throughout by the conviction that the fundamental principles of the whole Newtonian outlook were at stake. It was for this reason that his polemics against Newton were so strongly expressed, although he had no fondness for such controversies. In looking back on that part of the *Farbenlehre* which he had himself called 'Polemical' in the title, he said to Eckermann: 'I by no means disavow my severe dissections of the Newtonian statements; it was necessary at the time and will also have its value hereafter; but at bottom all polemical action is repugnant to my nature, and I can take but little pleasure in it.'

The reason why Goethe chose optics as the field of conflict, and devoted to it more than twenty years of research and reflection, amidst all the other labours of his rich life, lay certainly in his individual temperament — *'zum Sehen geboren, zum Schauen bestellt'*.[1] At the same time one must see here a definite guidance of humanity. Since the hour had struck for mankind to take the first step towards overcoming the world-conception of the one-eyed, colour-blind onlooker, what step could have been more appropriate than this of Goethe's, when he raised the eye's capacity for seeing colours to the rank of an instrument of scientific cognition?

In point of fact, the essential difference between Goethe's theory of colour and the theory which has prevailed in science (despite all modifications) since Newton's day, lies in this: While the theory of Newton and his successors was based on excluding the colour-seeing faculty of the eye, Goethe founded his theory on the eye's experience of colour.

* * * * *

In view of the present scientific conception of the effect

which a prismatic piece of a transparent medium has on light passing through it, Goethe's objection to Newton's interpretation and the conclusions drawn from it seems by no means as heretical as it did in Goethe's own time and for a hundred years afterwards. For, as Lord Rayleigh and others have shown, the facts responsible for the coming into being of the spectral colours, when these are produced by a diffraction grating, invalidate Newton's idea that the optical apparatus serves to *reveal* colours which are inherent in the original light. Today it is known that these colours are an *outcome* of the interference of the apparatus (whether prism or grating) with the light. Thus we find Professor R.W. Wood, in the opening chapter of his *Physical Optics*, after having described the historical significance of Newton's conception of the relation between light and colour, saying: 'Curiously enough, this discovery, which we are taking as marking the beginning of a definite knowledge about light, is one which we shall demolish in the last chapter of this book,[2] for our present ideas regarding the action of the prism more nearly resemble the idea held previous to Newton's classical experiments. We now believe that the prism actually manufactures the coloured light.'

As was mentioned in the previous chapter, Eddington dealt with this fact in his book, *The Philosophy of Physical Science*, under the heading 'Discovery or Manufacture?' where he, too, shows that the answer must be definitely in favour of 'manufacture'. Nevertheless, Eddington complains, experts, in spite of knowing better, keep to the traditional way of speaking about the spectral colours as being originally contained in the light. 'Such is the glamour of a historical experiment.'[3] It is for the same reason that Goethe's discovery continues to be unrecognised by the majority of scientists, who prefer, instead of examining the question for themselves, to join in the traditional assertion that 'Goethe never understood Newton'.

* * * * *

As Goethe relates at the conclusion of the 'historical' part

of his *Farbenlehre*,[4] he was drawn to study colour by his wish
to gain some knowledge of the objective laws of aesthetics. He
felt too close to poetry to be able to study it with sufficient
detachment, so he turned to painting — an art with which he
felt sufficiently familiar without being connected with it creatively
— hoping that if he could discover the laws of one art they would
prove applicable to others.

His visit to Italy, a land rich both in natural colour and in
works of art, gave him a welcome opportunity to pursue this
inquiry, but for a long time he made no headway. The paintings
he saw suggested no inherent law in their arrangement of colours,
nor could the painters he questioned tell him of one. The only
qualitative distinction they seemed to recognise was between
'cold' and 'warm' colours.

His own observations led him to a definite experience of the
quality of the colour blue, for which he coined the phrase 'feebleness of blue' (*'Ohnmacht des Blau'*). In some way this colour
seemed to him to be related to black. In order to rouse his artist
friends and to stimulate their reflections, he liked to indulge in
paradoxes, as when he asserted that blue was not a colour at all.
He found, however, as time went on, that in this way he came no
nearer his goal.

Although the splendour of colour in the Italian sky and the
Italian landscape made a powerful impression on Goethe, he
found not enough opportunity for systematic study to allow him
to arrive at more than a dim surmise of some law underlying
the occurrence of colour in nature. Still, there was one thing
he took home with him as a result of his labours. He had grown
convinced that 'the first approach to colours as physical phenomena had to be sought from the side of their occurrence in nature,
if one would gain an understanding of them in relation to art'.

Back at home, he strove to recollect the theory of Newton as
it was being taught in schools and universities — namely, that
'colours in their totality are contained in light'. Hitherto he had
had no occasion to doubt the correctness of this theory. Like
everyone else, he had heard it expounded in lectures as an incon-

testable result of empirical observation, though without this ever having been shown to him by way of experiment. He convinced himself by consulting a manual that his recollection was correct, but at the same time he found that the theory there set forth gave no help in answering his questions.[5] So he decided to examine the phenomena for himself.

For this purpose he borrowed a set of prisms from a friend living in nearby Jena, the physicist, Büttner. Since, however, he had at that time no opportunity of arranging a dark chamber on Newton's lines, where the necessary ray of light from a tiny hole in the window-covering was sent through a prism, he postponed the whole thing, until in the midst of all his many other interests and duties it was forgotten. In vain Büttner pressed many times for the return of the prisms; at last he sent a mutual acquaintance with the injunction not to return without them. Goethe then searched for the long-neglected apparatus and determined to take a rapid glance through one of the prisms before he gave them back.

He recalled dimly his pleasure as a boy at the vision of the world given him through a bit of similarly shaped glass. 'I well remembered that everything looked coloured, but in what manner I could no longer recollect. I was just then in a room completely white; remembering the Newtonian theory, I expected, as I put the prism to my eye, to find the whole white wall coloured in different hues and to see the light reflected thence into the eye, split into as many coloured lights.

'But how astonished was I when the white wall seen through the prism remained white after as before. Only where something dark came against it a more or less decided colour was shown, and at last the window-bars appeared most vividly coloured, while on the light-grey sky outside no trace of colouring was to be seen. It did not need any long consideration for me to recognise that a *boundary or edge is necessary to call forth the colours*, and I immediately said aloud, as though by instinct, that the Newtonian doctrine is false.'

For Goethe, there could be no more thought of sending

back the prisms, and he persuaded Büttner to leave them with him for some time longer.

Goethe adds a short account of the progress of the experiments he now undertook as well as of his efforts to interest others in his discovery. He makes grateful reference to those who had brought him understanding, and who had been helpful to him through the exchange of thoughts. Among these, apart from Schiller, whom Goethe especially mentions, we find a number of leading anatomists, chemists, writers and philosophers of his time, but not a single one of the physicists then active in teaching or research. The 'Guild' took up an attitude of complete disapproval or indifference, and so have things remained till a hundred years after his death, as Goethe himself prophesied.

One of the first systematic pieces of work which Goethe undertook in order to trace the cause of the Newtonian error was to go through Book I of Newton's *Optics*,[6] sentence by sentence, recapitulate Newton's experiments and rearrange them in the order which seemed to him essential. In so doing he gained an insight which was fundamental for all future work, and often proved very beneficial in the perfecting of his own methods. His examination of the Newtonian procedure showed him that the whole mistake rested on the fact that 'a complicated phenomenon should have been taken as a basis, and the simpler explained from the complex'. Nevertheless, it still needed 'much time and application in order to wander through all the labyrinths with which Newton had been pleased to confuse his successors'.

* * * * *

It seems a small thing, and yet it is a great one, which Goethe, as the above description shows, discovered almost by chance. This is shown by the conclusions to which he was led in the systematic prosecutions of his discovery. An account of them is given in his *Beiträge zur Optik*,[7] published in 1791, the year in which Galvani came before the public with his observations in the sphere of electricity.

Goethe describes in this book the basic phenomena of the creation of the prismatic colours, with particulars of a number of experiments so arranged that the truth he had discovered, contrary to Newton's view, comes to light through the very phenomena themselves. He did not publish the actual master-piece, *Entwurf einer Farbenlehre*,[8] until much later, in the year 1810, four years after he had brought the researches — which he had pursued most carefully the whole time — to a certain conclusion. (An English translation of the didactic part appeared about ten years after Goethe's death.)

While leaving a more detailed description of the composition of Goethe's *Entwurf* for our next chapter, we shall here deal at once with some of the essential conclusions to which the reader is led in this book. As already mentioned, Goethe's first inspection of the colour-phenomenon produced by the prism had shown him that the phenomenon depended on the presence of a boundary between light and darkness. Newton's attempt to explain the spectrum out of light alone appeared to him, therefore, as an inadmissible setting aside of one of the two necessary conditions. Colours, so Goethe gleaned directly from the prismatic pheno-menon, are caused by both light and its counterpart, darkness. Hence, to arrive at an idea of the nature of colour, which was in accord with its actual appearance, he saw himself committed to an investigation of the extent to which the qualitative differences in our experience of colours rests upon their differing proportions of light and darkness.

It is characteristic of Goethe's whole mode of procedure that he at once changed the question, 'What is colour?' into the question, 'How does colour arise?' It was equally characteristic that he did not, as Newton did, shut himself into a darkened room, so as to get hold of the colour-phenomenon by means of an artificially set-up apparatus. Instead, he turned first of all to nature, to let her give him the answer to the questions he had raised.

It was clear to Goethe that to trace the law of the genesis of colour in nature by reading her phenomena, he must keep a look-out for occurrences of colours which satisfied the conditions of the *Urphänomen*, as he had learned to know it. This meant that he must ask of nature where she let colours arise out of light and darkness in such a way that no other conditions contributed to the effect.

He saw that such an effect was presented to his eye when he turned his gaze on the one hand to the blue sky, and on the other to the yellowish luminous sun. Where we see the blue of the heavens, there, spread out before our eyes, is universal space, which as such is dark. Why it does not appear dark by day as well as by night is because we see it through the sun-illumined atmosphere. The opposite role is played by the atmosphere when we look through it to the sun. In the first instance it acts as a lightening, in the second as a darkening, medium. Accordingly, when the optical density of the air changes as a result of its varying content of moisture, the colour-phenomenon undergoes an opposite change in each of the two cases. Whilst with increasing density of the air the blue of the sky brightens up and gradually passes over into white, the yellow of the sun gradually darkens and finally gives way to complete absence of light.

The ur-phenomenon, having once been discovered in the heavens, could then easily be found elsewhere in nature on a large or small scale — as, for instance, in the blue of distant hills when the air is sufficiently opaque, or in the colour of the colourless, slightly milky opal which looks a deep blue when one sees it against a dark background, and a reddish yellow when one holds it against the light. The same phenomenon may be produced artificially through the clouding of glass with suitable substances, as one finds in various glass handicraft objects. The aesthetic effect is due to the treated glass being so fashioned as to present continually changing angles to the light, when both colour-poles and all the intermediate phases appear simultaneously. It is also possible to produce the ur-phenomenon experimentally by placing a glass jug filled with water before a black background, illuminating the jug from the side, and gradually clouding the water by the admixture of suitable substances. Whilst the brightness appearing in the direction of the light goes over from yellow and orange to an increasingly red shade, the darkness of the black background brightens to blue, which increases and passes over to a milky white.

It had already become clear to Goethe in Italy that all colour-experience is based on a polarity, which he found expressed by painters as the contrast between 'cold' and 'warm' colours. Now that the *coming-into-being* of the blue of the sky and of the yellow of the sun had shown themselves to him as two processes of opposite character, he recognised in them the objective reason why both colours are subjectively experienced by us as opposites. 'Blue is illumined darkness – yellow is darkened light' – thus could he assert the ur-phenomenon, while he expressed the relation to Light of colours in their totality by saying: 'Colours are Deeds and Sufferings of Light.' With this, Goethe had taken the first decisive step towards his goal – the tracing of man's aesthetic experience to objective facts of nature.

If we use the expressions of preceding chapters, we can say that Goethe, in observing the colour ur-phenomenon, had succeeded in finding how from the primary polarity, Light – Dark, the opposition of the yellow and blue colours arises as a secondary polarity. For such an interplay of light and darkness, the existence of the air was seen to be a necessary condition, representing in the one case a lightening, in the other, a darkening element. That it was able to play this double role arose from its being on the one hand pervious to light, while yet possessing a certain sub-stantial density. For a medium of such a nature Goethe coined the expression *trübes Medium*.

There seems to be no suitable word in English for rendering the term *trübe* in the sense in which Goethe used it to denote the optical resistance of a more or less transparent medium. The following remarks of Goethe's, reported by his secretary Riemer, will give the reader a picture of what Goethe meant by this term, clear enough to allow us to use the German word. Goethe's explanation certainly shows how inadequate it is to translate *trübe* by 'cloudy' or 'semi-opaque' as commentators have done.

'Light and Dark have a common field, a space, a vacuum in which they are seen to appear. This space is the realm of the transparent. Just as the different colours are related to Light and Dark as their creative causes, so is their corporeal part, their medium, *Trübe*, related to the transparent. The first diminution of the transparent, i.e. the first slightest filling of space, the first disposition, as it were, to the corporeal, i.e. the non-transparent — this is *Trübe*.'[9]

After Goethe had once determined from the macrotelluric phenomenon that an interplay of light and darkness within *Trübe* was necessary for the appearance of colour in space, he had no doubt that prismatic colours, too, could be understood only through the coming together of all these three elements. It was now his task to examine in what way the prism, by its being *trübe*, brings light and darkness, or, as he also expressed it, light and shadow, into interplay, when they meet at a boundary.

We must remember that on first looking through the prism Goethe had immediately recognised that the appearance of colour is always dependent on the existence of a boundary between light and darkness — in other words, that it is a border phenomenon. What colours appear on such a border depends on the position of light and darkness in relation to the base of the prism. If the lighter part is nearer to the base, then blue and violet tints are seen at the border, and with the reverse position tints of yellow and red. Along this path of study Goethe found no reason for regarding the spectrum-phenomenon as complete only when both kinds of border-phenomena appear simultaneously (let alone when — as a result of the smallness of the aperture through which the light meets the prism — the two edges lie so close that a continuous band of colour arises). Hence we find Goethe — unlike Newton — treating the two ends of the spectrum as two separate phenomena.

In this way, the spectrum phenomenon gave Goethe confirmation that he had succeeded in expressing in a generally valid form the law of the origin of the blue and yellow colours, as he had read it from the heavens. For in the spectrum, too, where the colour blue appears, there he saw darkness being lightened by a shifting of the image of the border between light and dark in the direction of darkness; where yellow appears, he saw light being darkened by a shifting of the image in the direction of light.

In the colours adjoining these — indigo and violet on the blue side, orange and red on the yellow side — Goethe recognised 'heightened' modifications of blue and yellow. Thus he had learnt from the macrotelluric realm that with decreasing density of the corporeal medium, the blue sky takes on ever deeper tones, while with increasing density of the medium, the yellow of the sunlight passes over into orange and finally red. Prismatic phenomenon and macrotelluric phenomenon were seen to correspond in this direction, too.

Faithful to his question, 'How does colour arise?' Goethe now proceeded to investigate under what conditions two borders, when placed opposite each other, provide a continuous band of colour — that is, a colour-band where, in place of the region of uncoloured light, green appears. This, he observed, came about if one brought one's eye, or the screen intercepting the light, to that distance from the prism where the steadily widening yellow-red and the blue-violet colour-cones merge. Obviously, this distance can be altered by altering the distance between the two borders. In the case of an extremely narrow light-space, the blue and yellow edges will immediately overlap. Yet the emergence of the green colour will always be due to a union of the blue and yellow colours which spread from the two edges. This convinced Goethe that it is inadmissible to place the green in the spectrum in line with the other colours, as is customary in the explanation of the spectrum since Newton's time.

This insight into the relation of the central colour of the continuous spectrum to its other colours still further strengthened Goethe's conviction that in the way man experiences nature in his soul, objective laws of nature come to expression. For just as we experience the colours on the blue side of the spectrum as cold colours, and those on the yellow side as warm colours, so does green give man the impression of a neutral colour, influencing us in neither direction. And just as the experience of the two polar colour-ranges is an expression of the objective natural law behind them, so too is the experience of green, the objective conditions of whose origin give it a neutral position between the two. With this it also became clear to Goethe why the vegetative part of the plant organism, the region of leaf and stem formation, where the light of the sun enters into a living union with the density of earthly substance, *must* appear in a garment of green.

* * * * *

Having in this way traced the true genesis of the spectrum, Goethe could not fail to notice that it called for another – a 'negative' spectrum, its polar opposite – to make the half into a whole. For he who has once learnt that light and darkness are two equally essential factors in the birth of colour, and that the opposing of two borders of darkness so as to enclose a light is a 'derived' (*abgeleitet*) experimental arrangement, is naturally free to alter the arrangement and to supplement it by reversing the order of the two borders, thus letting two lights enclose a darkness between them.

If one exposes an arrangement like this to the action of the prism, whose position has remained unchanged, colours appear on each of the two edges, as before, but in reverse order. The spectral phenomenon now begins at one side with light blue and passes into indigo and violet, with uncoloured darkness in the centre. From this darkness it emerges through red and passes through orange to yellow at the other end.

Again, where the two interior colour-cones merge, there an additional colour appears. Like green, it is of a neutral character, but at the same time its quality is opposite to that of green. In Newtonian optics, which assumes colour to be derived from light only, this colour has naturally no existence. Yet in an optics which has learnt to reckon with both darkness and light as generators of colour, the complete spectrum phenomenon includes this colour equally with green. For lack of an existing proper name for it, Goethe termed it 'pure red' (since it was free from both the blue tinge of the mauve, and the yellow tinge of the red end of the ordinary spectrum), or 'peach-blossom' (*pfirsichblüt*), or 'purple' (as being nearest to the dye-stuff so called by the ancients after the mollusc from which it was obtained).[10]

It needs only a glance through the prism into the sunlit world to make one convinced of the natural appearing of this delicate and at the same time powerfully luminous colour. For a narrow dark object on a light field is a much commoner occurrence in nature than the enclosing by two broad objects of a narrow space of light, the condition necessary for the emergence of a continuous colour-band with green in the middle. In fact, the spectrum which science since the time of Newton regards as the only one, appears much more rarely among natural conditions than does Goethe's counter-spectrum.

With the peach-blossom a fresh proof is supplied that what man experiences in his soul is in harmony with the objective facts of nature. As with green, we experience peach-blossom as a colour that leaves us in equilibrium. With peach-blossom, however, the equilibrium is of a different kind, owing to the fact that it arises from the union of the colour-poles, not at their original stage but in their 'heightened' form. And so green, the colour of the plant-world harmony given by nature, stands over against 'purple', the colour of the human being striving towards harmony. By virtue of this quality, purple served from antiquity for the vesture of those who have reached the highest stage of human development for their time. This characteristic of the middle colours of the two spectra was expressed by Goethe when he called green 'real totality', and peach-blossom 'ideal totality'.

From this standpoint Goethe was able to smile at the Newtonians. He could say that if they persisted in asserting that the colourless, so-called 'white' light is composed of the seven colours of the ordinary spectrum — red, orange, yellow, green, blue, indigo, violet — then they were in duty bound to maintain also that the colourless, 'black' darkness is composed of the seven colours of the inverted spectrum — yellow, orange, red, purple, violet, indigo, blue.

Despite the convincing force of this argument, the voice of the Hans Andersen child speaking through Goethe failed to gain a hearing among the crowd of Newtonian faithful. So has it been up to the present-day — regardless of the fact that, as we have shown, modern physics has reached results which make a contradiction of the Newtonian concept of the mutual relation of light and colour no longer appear so heretical as it was in Goethe's time.

*   *   *   *   *

When we compare the way in which Goethe, on the one hand, and the physical scientist, on the other, have arrived at the truth that what Newton held to be 'discovery' was in actual fact 'manufacture', we find ourselves faced with another instance of a fact which we have encountered before in our study of electricity. It is the fact that a truth, which reveals itself to the spectator-scientist only as the result of a highly advanced experimental research, can be recognised through quite simple observation when this observation is carried out with the intention of letting the phenomena themselves speak for their 'theory'.

Furthermore, there is a corresponding difference in the effect the knowledge of such truth has on the human mind. In the field of electricity we saw that together with the scientist's recognition of the absolute qualities of the two polar forms of electricity a false semblance of reality was lent to the hypothesis of the atomic structure of matter. Something similar has occurred in the field of optics. Here, after having been forced to recognise the fallacy of Newton's theory, the spectator's mind has been driven to form a concept of the nature of light which is further than ever from the truth. For what then remains of light is — in Eddington's words — a 'quite irregular disturbance, with no tendency to periodicity', which means that to light is assigned the quality of an undefined chaos (in the negative sense of this word) sprung from pure chance. Moreover, as Eddington shows, the question whether the optical contrivance 'sorts out' from the chaotic light a particular periodicity, or whether it 'impresses' this on the light, becomes just 'a matter of expression'.[11]

No such conclusions are forced upon the one who studies the spectrum phenomenon with the eyes of Goethe. Like the modern experimenter, he, too, is faced with the question 'Discovery or Manufacture?' and he, too, finds the answer to be 'Manufacture'. But to him nature can disclose herself as the real manufacturer, showing him how she goes to work in bringing about the colours, because in following Goethe he is careful to arrange his observations in such a way that they do not veil nature's deeds.

Chapter XV

SEEING AS 'DEED' – I

Having made ourselves so far acquainted with the fundamentals of Goethe's approach to the outer phenomena of colour involved in the spectrum, we will leave this for a while to follow Goethe along another no less essential line of inquiry. It leads us to the study of our own process of sight, by means of which we grow aware of the optical facts in outer space.

* * * * *

The importance which Goethe himself saw in this aspect of the optical problem is shown by the place he gave it in the didactic part of his *Farbenlehre*.[1] The first three chapters, after the Introduction, are called 'Physiological Colours', 'Physical Colours', and 'Chemical Colours'. In the first chapter, Goethe summarises a group of phenomena which science calls 'subjective' colours, since their origin is traced to events within the organ of sight. The next chapter deals with an actual physics of colour — that is, with the appearance of colours in external space as a result of the refraction, diffraction and polarisation of light. The third chapter treats of material colours in relation to chemical and other influences. After two chapters which need not concern us here comes the sixth and last chapter, entitled 'Perceptual-Spiritual Effect of Colour' (*'Sinnlich-sittliche Wirkung der Farben'*), which crowns the whole. There, for the first time in the history of modern science, a bridge is built between Physics, Aesthetics and Ethics. We remember it was with this aim in view that Goethe had embarked upon his search for the solution of the problem of colour.

In this chapter the experiencing of the various colours and

their interplay through the human soul is treated in many aspects, and Goethe is able to show that what arises in man's consciousness as qualitative colour experience is nothing but a direct 'becoming-inward' of what is manifested to the 'reader's' eye and mind as the objective nature of colours. So, in one realm of the sense world, Goethe succeeded in closing the abyss which divides existence and consciousness, so long as the latter is restricted to a mere onlooker relationship towards the sense world.

If we ask what induced Goethe to treat the physiological colours before the physical colours, thus deviating so radically from the order of customary science, we shall find the answer in a passage from the Introduction to his *Entwurf*. Goethe, in giving his views on the connection between light and the eye, says: 'The eye owes its existence to light. Out of indifferent auxiliary animal organs the light calls forth an organ for itself, similar to its own nature; thus the eye is formed by the light, for the light, so that the inner light can meet the outer.' In a verse which reproduces in poetic form a thought originally expressed by Plotinus, Goethe sums up his idea of the creative connection between eye and light as follows:

> *Wär' nicht das Auge sonnenhaft,*
> *Wie könnten wir das Licht erblicken?*
> *Lebt' nicht in uns des Gottes eigne Kraft,*
> *Wie könnt' uns Göttliches entzücken?*

> Unless our eyes had something of the sun,
> How could we ever look upon the light?
> Unless there lived within us God's own might,
> How could the Godlike give us ecstasy?
> (Transl. Stawell-Dickinson)

By expressing himself in this way in the Introduction to his *Farbenlehre*, Goethe makes it clear from the outset that when he speaks of 'light' as the source of colour phenomena, he has in mind an idea of light very different from that held by modern physics. For in dealing with optics, physical science turns at once to phenomena of light found outside man — in fact to phenomena in that physical realm from which, as the lowest of the kingdoms of nature, the observations of natural science are bound to start. Along this path one is driven, as we have seen, to conceive of light as a mere 'disturbance' in the universe, a kind of irregular chaos.

In contrast to this, Goethe sees that to gain an explanation of natural physical phenomena which will be in accord with nature, we must approach them on the path by which nature brings them into being. In the field of light this path is one which leads from light as creative agent to light as mere phenomenon. The highest form of manifestation of creative light most directly resembling its *Idea* is within man. It is there that light creates for itself the organ through which, as manifest light, it eventually enters into human consciousness. To Goethe it was therefore clear that a theory of light, which is to proceed in accord with nature, should begin with a study of the eye: its properties, its ways of acting when it brings us information of light's deeds and sufferings in external nature.

The eye with its affinity to light comes into being in the apparently dark space of the mother's womb. This points to the possession by the human organism of an 'inner' light which first forms the eye from within, in order that it may afterwards meet the light outside. It is this inner light that Goethe makes the starting-point of his investigations, and it is for this reason that he treats physiological colours before physical colours.

*   *   *   *   *

Of fundamental significance as regards method is the way in which Goethe goes on from the passage quoted above to speak of the activity of the inner light: 'This immediate affinity between light and the eye will be denied by none; to consider them identical in substance is less easy to comprehend. It will be more intelligible to assert that a dormant light resides in the eye, and that this light can be excited by the slightest cause from within or from without. In darkness we can, by an effort of imagination, call up the brightest images; in dreams, objects appear to us as in broad daylight; if we are awake, the slightest external action of light is perceptible, and if the organ suffers a mechanical impact light and colours spring forth.'

What Goethe does here is nothing less than to follow the development of sight to where it has its true origin. Let us remember that a general source of illusion in the modern scientific picture of the world lies in the fact that the onlooker consciousness accepts itself as a self-contained ready-made entity, instead of tracing itself genetically to the state of consciousness from which it has developed in the course of evolution. In reality, the consciousness kindled by outer sense-perception was preceded by a dreaming consciousness, and this by a sleeping consciousness, both for the individual and for humanity as a whole. So, too, outer vision by means of the physical apparatus of the eye was preceded by an inner vision. In dreams we still experience this inner vision; we use it in the activity of our picture-forming imagination; and it plays continuously upon the process of external sight. Why we fail to notice this when using our eye in the ordinary way, is because of that dazzling process mentioned earlier in this book. Goethe's constant endeavour was not to become the victim of this blindness – that is, not to be led by daytime experience to forget the night-side of human life. The passage quoted from the Introduction to his *Farbenlehre* shows how, in all that he strove for, he kept this goal in view.

In the section of his *Farbenlehre* dealing with 'physiological colours', Goethe devotes by far the most space to the so-called 'after-images' which appear in the eye as the result of stimulation by external light, and persist for some little time. To create such an after-image in a simple way, one need only gaze at a brightly-lit window and then at a faintly lit wall of the room. The picture of the window appears there, but with the light-values reversed: the dark cross-bar appears as light, and the bright panes as dark.

In describing this phenomena Goethe first gives the usual explanation, that the part of the retina which was exposed to the

light from the window-panes gets tired, and is therefore blunted
for further impressions, whereas the part on which the image of
the dark frame fell is rested, and so is more sensitive to the uniform impression of the wall. Goethe, however, at once adds that
although this explanation may seem adequate for this special
instance, there are other phenomena which can be accounted for
only if they are held to derive from a 'higher source'. Goethe
means experiences with coloured after-images. This will be confirmed by our own discussion of the subject.

What we first need, however, is a closer insight into the physiological process in the eye which causes the after-images as such.
Wherever Goethe speaks of a simple activity of the retina, we are
in fact concerned with a co-operation of the retina with other
parts of our organ of sight. In order to make this clear, let us
consider how the eye adapts itself to varying conditions of light
and darkness.

It is well known that if the eye has become adjusted to darkness it is dazzled if suddenly exposed to light, even though the
light be of no more than quite ordinary brightness. Here we enter
a border region where the seeing process begins to pass over into
a pathological condition.[2] A 'secret' of the effect of light on the
eye is here revealed which remains hidden in ordinary vision, for
normally the different forces working together in the eye hold
each other in balance, so that none is able to manifest separately.
This equilibrium is disturbed, however, when we suddenly expose
the eye to light while it is adapted to darkness. The light then
acts on the eye in its usual way, but without the immediate
counteraction which normally restores the balance. Under these
conditions we notice that the sudden dazzling has a painful
influence on the eye — that is, an influence in some way destructive. This will not seem surprising if we remember that when
light strikes on the background of the eye, consciousness is quick-
ened, and this, as we know, presupposes a breaking down of
substance in some part of the nervous system. Such a process
does in fact occur in the retina, the nerve-part of the eye, when
external light falls upon it. If the eye were solely a structure of

nerves, it would be so far destroyed by the impact of light that it could not be restored even by sleep, as are the more inward parts of the nervous system. But the eye receives also a flow of blood, and we know that throughout the threefold human organism the blood supplies the nervous system with building-up forces, polarically opposite to the destructive ones. In sleep, as we have already seen, the interruption of consciousness allows the blood to inundate the nervous system, as it were, with its healing, building-up acitivity. It is not necessary, however, for the whole of the body to pass into a condition of sleep before this activity can occur. It functions to some extent also in the waking state, especially in those parts of the organism which, like the eye, serve in the highest degree the unfolding of consciousness.

Having established this, we have a basis for an understanding of the complete process of vision. We see that it is by no means solely the nerve part of the eye which is responsible for vision, as the spectator-physiology was bound to imagine. The very fact that the place where the optic nerve enters the eye is blind indicates that the function of mediating sight cannot be ascribed to the nerve alone. What we call 'seeing' is far more the result of an interplay between the retina carrying the nerves, and the choroid carrying the blood-vessels. In this interplay the nerves are the passive, receptive organ for the inworking of external light, while the blood-activity comes to meet the nerve-process with a precisely correlated action. In this action we find what Goethe called 'inner light'.

The process involved in adaptation now becomes comprehensible. The cause of the dazzling effect of light of normal intensity on an eye adapted to the dark, is that in such an eye the blood is in a state of rest, and this prevents it from exercising quickly enough the necessary counteraction to the influence of the light. A corresponding effect occurs when one suddenly exposes to darkness the eye adapted to light. One can easily observe what goes on then, if, after looking for a time at an undifferentiated light surface such as the evenly luminous sky, one covers the opened eyes with the hollowed hands. It will then be found that the space before the eyes is filled by a sort of white light, and by paying close attention one recognises that it streams from the eyes out into the hollowed space. It may even be several minutes before the field of vision really appears black, that is, before the activity of the inner light in the choroid has so far died away that equilibrium prevails between the non-stimulated nerves and the non-stimulated blood.

With this insight into the twofold nature of the process of vision we are now able to describe more fully the negative after-image. Although in this case, as Goethe himself remarked, the ordinary explanation seems to suffice, yet in view of our later studies it may be well to bring forward here this wider conception.

On the basis of our present findings it is no longer enough to trace the appearing of the after-image solely to a differential fatigue in the retina. The fact is that as long as the eye is turned to the bright window-pane a more intensive blood-activity occurs in the portions of the eye's background met by the light than in those where the dark window-bar throws its shadow on the retina. If the eye so influenced is then directed to the faintly illumined wall of the room, the difference in the activity of the blood persists for some time. Hence in the parts of the eye adapted to darkness we experience the faint brightness as strongly luminous, even dazzling, whereas in the parts more adapted to light we feel the same degree of brightness to be dark. That the action of the inner light is responsible for the differences becomes clear if, while the negative after-image is still visible, we darken the eye with the hollowed hands. Then at once in the dark field of vision the positive facsimile of the window appears, woven by the activity of the blood which reproduces the outer reality.

* * * * *

Having traced the colourless after-image to 'higher sources' — that is, to the action of the inner light — let us now examine coloured after-images.

Just as the simple light-dark after-image shows a reversal of light-values in relation to the external picture, so in the coloured after-images there is a quite definite and opposite relationship of their colours to those of the original picture. Thus, if the eyes are exposed for some time to an impression of the colour red, and then directed to a neutral surface, not too brightly illuminated, one sees it covered with a glimmering green. In this way there is a reciprocal correspondence between the colour pairs Red/Green, Yellow/Violet, Blue/Orange. To whichever of these six colours one exposes the eye, its contrast colour always appears as after-image, thereby forming a pair of opposites.

We must here briefly recall how this phenomenon is generally explained on Newtonian lines. The starting-point is the assumption that the eye becomes fatigued by gazing at the colour and gradually becomes insensitive to it. According to Newton's theory, if an eye thus affected looks at a white surface, the sum of all the colours comes from there to meet it, while the eye has a reduced sensitivity to the particular colour it has been gazing at. And so among the totality of colours constituting the 'white' light, this one is more or less non-existent for the eye. The remaining colours are then believed to cause the contrasting colour-impression.

Goethe's view of the appearance of the contrast-colours in the after-images was of a different make. Nature outside man had taught him that life on all levels takes its course in a perpetual interplay of opposites, manifested externally in an interplay of diastole and systole comparable to the process of breathing. He, therefore, traced the interchange of light-values in colourless after-images to a 'silent resistance which every vital principle is forced to exhibit when some definite condition is presented to it. Thus, inhalation presupposes exhalation; thus every systole, its diastole. When darkness is presented to the eye, the eye demands brightness, and vice versa: it reveals its vital energy, its fitness to grasp the object, precisely by bringing forth out of itself something contrary to the object.' He summarises his reflections on coloured after-images and their reversals of colour in these words: 'The eye demands actual completeness and closes the colour-circle in itself.'

In order to bring Goethe's views to our immediate experience, we need only to expose the eyes for some time to an intense light, and then darken them for a similar period. Nothing in external nature resembles in beauty and radiance the play of colour which then arises, unless it be the colour phenomenon of the rainbow under exceptionally favourable circumstances.

The physiological process which comes to consciousness in this way as an experience of vision is exactly the same as the process which gives us experiences of vision in dreams. There is indeed evidence that when one awakens in a brightly lit room out of vivid dreaming, one feels less dazzled than on waking from dreamless sleep. This indicates that in dream vision the blood in the eye is active, just as it is in waking vision. The only difference is that in waking consciousness the stimulus reaches the blood from outside, through the eye, whereas in dreams it comes from causes within the organism. The nature of these causes does not concern us here; it will be dealt with later. For the moment it suffices to establish the fact that our organism is supplied with a definite activity of forces which we experience as the appearance of certain images of vision, no matter from which side the stimulus comes. All vision, physiologically considered, is of the nature of dream vision; that is to say, *we owe our day-waking sight to the fact that we are able to encounter the pictures of the outer world, brought to us by the light, with a dreaming of the corresponding after-images.*

It follows that the appearance of the contrast-colour in the field of vision is not, as the Newtonian theory asserts, the result of fatigue, but of an intensified activity of the eye, which continues even after the colour impression which gave rise to it has ceased. What is seen on the neutral surface (it will be shown later why we studiously avoid speaking of 'white light') is no outwardly existing colour at all. It is the activity of the eye itself, working in a dreamlike way from its blood-vessel system, and coming to our consciousness by this means. Here again, just as in the simple opposition of light and dark, the perception of coloured after-images is connected with a breaking-down process in the nerve region of the eye, and a corresponding building-up activity coming from the blood. Only in this case the eye is not affected by simple light, but by light of a definite colouring. The specific destructive process caused by this light is answered with a specific building-up process by the blood. Under certain conditions we can become dreamily aware of this process which normally does not enter our consciousness. In such a case we see the contrasting colour as coloured after-image.

Only by representing the process in this way do we do justice to a fact which completely eludes the onlooker-consciousness – namely, that the eye produces the contrasting colour even while it is still exposed to the influence of the outer colour. Since this is so, all colours appearing to us in ordinary vision are already tinged by the subdued light of the opposite colour, produced by the eye itself. One can easily convince oneself of this through the following experiment. Instead of directing the eye, after it has been exposed to a certain colour, to a neutral surface, as previously, gaze at the appropriate contrasting colour. (The first and second coloured surfaces should be so arranged that the former is considerably smaller than the latter.) Then, in the middle of the second surface (and in a field about the size of the first), its own colour appears, with a strikingly heightened intensity.

Here we find the eye producing, as usual, a contrast-colour from out of itself, as an after-image, even while its gaze is fixed on the same colour in the outer world. The heightened brilliance within the given field is due to the addition of the after-image colour to the external colour.

The reader may wonder why this phenomenon is not immediately adduced as a decisive proof of the fallacy of the whole Newtonian theory of the relation of 'white' light to the various colours. Although it does in fact offer such a proof, we have good reason for not making this use of it here. Throughout this book it is never our intention to enter into a contest of explanations, or to defeat one explanation by another. How little this would help will be obvious if we realise that research was certainly not ignorant of the fact that the opposite colour arises even when the

eye is not turned to a white surface. In spite of this, science did
not feel its concept of white light as the sum of all the colours
to be an error, since it has succeeded in 'explaining' this phenomenon too, and fitting it into the prevailing theory. To do so is
in thorough accord with spectator-thinking. Our own concern,
however, as in all earlier cases, is to replace this thinking with all
its 'proofs' and 'explanations' by learning to *read* in the phenomena themselves. For no other purpose than this the following
facts also are now brought forward.

* * * * *

Besides Rudolf Steiner's fundamental insight into the spiritual-
physical nature of the growing human being, through which he
laid the basis of a true art of education, he gave advice on many
practical points. For example, he indicated how by the choice
of a suitable colour environment one can bring a harmonising
influence to bear on extremes of temperament in little children.
Today it is a matter of practical experience that excitable children
are quietened if they are surrounded with red or red-yellow
colours, or wear clothes of these colours, whereas inactive, lethargic
children are roused to inner movement if they are exposed to the
influence of blue or blue-green colours.

This psychological reaction of children to colour is not surprising if one knows the role played by the blood in the process
of seeing, and how differently the soul life of man is connected
with the blood-nerve polarity of his organism in childhood and in
later life. What we have described as the polar interplay of blood
and nerve in the act of sight is not confined to the narrow field
of the eye. Just as the nerve processes arising in the retina are
continued to the optic centre in the cerebrum, so must we look
for the origin of the corresponding blood process not in the
choroid itself, but in the lower regions of the organism. Wherever,
therefore, the colour red influences the whole nerve system, the
blood system as a whole answers with an activity of the metabolism corresponding to the contrasting colour, green. Similarly

it reacts as a whole to a blue-violet affecting the nerve system, this time with a production corresponding to yellow-orange.

The reason why in later years we notice this so little lies in a fact we have repeatedly encountered. The consciousness of the grown man today, through its one-sided attachment to the death-processes in the nerve region, pays no attention to its connection with the life-processes centred in the blood system. In this respect the condition of the little child is quite different. Just as the child is more asleep in its nerve system than the grown-up person, it is more awake in its blood system. Hence in all sense-perceptions a child is not so much aware of how the world works on its nerve system as how its blood system responds. And so a child in a red environment feels quietened because it experiences, though dimly, how its whole blood system is stimulated to the green production; bluish colours enliven it because it feels its blood answer with a production of light yellowish tones.

From these latter phenomena we see once more the significance of Goethe's arrangement of his *Farbenlehre*. For we are now able to realise that to turn one's attention to the deeds and sufferings of the *inner* light means nothing less than to bring to consciousness the processes of vision which in childhood, though in a dreamlike way, determine the soul's experience of seeing. Through placing his examination of the physiological colours at the beginning of his *Farbenlehre*, Goethe actually took the path in scientific research to which Thomas Reid pointed in philosophy. By adapting Reid's words we can say that Goethe, in his *Farbenlehre*, proclaims as a basic principle of a true Optics: that we must become again as little children if we would reach a philosophy of light and colours.

*   *   *   *   *

As the following quotation will show, Reid himself uttered thoughts — and so did Ruskin in his own way — about the eye and the outer action of the light that are quite close to Goethe's.

In his *Inquiry*, at the beginning of his review of visual

perceptions, Reid says:

'The structure of the eye, and of all its appurtenances, the admirable contrivances of nature for performing all its various external and internal motions and the variety in the eyes of different animals, suited to their several natures and ways of life, clearly demonstrate this organ to be a masterpiece of nature's work. And he must be very ignorant of what hath been discovered about it, or have a very strange cast of understanding, who can seriously doubt, whether or not *the rays of light and the eye were made for one another with consummate wisdom, and perfect skill in optics.*'[3]

The following passage from Ruskin's *Ethics of the Dust* (Lecture X) brings out his criticism of the scientific way of treating of optical phenomena:

'With regard to the most interesting of all their [the philosophers'] modes of force — light; they never consider how far the existence of it depends on the putting of certain vitreous and nervous substances into the formal arrangement which they call "eye". The German philosophers began the attack, long ago, on the other side, by telling us there was no such thing as light at all, unless we choose to see it.[4] Now, German and English, both, have reversed their engines, and insist that light would be exactly the same light that it is, though nobody could ever see it. The fact being that the force must be there, and the eye there, and light means the effect of the one on the other — and perhaps, also — (Plato saw farther into that mystery than anyone has since, that I know of) — on something a little way within the eyes.'

Remarks like these, and the further quotation given below, make it seem particularly tragic that Ruskin apparently had no knowledge of Goethe's *Farbenlehre*. This is the more remarkable in view of the significance which Turner, with whom Ruskin stood in such close connection, ascribed to it from the standpoint of the artist. For the way in which Ruskin in his *Modern Painters* speaks of the effect of the modern scientific concept of colours upon the ethical-religious feeling of man, shows that he deplores the lack of just what Goethe had long since achieved in his

Farbenlehre where starting with purely physical observations, he had been able to develop from them a 'physical-moral' theory of colour.

Ruskin's alertness to the effect on ethical life of a scientific world-picture empty of all qualitative values led him to write:

'It is in raising us from the first state of inactive reverie to the second of useful thought, that scientific pursuits are to be chiefly praised. But in restraining us at this second stage, and checking the impulses towards higher contemplation, they are to be feared or blamed. They may in certain minds be consistent with such contemplation, but only by an effort; in their nature they are always adverse to it, having a tendency to chill and subdue the feelings, and to resolve all things into atoms and numbers. For most men, an ignorant enjoyment is better than an informed one, it is better to conceive the sky as a blue dome than a dark cavity, and the cloud as a golden throne than a sleety mist. I much question whether anyone who knows optics, however religious he may be, can feel in equal degree the pleasure and reverence an unlettered peasant may feel at the sight of a rainbow.' [5]

Chapter XVI

SEEING AS 'DEED' – II

The observation of our own visual process, which we began in the last chapter, will serve now to free us from a series of unreal concepts which have been connected by the onlooker-consciousness with the phenomena brought about by light, and to replace them with concepts taught by the phenomena themselves.

There is first the general assumption that light as such is visible. In order to realise that light is itself an invisible agent, we need only consider a few self-evident facts – for instance, that for visibility to arise light must always encounter some material resistance in space. This is, in fact, an encounter between light, typifying levity, and the density of the material world, typifying gravity. Accordingly, wherever visible colours appear we have to do with light meeting its opposite.

Optics, therefore, as a science of the physically perceptible is never concerned with light alone, but always with light and its opposite together. This is actually referred to in Ruskin's statement, quoted in the last chapter, where he speaks of the need of the 'force' and of the intercepting bodily organ before a science of optics can come into existence. Ruskin's 'light', however, is what we have learnt with Goethe to call 'colour', whereas that for which we reserve the term 'light' is called by him simply 'force'.

All this shows how fallacious it is to speak of 'white' light as synonymous with plain light, in distinction to 'coloured' light. And yet this has been customary with scientists from the time of Newton until today, not excluding Newton's critic, Eddington. White, as a content of visual perception belongs to the phenomenal world, and is therefore properly characterised as a colour. This is, therefore, how Goethe spoke of it. We shall see presently the special position of white (and likewise of black), as a colour among colours. What matters first of all is to realise that white must be strictly differentiated from light as such, for the function of light is to make visible the material world without itself being visible.

To say that light is invisible, however, does not mean that it is wholly imperceptible. It is difficult to bring the perception of light into consciousness, for naturally our attention, when we look out into light-filled space, is claimed by the objects of the illuminated world, in all their manifold colours and forms. Nevertheless the effect of pure light on our consciousness can be observed – during a railway journey, for instance, when we leave a tunnel that has been long enough to bring about a complete adaptation of the eyes to the prevailing darkness. Then, in the first moments of the lightening of the field of vision, and before any separate objects catch the attention, we can notice how the light itself exercises a distinctly expanding influence on our consciousness. We feel how the light calls on the consciousness to participate, as it were, in the world outside the body.

It is possible also to perceive directly the opposite of light. This is easier than the direct perception of light, for in the dark one is not distracted by the sight of surrounding objects. One need only pay attention to the fact that, after a complete adapting of the eyes to the dark, one still retains a distinct experience of the extension of the field of vision of both eyes. We find here, just as in the case of light, that our will is engaged within the eye in a definite way; a systolic effect proceeds from dark, a diastolic effect from light. We have a distinct perception of both, but not of anything 'visible' in the ordinary sense.

With regard to our visual experience of white and black, it is quite different. We are concerned here with definite conditions of corporeal surfaces, just as with other colours, although the conditions conveying the impressions of white or black are of a special character. A closer inspection of these conditions reveals a property of our act of seeing which has completely escaped scientific observation, but which is of fundamental importance for the understanding of optical phenomena dynamically.

It is well-known that a corporeal surface, which we experience as white, has the characteristic of throwing back practically all the light that strikes it, whereas light is more or less completely absorbed by a surface which we experience as black. Such extreme forms of interplay between light and a corporeal surface, however, do not only occur when the light has no particular colour, but also when a coloured surface is struck by light of the same or opposite colour. In the first instance complete reflection takes place; in the second, complete absorption. And both these effects are registered by the eye in precisely the same manner as those mentioned before. For example, a red surface in red light looks simply white; a green surface in red light looks black.

The usual interpretation of this phenomenon, namely, that it consists in a subjective 'contrast' impression of the eye — a red surface in red light looking brighter, a green surface darker, than its surroundings, and thereby causing the illusion of white or black — is a typical onlooker-interpretation against which there stands the evidence of unprejudiced observation. The reality of the 'white' and the 'black' seen in such cases is so striking that a person who has not seen the colours of the objects in ordinary light can hardly be persuaded to believe that they are not 'really' white or black. The fact is that the white and the black that are seen under these conditions are just as real as 'ordinary' white and black. When in either instance the eye registers 'white' it registers exactly the same event, namely, the total reflection of the light by the surface struck by it. Again, when the eye registers 'black' in both cases it registers an identical process, namely, total absorption of the light.[1]

Seen thus, the phenomenon informs us of the significant fact that our eye is not at all concerned with the colour of the light that enters its own cavity, but rather with what happens between the light and the surface on which the light falls. In other words, the phenomenon shows that *our process of seeing is not confined to the bodily organ of the eye, but extends into outer space to the point where we experience the visible object to be.*[2]

* * * * *

This picture of the visual process, to which we have been led here by simple optical observation, was reached by Thomas Reid through his own experience of how, in the act of perceiving the world, man is linked intuitively with it. We remember that he intended in his philosophy to carry *ad absurdum* the hypothesis that 'the images of the external objects are conveyed by the organs of sense to the brain and are there perceived by the mind'. Common Sense makes Reid speak as follows: 'If any man will shew how the mind may perceive images of the brain, I will undertake to shew how it may perceive the most distant objects; for if we give eyes to the mind, to perceive what is transacted at home in its dark chamber, why may we not make the eyes a little longer-sighted? And then we shall have no occasion for that unphilosophical fiction of images in the brain.' (*Inq.*, VI, 12.) Reid proceeds to show this by pointing out, first, that we must only use the idea of 'image' for truly visual perceptions; secondly, that the sole place of this image is the background of the eye, and not any part of the nervous system lying beyond; thirdly, that even this retina-image, as such, does not come to our consciousness, but serves only to direct the consciousness to the cause of the image, namely, the external object itself. In what follows we shall deal with an observation which will show how right Reid was in this respect.

* * * * *

Those familiar with this observation (well-known indeed to those living in hilly and mountainous districts) know that when distant features of the landscape, in an otherwise clear and sunlit atmosphere, suddenly seem almost near enough to touch, rainy weather is approaching. Likewise a conspicuous increase in distance, while the sky is still overcast, foreshadows fine weather.

This effect (the customary 'explanation' of which is, as usual, of no avail to us and so need not concern us here) ranks with phenomena described in optics under the name of 'apparent optical depth', a subject we shall discuss more fully in the next chapter. It suffices here to state that it is the higher degree of humidity which, by lending the atmosphere greater optical density, without changing its clarity, makes distant objects seem to be closer to the eye, and vice versa. If we could substitute for the air a much lighter gas — say, hydrogen — then the things we see through it would look farther off than they ever do in our atmosphere.

This observation tells us the following about the process of vision.

We see the surrounding world always through a medium of some density. Through this medium the light carries towards us the images of the corporeal content of that world. When this external light strikes the retina of our eye, our inner light is stimulated to move out of the eye towards it; in pressing outward, this inner light meets with a certain resistance, and the extent of this determines at what distance from the eye our visual ray comes to rest as the result of a kind of exhaustion. Just as the outer light reaches an inner boundary at our retina, so does the inner light meet with an outer boundary, set by the optical density of the medium spread out before the eye. Outer and inner light interpenetrate each other along the whole tract between these two boundaries, but normally we are not conscious of this process. We first become conscious of it where our active gaze — that is, the inner light sent forth through the eye — reaches the limit of its activity. At that point we become aware of the object of our gaze. So here we find confirmed a fact noted earlier, that consciousness — at least at its present state of evolution — arises where for some reason or other our volition comes to rest.

* * * * *

The foregoing observations have served, first of all, to awaken us in a preliminary way to the fact that an essential part of our act of seeing takes place outside our bodily organ of vision and that our visual experience is determined by what happens out there between our gaze and the medium it has to penetrate. Our next task will be to find out how this part of our visual activity is affected by the properties of the different colours. We shall thereby gain a further insight into the nature of the polarity underlying all colour-phenomena, and this again will enable us to move a step further towards becoming conscious of what happens in our act of seeing.

We shall start by observing what happens to the two sides of the colour-scale when the optical medium assumes various degrees of density.

For the sky to appear blue by day a certain purity of the atmosphere is needed. The more veiled the atmosphere becomes the more the blue of the sky turns towards white; the purer and rarer the atmosphere, the deeper the blue, gradually approaching black. To mountain climbers and those who fly at great heights it is a familiar experience to see the sky assume a deep indigo hue, and recent observations have shown that further up the colour of the sky passes over into violet and ultimately into pure black. Thus in the case of blue the field of vision owes its darkening to a decrease in the resistance by which the visual ray of our gaze is met in the optical medium. It is precisely the opposite with yellow. For here, as the density of the medium increases, the colour-effect grows darker by yellow darkening first to orange and then to red, until finally it passes over into complete darkness.

This shows that our visual ray is subject to entirely different dynamic effects at the two poles of the colour-scale. At the blue pole, the lightness-effect springs from the resistant medium through which we gaze, a medium under the influence of gravity, while the darkness is provided by the anti-gravity quality of cosmic space, which as a 'negative' resistance exercises a suction on the eye's inner light. At the yellow pole it is just the reverse. Here, the resistant medium brings about a darkening of our field of vision, while the lightness-effect springs from a direct meeting of the eye with light, and so with the suctional effect of negative density.

Our pursuit of the dynamic causes underlying our apperception of the two poles of the colour-scale has led us to a point where it becomes necessary to introduce certain new terms to enable us to go beyond Goethe's general distinction between *Finsternis* (darkness) and *Licht* (light). Following Goethe, we have so far used these two terms for what appears both in blue and yellow as the respective light and dark ingredients. This distinction cannot satisfy us any more. For through our last observations it has become clear that the *Finsternis* in blue and the *Licht* in yellow are opposites only in appearance, because they are both caused by Levity, and similarly that the lightening effect in blue and the darkening effect in yellow are both effected by Gravity. Therefore, to distinguish between what appertains to the primary polarity, Levity-Gravity, on the one hand, and their visible effects on the secondary polarity of the colours, on the other, we shall henceforth reserve the term *darkness* and, with it, *lightness* for instances where the perceptible components of the respective colours are concerned, while speaking of *Dark* and *Light* where reference is made to the generating primary polarity.

* * * * *

If we are justified in thus tracing the colour-polarity to a polarically ordered interplay between levity and gravity, we may then pursue the following line of thought. We know from earlier considerations that wherever such an interplay between the poles of the primary polarity takes place, we have to do, in geometric terms, with the polarity of sphere and radius. We may therefore conclude that the same characteristics will apply to the way in which the blue of the sky and the yellow of the sunlight are encountered spatially. Now we need only observe how the blue heavens arch over us spherically, on the one hand, and how the yellow brightness of the sun penetrates the air raywise, on the other, in order to realise that this really is so.

Having thus established the connection of the two poles of the colour-scale with the spherical and radial structure of space, we are now able to express the dynamic of the ur-phenomenon more distinctly than Goethe could do it. On the one hand, we see the blue of the heavens emerging when levity is drawn down by gravity from its primal invisibility into spherically orientated manifestation. In the yellow of the sunlight, on the other hand, we see gravity, under the influence of the sun's levity, gleaming up radially into visibility. The aspect of the two colour-poles which thus arises before us prompts us to replace Goethe's 'lightened Dark' by *Earthward-dawning-Levity*, and his 'darkened Light' by *Heavenward-raying-Gravity*.

* * * * *

We have now to show that this picture of the dynamic relationship which underlies the appearance of the colour-polarity in the sky is valid also for other cases which are instances of the ur-phenomenon of the generation of colour in Goethe's sense, but seem not to lend themselves to the same cosmic interpretation. Such a case is the appearance of yellow and blue when we look through a clouded transparent medium towards a source of light or to a black background. There is no special difficulty here in bringing the appearance of yellow into line with its macrotelluric counterpart, but the appearance of blue requires some consideration.

We have seen that a corporeal surface appears as black if light striking it is totally absorbed by it. Thus, wherever our eye is met by the colour black, our visual ray is engaged in a process whereby light disappears from physical space. Now we need only bring this process into consciousness – as we have tried to do before in similar instances – to realise that what happens here to the visual ray is something similar to what it undergoes when it is directed from the earth into cosmic space.

Note, in this respect, the principle of the mirror as another instance of the fact that the interplay between light and an illumined surface can have on the visual ray an effect similar to that of external space. For the optical processes which occur on the surface of a mirror are such that, whilst taking place on a two-dimensional plane, they evoke in our consciousness pictures of exactly the same nature as if we were looking through the mirror into the space behind it.[3]

* * * * *

Our picture of the colour-polarity receives further confirmation if we observe how natural phenomena based on the same kind of polarity in other realms of nature fit in with it. We remember that one of Goethe's starting-points in his investigation of the riddle of colour was the observation that of the totality of colours one part is experienced as 'warm' and the other as 'cold'. Now we can go further and say that the colours of the spherical pole are experienced as cold, those of the radial pole as warm. This corresponds precisely to the polarity of snow-formation and volcanic activity. The former, being the spherically directed process, requires physically low temperatures; the latter, being the radially directed process, requires high temperatures. Here, once more, we see with what objectivity the human senses register the facts of the outer world.

Another realm of phenomena based on a similar polar order is that of electricity. When we studied the negative and positive poles of the vacuum tube, with regard to the polar distribution of radius and sphere, we hinted at the colours appearing on the two electrodes — red at the (positive) anode, blue at the (negative) cathode. Again we find a coincidence with the natural order of the colours.

Note how the qualitative dynamic method employed here brings into direct view the relationship between light and electricity, while it precludes the mistake of tracing light processes to those of electricity, as modern science does. Nor are electric processes 'explained' from this point of view merely as variations of light processes. Rather is the relation between light and electricity seen to be based on the fact that all polarities arising perceptibly in nature are creations of the same primeval polarity, that of Levity and Gravity. The interplay of Levity and Gravity can take on many different forms which are distinguished essentially by differences in cosmic age. Thus the colour-polarity in its primal form, made manifest by the heavens, differs as much from the corresponding polarity shown by the vacuum tube, as does the lightning in the heights from the electric spark.

* * * * *

With the aid of what we have learnt here concerning outer light-processes we shall turn once more to the activity of our own inner light.

We may expect by now that our eye is fitted with two modes of seeing activity, polar to each other, and that the way in which they come into operation depends on whether the interplay of positive and negative density outside the eye leads to the appearance of the blue-violet or the yellow-red side of the colour-scale. Such a polarity in the activity of the eye can indeed be established. Along with it goes a significant functional difference between the two eyes, not unlike that shown in the two hands.

To observe this we need simply to compare the two eyes of a person in a photograph by covering alternately the right and the left half of the face. Nearly always it will be found that the right eye looks out clearly into the world with an active expression, and the left eye with a much gentler one, almost held back. Artists are well aware of this asymmetry, as of others in the human countenance, and are careful to depict it. An outstanding example is Raphael's Sistine Madonna, where in the eyes and whole countenance both of Mother and Child this asymmetry can be studied in a specially impressive way.

Inner observation leads to a corresponding experience. A convenient method is to exercise the two eyes in complete darkness, in the following way. One eye is made to look actively into the space in front of it, as if it would pierce the darkness with its visual ray, while the activity of the other eye is held back, so that its gaze rests only superficially, as it were, on the darkness in front of it. Experience shows that most people find it natural to give the active note to the right eye, and the passive note to the left.

Once one has grown conscious of this natural difference between the two eyes, it is quite easily detected while one is looking normally into the light-filled environment. We thereby realise that for the two eyes to act differently in this way is the usual thing.

As an instance where this fact is well observed and effectively made use of, that of shooting may be mentioned here, especially shooting at flying game. Those who train in this sport learn to make a completely different use of the two eyes in sighting the target. The naturally more active eye — only once in about fifty cases is it the left — is called by them the 'master-eye'. Whilst the less actively gazing eye is usually employed for surveying the field as a whole into which the target is expected to enter, the master-eye is used for making active contact with the target itself ('throwing' oneself on the target 'through' the eye).

One further observation may be added. If one looks with rested eyes and in very faint daylight (perhaps in the early morning on awakening) at a white surface, while opening and closing the eyes alternately, then the white surface looks faintly reddish to the 'master-eye', and faintly bluish to the other.

* * * * *

Following the lines of our treatment of after-images in the last chapter, we will next inquire into the anatomical and physiological basis of the two opposite sight-activities. In the previous instance we found this in the polarity of nerve and blood. This time we must look for it in a certain twofold structure of the eye itself. We shall best perceive this by watching the 'becoming' of the eye, thus again following a method first shown by Goethe.

Fig. 14 shows the human eye in different stages of its embryonic formation. The eye is clearly seen to consist of two parts essentially different in origin. Growing out from the interior of the embryonic organism is a structure that is gradually pushed in, and in its further development becomes the entire posterior part of the eye, destined to carry its life-imbued functions. A second independent part grows towards this from outside; this

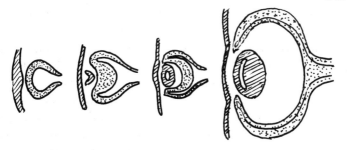

Fig. 14

is at first a mere thickening of the embryonic skin formation, but later it loosens itself and presses forward into the interior of the cup-shaped structure. It is gradually enclosed by this and evolves finally into that part of the finished eye which embodies the optical apparatus functioning according to purely physical laws.

This series of forms shows that in the embryonic formation of the eye we are confronted with two processes, one of spherical, and the other of radial orientation. Consequently the two parts of the eye are differentiated in such a way that the posterior part, which has grown forth radially from the embryonic organism, as the life-filled element represents the *sulphur*-pole of the total eye, while the anterior part, with its much more crystalline nature, having grown spherically towards the organism, represents the eye's *salt*-pole.

Closer inspection into the connection of the two visual activities of the eye with its basic corporeal parts reveals that here, at the outermost boundary of the human organism, we encounter once more that peculiar reversal of functions which we have already several times met in various realms of nature. For the anterior part of the eye – its salt-pole – which has come into being through a spherically directed formative process, seems to be the one through which we exercise the perceptive activity streaming out radially from the eye, whilst the posterior part – the eye's sulphur-pole – which has come into being through radially directed formative action, serves that form of seeing which is more receptive and is carried out in a plane-wise manner.

Considerations of this kind, and they alone, enable us also to draw true comparison between the different sense-organs. Take the organ of hearing. Usually the ear is assumed to fill the same role in the field of hearing as does the eye in the field of seeing. In fact the ear corresponds to only one half of the eye; the other half must be looked for in the larynx. In other words, the two parts of the eye are represented in the realm of hearing by two separate organs, ear and larynx. Speaking from the aspect of metamorphosis, the vital part of our eye may be regarded as our 'light-ear'; the crystalline part, as our 'light-larynx'. In order to come consciously to a perception of sight we must 'listen' to the 'deeds and sufferings' of light, while at the same time we meet them with the help of the 'speaking' of our inner light. Something similar holds good for hearing. In fact, observation reveals that we take in no impression of hearing unless we accompany it with an activity of our larynx, even though a silent one.

* * * * *

Our insight into the polar nature of visual activity will enable us now to link the external interplay of Light and Dark — to which the physical colours owe their existence — to that play of forces which we ourselves set in motion when our eye meets the world of colours in their polar differentiation.

We established earlier that in the cold colours the role of darkness belongs to the pole of levity or negative density, and the role of lightness to the pole of gravity or positive density, whereas in the case of the warm colours the roles are reversed. Let us now unite with this the insight we have meanwhile gained into the two kinds of activity in seeing — the receptive, 'left-eyed' and the radiating, 'right-eyed' — which mediate to us the experience of the positive or negative density of space spread out before our eyes. Taking together the results of outer and inner observation, we can express the polarity ruling in the realm of colour as follows:

If lightness and darkness, as elements of colour, meet us in such a way that lightness, by reason of its positive density, calls forth 'left-eyed' activity, and darkness, by reason of its negative density, 'right-eyed' activity, then our soul receives the impression of the colour blue and colours related to blue. If lightness and darkness meet us so that we see the former in a 'right-eyed', and the latter in a 'left-eyed' way, then we experience this as the presence of yellow and the colours related to it.

The reason why we usually fail to observe the different kinds of interplay of the two modes of seeing, when we perceive one or other of the two categories of colour, is because in ordinary sight both eyes exercise each of the two activities without our becoming aware which is the leading one in a particular eye. If, however, one has come to a real experience of the inner polarity of the visual act, one needs only a little practice to realise the distinction. For example, if one looks at the blue sky, notably at noon-time, on the side away from the sun, or at the morning or evening sky, shining yellow and red, one quickly becomes conscious of how our eyes take hold of the particular contribution which Light and Dark make to one or other of the two colour appearances.

* * * * *

In the natural course of our argument we had to keep at first to the appearance of colours as they come freely before us in space. The results we have obtained, however, hold good equally well for the permanent tints of material objects, as the following example – known as 'Purkinje's phenomenon' – will show.

Red and blue surface colours, when illumined by light of steadily diminishing intensity, are known to reverse their normal ratio of brightness. This phenomenon can be seen in nature, if, for instance, one observes a bed of blue and red flowers in the fading evening light and compares the impression with that which the same flowers make in bright daylight. If the phenomenon is reproduced artificially, the actual transition from one state to the other can be clearly observed. The easiest way is to place a red and a blue surface side by side under an electric light whose intensity can be gradually lessened by means of a sliding resistance.

Here, as much as in the natural phenomenon, our reason finds it difficult to acknowledge that the surface gleaming in a whitish sheen should be the one which ordinarily appears as darkening blue, and that the one disappearing into darkness should be the surface which normally presents itself as radiant red.

This riddle is readily solved if we apply what we have learnt about the particular shares of lightness and darkness in these two colours, and if we link this up with the respective forms of seeing exercised by our two eyes. To the dim light, clearly, our eyes will respond more with the 'left-eyed' than with the 'right-eyed' form of vision. Now we know that it is 'left-eyed' vision which is roused by the lightness-component in blue and the darkness-component in red. It is only to be expected, therefore, that these elements should become conspicuous when in the dim light our seeing is mainly 'left-eyed'. This solution of the problem makes us realise further, that the laws which Goethe first found for the coming into appearance of colours freely hovering in space are indeed applicable to the fixed material colours as well.

Chapter XVII

OPTICS OF THE DOER

Three basic concepts form the foundation for the present-day scientific description of a vast field of optical phenomena, among them the occurrence of the spectral colours as a result of light passing through a transparent medium of prismatic shape. They are: 'optical refraction', 'light-ray', and 'light-velocity' — the latter two serving to explain the first. As the following discussion will show, they are all concepts to which nothing corresponds in the realm of actual phenomena. In the way they have been formed, they are purely kinematic concepts typical of the onlooker-way of conceiving things.

It will be the aim of the present chapter to fill these concepts with new meaning, or else to replace them by other concepts read from the actual phenomena. Once this is done the way will be free for the development of the picture of the spectrum pheno-menon which is in true accord with the Goethean conception of Light and Colour.

* * * * *

The first to be brought in this sense under our examination is the concept of the 'light-ray'.

In present-day optics this concept signifies a geometrical line of infinitely small width drawn, as it were, by the light in space, while the cone or cylinder of light actually filling the space is described as being composed of innumerable such rays. In the same way the object producing or reflecting light is thought of as composed of innumerable single points from which the

light-rays emerge. All descriptions of optical processes are based
upon this conception.

Obviously, we cannot be satisfied with such a reduction of
wholes into single geometrically describable parts, followed by a
reassembling of these parts into a whole. For in reality we have to
do with realms of space uniformly filled with light, whether
conical or cylindrical in form, which arise through certain boundaries being set to the light. In optical research we have therefore
always to do with *pictures*, spatially bounded. Thus what comes
before our consciousness is determined equally by the light
calling forth the picture, and by the unlit space bordering it.

Remembering the results of our earlier study, we must say
further of such a light-filled realm that it lacks the quality of
visibility and therefore has no colour, not even white. Goethe and
other 'readers', such as Reid and Ruskin, tried continually to
visualise what such a light-filled space represents in reality. Hence
they directed their attention first to those spheres where light
manifests its form-creative activity, as in the moulding of the
organ of sight in animal or man, or in the creation of the many
forms of the plant kingdom — and only then gave their mind
to the purely physical light-phenomena. Let us use the same
method to form a picture of a light-filled space, and to connect
this with the ideas we have previously gained on the co-operation
in space of levity and gravity.

Suppose we have two similar plant-seeds in germ; and let one
lie in a space filled with light, the other in an unlit space. From
the different behaviour of the two seeds we can observe certain
differences between the two regions of space. We note that within
the light-filled region the spiritual archetype of the plant belonging
to the seed is helped to manifest itself physically in space, whereas
in the dark region it receives no such aid. For in the latter the
physical plant, even if it grows, does not develop its proper forms.
This tells us, in accordance with what we have learnt earlier,
that in the two cases there is a different relation of space to the
cosmically distant, all-embracing plane. Thus inside and outside
the light-region there exists a quite different relation of levity

and gravity — and this relation changes abruptly at the boundaries of the region. (This fact will be of especial importance for us when we come to examine the arising of colours at the boundary of Light and Dark, when light passes through a prism.)

* * * * *

To what extent the conception of light as consisting of single light-rays has impeded the appreciation of the true properties of light, is shown by the case of the 'pin-hole camera'. The phenomenon, in itself well-known, becomes in this way another example of what Goethe called 'while seeing, to see past the thing'. It is easily produced by means of a keyhole in a closed door whch on one side faces a window and on the other leads to a comparatively dark room. If conditions are favourable, a reversed image will appear on the wall opposite the keyhole of the objects extending outside the window.

The usual explanation of the phenomenon is that light-rays, emanating from every point outside, cross each other in the aperture of the camera and so — again point by point — create the inverted image. No such explanation, clearly, is open to us. For the world of external objects is a whole, and so is its image appearing in the camera. Equally, the light entering the camera is not a sum of single rays. Pure observation leads to the following description of the optical process.

By surveying the path which the light takes from the illuminated surface of the outer objects via the pin-hole to the optical image inside the camera, we realise that the light-realm engaged in this process has the shape of a double cone, with its apex in the opening of the camera. Within this cone the light carries the image across the space stretching in front of the light-reflecting objects up to the point where the image becomes visible by being caught on the back wall of the camera. Thus in every section of the cone the image is present in its totality — even in the very apex of the cone. There, too, the image in all its details is present as a whole, though without (ideally) any spatial extension.

Seen thus, the phenomenon reveals as an essential characteristic of light its faculty of making present in a spaceless point an
image originally expanded in space, and of letting it emerge from
this point in spatial expansion.

Further, there is the fact that, wherever we set up a pin-hole
camera, the aperture in its front will cause the formation of an
optical image inside it. This shows that each point in space filled
with light is the bearer of an optical image, contracted to a point,
of the entire world of light-reflecting objects surrounding it. All
we do with such a camera is to select a particular image and bring
it to separate visibility.

Through these observations, properly read, we grow aware of
light's faculty of communicating simultaneously to space as a
whole, and to each point in it, a potential image of the light-
reflecting object. In a later context (Chapter XIX) we shall again
meet this faculty of light at a higher stage of nature.

*   *   *   *   *

After having replaced the customary concept of the light-
bundle composed of single rays by the conception of two dynamically distinguished realms of space bordering each other, we turn
to the examination of what is going on dynamically inside these
realms. This will help us to gain a proper concept of the propagation
of light through space.

In an age when the existence of a measurable light-velocity
seems to belong to the realm of facts long since experimentally
proved; when science has begun to measure the universe, using
the magnitude of this velocity as a constant, valid for the whole
cosmos; and when entire branches of science have been founded
on results thus gained, it is not easy, and yet it cannot be avoided,
to proclaim that *neither has an actual velocity of light ever been
measured, nor can light as such ever be made subject to such
measurement by optical means* — and that, moreover, light, by
its very nature, forbids us to conceive of it as possessing any
finite velocity.

With the last assertion we do not mean to say that there is nothing going on in connection with the appearance of optical phenomena to which the concept of a finite velocity is applicable. Only, what is propagated in this way is not the entity we comprise under the concept of 'light'. Our next task, therefore, will be to create a proper distinction between what moves and what does not move spatially when light is active in the physical world. Once more an historical retrospect will help us to establish our own standpoint with regard to the existing theories.

The first to think of light as possessing a finite velocity was Galileo, who also made the first, though unsuccessful, attempt to measure it. Equally unsuccessful were attempts of a similar nature made soon afterwards by members of the Accademia del Cimento. In both cases the obvious procedure was to produce regular flashes of light and to try to measure the time which elapsed between their production and their observation by some more or less distant observer. The failure of these experiments did not manage to shake the conviction of the existence of such a velocity. In fact, this conviction was so deeply ingrained in the minds of men that, when later observations succeeded in establishing a finite magnitude for what seemed to be the rate of the light's movement through space, these observations were hailed much more as the quantitative value of this movement than as proof of its existence, which was already taken for granted.

A clear indication of man's state of mind in regard to this question is given in the following passage from Huygens's famous *Traité de la Lumière*, by which the world was first made acquainted with the concept of light as a sort of undulatory movement.

'One cannot doubt that light consists in the movement of a certain substance. For if one considers its production one finds that here on the earth it is chiefly produced by fire and flame, which without doubt contain bodies in rapid motion, for they dissolve and melt numberless other bodies. Or, if one considers its effects, one sees that light collected, for instance, by a concave mirror has the power to heat like fire, i.e. to separate the parts of the bodies; this assuredly points to movement, at least in true philosophy in which one traces all natural activity to mechanical causes. In my opinion one must do this, or quite give up all hope of ever grasping anything in physics.'

* * * * *

In these words of Huygens it must strike us how he first provides an explanation for a series of phenomena as if this explanation were induced from the phenomena themselves. After he has drawn quite definite conclusions from it, he then derives its necessity from quite other principles – namely, from a certain method of thinking, accepting this as it is, unquestioned and unalterably established. We are here confronted with an 'unlogic' characteristic of human thinking during its state of isolation from the dynamic substratum of the world of the senses, an unlogic which one encounters repeatedly in scientific argumentation once one has grown aware of it. In circles of modern thinkers where such awareness prevails (and they are growing rapidly today) the term 'proof of a foregone conclusion' has been coined to describe this fact.[1]

'Proof of a foregone conclusion' is indeed the verdict at which one arrives in respect of all the observations concerned with the velocity of light – whether of existing phenomena detectable in the sky or of terrestrial phenomena produced artificially – if one studies them with the attitude of mind represented by the child in Hans Andersen's story. In view of the seriousness of the matter it will not be out of place if we discuss them here as briefly as possible, one by one.[2]

The relevant observations fall into two categories: observations of certain astronomical facts from which the existence of a finite velocity of light and its quantity as an absolute property of it has been inferred; and terrestrial experiments which permitted direct observation of a process of propagation connected with the establishment of light in space resulting in the measurement of its speed. To the latter category belong the experiments of Fizeau (1849) and Foucault (1850) as well as the Michelson-Morley experiment with its implications for Einstein's Theory of Relativity. The former category is represented by Roemer's observations of certain apparent irregularities in the times of revolution of one of Jupiter's moons (1676), and by Bradley's investigation into the reason for the apparent rhythmic changes of the positions of the fixed stars (1728).

We shall start with the terrestrial observations, because in their case alone is the entire path of the light surveyable, and what is measured therefore is something appertaining with certainty to every point of the space which spreads between the source of the light and the observer. For this reason textbooks quite rightly say that only the results drawn from these terrestrial observations have the value of empirically observed facts. (The interpretation given to these facts is another question.)

Now, it is a common feature of all these experiments that by necessity they are based on an arrangement whereby a light-beam can be made to appear and disappear alternately. In this respect there is no difference between the first primitive attempts made by Galileo and the Academicians, and the ingeniously devised experiments of the later observers, whether they operate with a toothed wheel or a rotating mirror. It is always a *flash of light* – and how could it be otherwise? – which is produced at certain regular intervals and used for determining the speed of propagation.

Evidently what in all these cases is measured is the speed with which a beam of light establishes itself in space. *Of what happens within the beam, once it is established, these observations tell nothing at all.* The proof they are held to give of the existence of a finite speed of light, as such, is a 'proof of a foregone conclusion'. All they tell us is that the beam's front, at the moment when this beam is first established, travels through space with a finite velocity and that the rate of this movement is such and such. And they tell us nothing at all about other regions of the cosmos.

That we have to do in these observations with the speed of the light-front only, and not of the light itself, is a fact fully acknowledged by modern physical optics. Since Lord Rayleigh first discussed this matter in the eighties of the last century, physicists have learnt to distinguish between the 'wave-velocity' of the light itself and the velocity of an 'impressed peculiarity', the so-called 'group-velocity', and it has been acknowledged that only the latter has been, and can be, directly measured. More recently, a third aspect of velocity has been added, termed 'signal velocity' by analogy to the observations made with the aid of radio-waves. This velocity is held to be actually responsible for our receiving the optical image. There is no possibility of measuring the wave-velocity itself, this being the velocity with which the light is believed to travel through the medium when a signal is being received continually. Nevertheless, the modern mind allows itself to be convinced that light possesses a finite velocity and that this has been established by actual measurement. We feel reminded here of Eddington's comment on Newton's famous observations: 'Such is the glamour of a historical experiment.'

Let us now turn to Roemer and Bradley. In a certain sense Roemer's observations and even those of Bradley rank together with the terrestrial measurements. For Roemer used as optical signals the reappearance in the telescope of one of Jupiter's moons in the course of its revolution round the planet; thus he worked with light-*flashes*, as the experimental investigations do. Hence, also, his measurements were concerned — as optical science acknowledges — with group-velocity only. In fact, even Bradley's observations, although he was the only one who operated with continuous light-phenomena, are exposed to the charge that they give information of the group-velocity of light, and not of its wave-velocity. However, we shall ignore these limitations in both cases, because there are quite other factors which invalidate the proofs they are held to give, and to gain a clear insight into these factors is of special importance for us.

Roemer observed a difference in the length of time which a certain moon of Jupiter needed to resume its former position, and found that this difference underwent regular changes coincident with the changes in the earth's position in relation to Jupiter and the sun. Seen from the sun, the earth is once a year in conjunction with Jupiter, once in opposition to it. It seemed obvious to explain the time-lag in the moon's reappearance, when the earth was on the far side of the sun, by the time the light from the moon needed to cover the distance marked by the two extreme positions of the earth — that is, a distance equal to the diameter of the earth's orbit. On dividing the observed interval of time by the accepted value of this distance, Roemer obtained for the velocity of light a figure not far from the one found later by terrestrial measurements.

We can here leave out of account the fact that Roemer's reasoning is based on the assumption that the Copernican conception of the relative movements of the members of our solar system is the only valid conception, an assumption which, as later considerations will show, cannot be upheld in a science which strives for a truly dynamic understanding of the world. For the change of aspect which becomes necessary in this way does not invalidate Roemer's observation as such; it rules out only the customary interpretation of it. Freed from all hypothetical by-thought, Roemer's observation tells us, first, that the time taken by a light-signal travelling from a cosmic light-source to reach the earth varies to a measurable extent, and, secondly, that this difference is bound up with the yearly changes of the earth's position in relation to the sun and the relevant planetary body.

We leave equally out of account the fact that our considerations of the nature of space in Chapter X render it impermissible to conceive of cosmic space as something 'across' which light (or any other entity) can be regarded as travelling this or that distance in this or that time. What matters to us here is the validity of the conclusions drawn from Roemer's discovery within the framework of thought in which they were made.

Boiled down to its purely empirical content, Roemer's observation tells us solely and simply that *within the earth's cosmic orbit* light-flashes travel with a certain measurable speed. To regard this information as automatically valid, firstly for light which is continuously present, and secondly for everywhere in the universe, rests again on nothing but a foregone conclusion.

Precisely the same criticism applies to Bradley's observation, and to an even higher degree. What Bradley discovered is the fact that the apparent direction in which we see a fixed star is dependent on the direction in which the earth moves relatively to the star, a phenomenon known under the name of 'aberration of light'. This phenomenon is frequently brought to students' understanding by means of the following or some similar analogy.

Imagine that a gun in a fixed position has sent its projectile right across a railway-carriage so that both the latter's walls are pierced. If the train is at rest, the position of the gun could be determined by sighting through the shot-holes made by the entrance and exit of the bullet. If, however, the train is moving at high speed, it will have advanced a certain distance during the time taken by the projectile to cross the carriage, and the point of exit will be nearer the rear of the carriage than in the previous case. Let us now think of an observer in the train who, while ignorant of the train's movement, undertook to determine the gun's position by considering the direction of the line connecting the two holes. He would necessarily locate the gun in a position which, compared with its true position, would seem to have shifted by some distance in the direction of the train's motion. On the other hand, given the speed of the train, the angle which the line connecting the two holes forms with the true direction of the course of the projectile — the so-called angle of aberration — provides a measure of the speed of the projectile.

Under the foregone conclusion that light itself has a definite velocity, and that this velocity is the same throughout the universe, Bradley's observation of the aberration of the stars seemed indeed to make it possible to calculate this velocity from the knowledge of the earth's own speed and the angle of aberration. This angle could be established by comparing the different directions into which a telescope has to be turned at different times of the year in order to focus a particular star. But what does Bradley's observation tell us, once we exclude all foregone conclusions?

As the above analogy helps towards an understanding of the

concept of aberration, it will be helpful also to determine the limits up to which we are allowed to draw valid conclusions from the supposed occurrence itself. A mind which is free from all preconceived ideas will not ignore the fact that the projectile, by being forced to pierce the wall of the carriage, suffers a considerable diminution of its speed. The projectile, therefore, passes through the carriage with a speed different from its speed outside. Since, however, it is the speed from hole to hole which determines the angle of aberration, no conclusion can be drawn from the latter as to the original velocity of the projectile. Let us assume the imaginary case that the projectile was shot forth from the gun with infinite velocity, and that the slowing-down effect of the wall was great enough to produce a finite speed of the usual quantity, then the effect on the position of the exit hole would be precisely the same as if the projectile had moved all the time with this speed and not been slowed down at all.

Seeing things in this light, the scientific Andersen child in us is roused to exclaim: 'But all that Bradley's observation informs us of with certainty is a finite velocity of the optical process going on *inside the telescope!*' Indeed, if someone should claim with good reason (as we shall do later on) that light's own velocity is infinite, and (as we shall *not* do) that the dynamic situation set up in the telescope had the effect of slowing down the light to the measured velocity — there is nothing in Bradley's observation which could disprove these assertions.

* * * * *

Having thus disposed of the false conclusions drawn by a kinematically orientated thinking from the various observations and measurements of the velocity which appears in connection with light, we can carry on our own studies undisturbed. Two observations stand before us representing empirically established facts: one, that in so far as finite velocity has been measured or calculated from other observations, nothing is known about the existence or quantity of such a velocity except within the boundaries of the dynamic realm constituted by the earth's presence in the universe; the other, that this velocity is a signal-velocity, that is, the velocity of the front of a light-beam in process of establishment. Let us see what these two facts have to tell us when we regard them as letters of the 'word' which light inscribes into the phenomenal world as an indication of its own nature.

Taking the last-named fact first, we shall make use of the following comparison to help us realise how little we are justified in drawing from observations of the front speed of a light-beam any conclusions concerning the kinematic conditions prevailing in the interior of the beam itself. Imagine the process of constructing a tunnel, with all the efforts and time needed for cutting its passage through the resisting rock. When the tunnel is finished the activities necessary to its production are at an end. Whereas these continue for a limited time only, they leave behind them permanent traces in the existence of the tunnel, which one can describe dynamically as a definite alteration in the local conditions of the earth's gravity. Now, it would occur to no one to ascribe to the tunnel itself, as a lasting quality, the speed with which it had been constructed. Yet something similar happens when, after observing the velocity required by light to lay hold on space, this velocity is then attributed to the light as a quality of its own. It was reserved for a mode of thought that could form no concept of the real dynamic of Light and Dark, to draw conclusions as to the qualities of light from experiences obtained through observing its original spreading out into space.

To speak of an independently existing space within which light could move forward like a physical body, is, after what we have learnt about space, altogether forbidden. For space in its relevant structure is itself but a result of a particular co-ordination of levity and gravity, or in other words, of Light and Dark. What we found earlier about the qualities of the two polar spaces now leads us to conceive of them as representative of two limiting conditions of velocity: absolute contraction representing zero velocity; absolute expansion, infinite velocity (each in its own way a state of 'rest'). Thus any motion with finite velocity is a mean between these two extremes, and as such the result of a particular co-ordination of levity and gravity. This makes it evident that to speak of a velocity taking its course *in* space, whether with reference to light or to a physical body in motion, is something entirely unreal.

Let us now see what we are really told by the number 186,000 miles a second, as the measure of the speed with which a light-impulse establishes itself spatially. In the preceding chapter we learnt that the earth's field of gravity offers a definite resistance to our visual ray. What is true for the inner light holds good equally for the outer light. Using an image from another dynamic stratum of nature we can say that light, while appearing within the field of gravity, 'rubs' itself on this. On the magnitude of this friction depends the velocity with which a light-impulse establishes itself in the medium of the resisting gravity. Whereas light itself as a manifestation of levity possesses infinite velocity, this is forced down to the known finite measure by the resistance of the earth's field of gravity. Thus the speed of light which has been measured by observers such as Fizeau and Foucault reveals itself as a function of the gravitational constant of the earth, and hence has validity for this sphere only.[3] The same is true for Roemer's and Bradley's observations, none of which, after what we have stated earlier, contradicts this result. On the contrary, seen from this viewpoint, Roemer's discovery of the light's travelling with finite speed within the cosmic realm marked by the earth's orbit provides an important insight into the dynamic conditions of this realm.

* * * * *

Now that we have realised that it is inadmissible to speak of light as consisting of single rays, or to ascribe to it a finite velocity, the concept of the refraction of light, as understood by optics today and employed for the explanation of the spectrum, also becomes untenable. Let us find out what we must put in its place.

The phenomenon which led the onlooker-consciousness to form the idea of optical refraction has been known since early times. It consists in the fact, surprising at first sight, that an

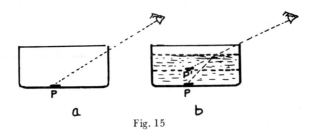

Fig. 15

object, such as a coin, which lies at the bottom of a vessel hidden from an observer by the rim, becomes visible when the vessel is filled with water. Modern optics has explained this by assuming that from the separate points of the floor of the vessel light-rays go out to all sides, one ray falling in the direction of the eye of the observer. Hence, because of the positions of eye and intercepting rim there are a number of points from which no rays can reach the eye. One such point is represented by the coin (P in Fig. 15a). Now if the vessel is filled with water, light-rays emerging from it are held to be refracted, so that rays from the points hitherto invisible also meet the eye, which is still in its original position. The eye itself is not conscious of this 'break' in the light-rays, because it is accustomed to seeing the object in the direction of the light which enters its own cavity. (Fig. 15b). Hence, it sees P in the position of P'. This is thought to be the origin of the impression that the whole bottom of the vessel is raised.

This kind of explanation is quite in line with the peculiarity of the onlooker-consciousness, noted earlier, to attribute an optical illusion to the eye's way of working, while charging the mind with the task of clearing up the illusion. In reality it is just the reverse. Since the intellect can form no other idea of the act of seeing than, that this is a passive process taking place solely within the eye, it falls, itself, into illusion.

Once more, it is not our task to replace this way of 'explaining' the phenomenon by any other, but rather to combine the phenomenon given here with others of kindred nature so that the theory contained in them can be read from them direct. One other such phenomenon is that of so-called apparent optical depth, which an observer encounters when looking through transparent media of varying optical density. What connects the two is the fact that the ratio of the actual depth to the apparent depth, and the ratio which measures the change in the direction of light (see page 370), are the same for the same two media.

In present-day optics this phenomenon is explained with reference to the former. In proceeding like this, optical science makes the very mistake which Goethe condemned in Newton, saying that a complicated phenomenon was made the basis, and the simpler derived from the complex. For of these two phenomena, the simpler, since it is independent of any secondary condition, is the one showing that our experience of depth is dependent on the density of the optical medium. The latter phenomenon we met once before, though without reference to its quantitative side, when in looking at a landscape we found how our experiences of depth change in conformity with alterations in atmospheric conditions. This, then served to make us aware that the way we apprehend things optically is the result of an interplay between our visual ray and the medium outside us which it meets.

It is exactly the same when we look through a vessel filled with water and see the bottom of it as if raised in level. This is in no sense an optical illusion; it is the result of what takes place objectively and dynamically within the medium, when our visual ray passes through it. Only our intellect is under an illusion when, in the case of the coin becoming visible at the bottom of the vessel, it deals with the coin as if it were a point from which an individual light went out.... etc., instead of conceiving the phenomenon of the raising of the vessel's bottom as one indivisible whole, wherein the coin serves only to link our attention to it.

There is a certain metamorphosis of the phenomenon, studied so far, which forms an important link in the chain of optical

events leading to the spectrum phenomenon. This is the displacement of the image of an object when the latter is looked at
obliquely through a denser medium with parallel plane surfaces.
Again we find that our gaze, while penetrating the medium, contracts the distance of the image proportionally to the greater
density of the medium. Further, as a result of the oblique direction, our visual ray does not take the shortest distance through the
medium. Hence the distance is shortened also through a shifting of
the image parallel to itself. Fig. 16 shows this in the usual style of
representation (without the contraction of the depth). The
straight lines here do not signify a refracted and unrefracted light-
ray, but the relevant directions of the eye's visual activity.

In accordance with the principle stated before, that the entire
field of vision, undivided, must always be taken into account as
being involved in the optical process, the phenomenon under consideration must be described as follows:

When we look in the manner described at, say, a white spot on
a black ground, not only the image of the spot is optically shifted,

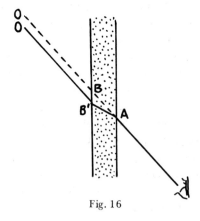

Fig. 16

but equally the entire surrounding area. The Light-Dark contrast
offered to our eye by such a picture serves only to bring the effect
to our consciousness. The same thing happens when we look in this
way at a uniformly coloured surface: what we lack is simply the

point of support which would enable our consciousness to notify it. In the next chapter we shall make use of what we have thus come to realise for comprehending the coming into being of colours as a result of light passing through a medium with surfaces other than parallel.

* * * * *

Having thus cleared away the purely kinematic interpretation of the so-called refraction phenomenon, we may pass on to discuss the optical effect through which the so-called law of refraction was first established in science. Instead of picturing to ourselves, as is usually done, light-rays which are shifted away from or towards the perpendicular at the border-plane between two media of different optical properties, we shall rather build up the picture as light itself designs it into space.

We have seen that our inner light, as well as the outer light, suffers a certain hindrance in passing through a physical medium — even such as the earth's gravity field. Whilst we may not describe this retardation, as is usually done, in terms of a smaller velocity of light itself within the denser medium, we may rightly say that density has the effect of lessening the intensity of the light. (It is the time required for the initial establishment of a light-filled realm which is greater within such a medium than outside it.) Now by its very nature the intensity of light cannot be measured in spatial terms. Yet there is a phenomenon by which the decrease of the inner intensity of the light becomes spatially apparent and thus spatially measurable. It consists in the alteration undergone by the aperture of a cone of light when passing from one optical medium to another.

If one sets in the path of a luminous cone a glass-walled trough filled with water, then, if both water and surrounding air are slightly clouded, the cone is seen to make a more acute angle within the water than outside it (Fig. 17). Here in an external phenomenon we meet the same weakening in the light's tendency to expand that we recognise in the shortening of our experience of depth on looking through a dense medium. Obviously, we expect

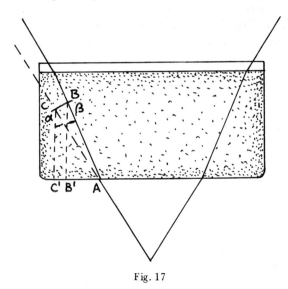

Fig. 17

the externally observable narrowing of the light-cone and the subjectively experienced change of optical depth to show the same ratio.

In order to compare the expansion of a luminous cone inside and outside water, we must measure by how much less the width of the cone increases along the same distance within the water than it does outside, this distance being some equal length on the edge of each cone respectively, because that is the length of the way practically traversed by the light in each case. (AB = AC in Fig. 17.) In the diagram, the lengths AB', and AC', indicate the relative increase of the cone's width. Observation shows that this ratio is the same as that by which the bottom of a vessel appears to be raised when the vessel is filled with water (4:3).

Thus, by means of simple reasoning based on pure observation penetrated by adequate thought, we have arrived at what is known to physical optics as Snell's Law of Refraction. For, seen trigonometrically, the two distances AB', and AC', represent the sine of the angle of aperture (more precisely half the angle) of the respective light cones: $\dfrac{AC'}{AB'} = \dfrac{\sin\alpha}{\sin\beta}$ This law, in itself the result of pure observation, was clothed by the spectator-mind in a conceptual form devoid of reality. For in this form direct reference is made to the two angles which are conceived as the angles between the ray of light in either medium, with a line at right angles to the boundary surface between the two media, and it is said that the ray is 'broken' towards or away from this perpendicular. On the other hand, the idea that the boundary of a luminous cone is spatially displaced when its expansion is impeded by an optical medium of some density, and that the measure of this displacement is equal to the shortening of depth which we experience in looking through this medium, is directly evident, since all its elements are taken from observation. Thus it is justified to assert that by means of a sufficiently developed power of intuition it would have been possible in principle, with the aid simply of observation and measurement of the optical alteration of depth, to infer along pure lines of thought the law of refraction as a necessary metamorphosis of it.

* * * * *

From what we have here found we may expect that in order to account for the numerical relationships between natural phenomena (with which science in the past has been solely concerned), we by no means require the artificial theories to which the onlooker in man, confined as he is to abstract thinking, has been unavoidably driven. Indeed, to an observer who trains himself on the lines indicated in this book, even the *quantitative* secrets of nature will become objects of intuitive judgment, just as Goethe, by developing this organ of understanding, first found access to nature's *qualitative* secrets.[4]

Chapter XVIII

THE SPECTRUM AS A SCRIPT OF THE SPIRIT

The realisation that Newton's explanation of the spectrum fails to meet the facts prompted Goethe to engage in all those studies which made him the founder of a modern optics based on intuitive participation in the deeds and sufferings of light. In spite of all that he achieved, however, he never reached a real solution to the riddle of the colour-phenomenon produced when light passes through a transparent body of prismatic shape. A brief recapitulation of the contents of the foregoing chapters will help us to see what hindered Goethe in this field and what we have to do in his place.

* * * * *

Goethe's realism enabled him to recognise as the actual object of optical research the optical *image* woven by Light and Dark. An image, in this sense, can be a Light and Dark area, with one area confining the other externally, or else a colour phenomenon woven by an inward interaction between Light and Dark. It is in this sense that Goethe in fact understood the nature of the optical image, and as such he studied it. But he kept his experience limited on the one hand to the appearance of the image within the eye, and on the other to its outer appearance on the surface where it is met by the gaze. The objects of his contemplation, therefore, were all, in some way, of a two-dimensional character, which indeed seems to be the intrinsic nature of the image. In our inquiry we could not rest content with Goethe's planar form of observation. Instead, we widened it to a three-dimensional observation both in respect of the process giving rise to the after-images in the eye, which we learnt to derive from the entire blood- and nerve-activity of the organism extending behind the eye, and in respect of the happenings between the visual ray and the outer light in the realm lying between the eye and the object. Hence we had to inquire into the fate of light as a result of its interaction with space. This then made it necessary to differentiate Goethe's concepts of Light and Dark into Light and Dark proper as representatives of the basic polarity of Levity and Gravity, and into lightness and darkness as forms of visual appearance of these two. Further, we found the act of seeing to be of two kinds, 'right-eyed' and 'left-eyed', depending on the way in which gravity and levity (positive and negative density) represent the factor producing lightness or darkness.

In the sense of his more plane-bound mode of contemplation, Goethe also tried to explain the prismatic colours. He assumed that the prism gives rise, alongside the original (primary) image, to another (secondary) image which, being shifted in respect of the former, overlaps with it so that, at the respective edges, lightness and darkness interweave, thus giving rise to the appearance of the respective colours. But he failed to find in this way a satisfying answer to the question of the origin of the spectrum phenomenon.[1] This becomes possible only by penetrating into the actual process which goes on spatially between the source of light and the final phenomenal effect in the eye, as we have indeed already done. From our past observations it is clear that we are not here abandoning the principle that the *image* must be regarded as the true object of optical research.

The result of this kind of inquiry into the coming-into-being of the spectral colours will, it is hoped, help future research to gain a corresponding insight into related optical facts, such as diffraction, polarisation, and others.

* * * * *

For a spatially orientated observation, the process of the formation of the spectrum by light that passes through a prism can be divided into two essentially different parts. The first consists in the influence which the light undergoes in the prism as a result of the latter's special shape, the second, in what happens in consequence of this at the boundary between the Light-space and the surrounding Dark-space. Accordingly, we will study these two parts of the process separately.

Let us remember that it is a characteristic of an ordinary light-impulse, if not interfered with, to direct itself through space in a straight line and to illuminate equally any cross-section of the area it occupies. Both these features are altered when the light is exposed to a transparent medium of prismatic shape — that is, to an optically resistant medium so shaped that the length of the light's passage through it changes from one side of the beam to the other, being least at the so-called refracting angle of the prism, greatest at the base opposite to that. The dimming effect of the medium, therefore, has a different quantity at each point of the width of the beam. Obviously, the ratio between levity and gravity inside such a light-realm, instead of being constant, varies from one side to the other. The result is a transverse dynamic impulse which acts from that part of the light-realm where the weakening influence of the prism is least towards the part where it is strongest.[2] The light-realm possesses now what we may call a transverse field-gradient. This gradient manifests in the deflection of the light from its original course. Let us imagine that we could arrange the experiment by making, for instance, the dimensions of all the parts involved sufficiently large and in such a form that an observer's eye would not be met by the colours appearing at the two borders of the light-path. For such an observer's eyesight, the phenomenon on the screen would not differ from what it would be if no prism intervened in the path of the light. While seeing nothing but an area illumined by colourless light, he would not surmise that the dynamic condition of this light was not the normal one. For the additional field-gradient, being parallel to the surface of the screen, has no effect on it. (The surface of the screen must, of course, be sufficiently smooth, and free from any darkening impurity.)

All the greater will be the observer's surprise (whom we imagine not to be acquainted with elementary optics) when we proceed to narrow down the light-realm from one side or the other. For instead of nothing but a black shadow appearing on the screen from one side or the other, as he would expect, the rim of the shadow will appear as coloured, and in different ways, according to the side from which we introduce the shadow-casting object. The observer must needs conclude from this phenomenon that the light is indwelt by a mysterious, one-sided dynamic. We then proceed to demonstrate that this is indeed so by showing the deflection of the light and how it is being deflected.

What is it that takes place at the borders of such a deflected light-realm as a result of the immanent transverse impulse? It is evident that where the light-realm borders upon the dark-realm a sudden jump occurs in the relation between levity and gravity, and it is equally evident that the effect of the transverse impulse will be different, according to the nature of the discontinuity: whether it is from light to dark or the opposite. Our eyes witness to this difference by seeing the colours of the *blue* pole of the colour-scale when the discontinuity is in *front* of the gradient, and the colours of the *yellow* pole when it is at the *back* of the gradient. On the ground of what we have already learnt about the characteristics of the two colour-poles, we are now in a position to describe the dynamic happenings in the two coloured bands as follows.

On the side towards which the lateral impulse points — i.e. where the blue, etc., appears — the interaction between negative and positive density is such that the latter makes for lightness and the former for darkness, whereas on the opposite side they interact contrariwise. Further, there is the striking fact that on both sides the darkness element in the colour-band increases in the direction away from the light-realm. This tells us that in this direction a gradual decrease in positive density, and an increase in negative density occur on the blue-violet side, while on the yellow-red side positive density increases in the direction away from the light-realm, and negative density decreases. Thus, at the edge towards which the gradient is directed we find that the *Trübe*, imprinted on the light within the prism, is arrested, and the light, following its transverse impulse, rays with increasing independence into the adjacent space, until beyond the violet it vanishes from the eye for lack of admixed *Trübe*. On the opposite side we find the imparted *Trübe* penetrating into the part of the space where through the absence of the deflected light, some kind of dynamic vacuum prevails. Being directed away from the light, the *Trübe* can increasingly gain the upper hand. Whereas on the blue-violet side the light escapes, as it were, from the dark which is lagging behind, on the yellow-red side they counteract each other. Our visual ray, when penetrating into the respective border-realms, thus meets conditions which correspond entirely with those it meets when we either gaze into cosmic space across the light-filled expanse of the steadily thinning atmosphere, or when through the darkening air the light of the sun comes towards us.

From what we have found concerning the two kinds of dynamic co-ordination of positive and negative density at the two ends of the spectrum, we may infer that the spatial conditions at one end must be quite different from those at the other. Our immediate perception confirms this. In fact, if we believe that we see both ends of the spectrum lying, as it were, flatly on the surface of the observation screen, this is merely an illusion due to our superficial way of using our eyes. If we gaze with our visual ray (activated in the manner previously described) into the two sides of the spectrum, while turning our eyes alternately in one or other direction, we soon notice that the colours of the yellow-red side rise towards the eye so as to give the impression of protruding almost corporeally from the surface of the screen. We feel: Density obtains here in a state of fiery radiation. When turning to the other side we feel our visual ray, instead of being as before caught up in the colours, passing freely across the colours as if carried by them into the infinite. On the blue-violet side, space itself seems to fluoresce mysteriously. Following Goethe's conception of the physical-moral effect of colours, we may describe the experience received thus from the two poles of the spectrum by saying that an 'other-worldly' character belongs to the colours of the blue-violet pole; an 'earthly' character to those of the yellow-red; while that of green, which appears when both sides are made to overlap, witnesses to its mediating nature between the two.[3]

* * * * *

There is still another way of coming to understand the spectrum phenomenon. It is, in fact, the way used by Goethe, and therefore also by us at the outset of our optical studies in Chapter XIV. In this method it is not the outer light which is watched when exposed to the working of the prism; we watch our own gaze by looking through it. In the science of optics this spectral appearance is termed, not very happily, 'subjective', in contrast to the 'objective' spectrum obtained by the other means.

In comparison with the latter, the spectrum, as the eye perceives it across the prism, now springs a surprise on the observer. For here the displacement of the image does not occur, as in the other case, towards, but away from the base of the prism. Consequently, the two coloured bands also appear in reversed distribution, although the whole phenomenon remains consistent in that, where the shifting is from light to dark, the blue-violet colours appear, etc.

From our earlier studies we know that outer and inner light correspond to each other in every respect, and that their response to the same cause therefore is the same. This makes it possible to apply to the present case the insight obtained before. In Chapter XVII we saw that the displacement of the image, when looked at obliquely across an optically denser medium with parallel surfaces, is caused by the gaze shortening the path across the medium through altering its direction inside the medium. Something similar happens when we look through a transparent body whose surfaces are plane, but not parallel, as with the prism. Whereas in the former case the natural homogeneity of the gaze over the width of the field of vision remains unaltered, it does become altered by the prism. It receives an additional transverse dynamic, as the outer light does in the other case, but now in the sense that the gaze presses from the side of the major resistance towards that of the minor one — i.e. away from the base of the prism towards its edge. Evidently, a gaze transformed dynamically in this way does not only lay hold of the image in the nearest agreeable position, as in the case of the medium with parallel surfaces, but it presses towards the object with a transverse dynamic of its own. If a light and dark area bordering upon each other are exposed to the gaze, then the gaze presses from dark to light, if the order of the two areas is such that the dark one is on the side of the base of the prism; and, correspondingly, if the order of the two is reversed. In the first instance, therefore, the border appears in the yellow-red colours; in the second instance, in the blue-violet. Here, too, the former colours are experienced as raying towards the eye, the latter as carrying the gaze away with them.

* * * * *

In our endeavour to view the fundamental experiement of Newtonian optics with the eyes of Goethe we have been led from the wide expanse of the earth's sunlit periphery into the confines of the darkened experimental chamber. With the aid of the results gained from studying the artificially produced spectrum phenomenon, we shall now return to our original field of observation in order to study the same phenomenon in nature. There it meets us in the form of the rainbow, which we shall now be able to read as a chapter in the great book of nature.

From what we have learnt already we can say at once that the rainbow must represent some sort of border-phenomenon, thus pointing to the existence of a boundary between two space-regions of differing illumination. Our question therefore must be: what is the light-image whose boundary comes to coloured manifestation in the phenomenon of the rainbow? There can be no doubt that the image is that of the sun-disk, shining in the sky. When we see a rainbow, what we are really looking at is the edge of an image of the sun-disk, caught and reflected, owing to favourable conditions, in the atmosphere. (Observe in this respect that the whole area inside the rainbow is always considerably brighter than the space outside.)

Once we realise this to be the true nature of the rainbow, the peculiar order of its colours begins to speak a significant language. The essential point to observe is that the blue-violet part of the spectrum lies on the inner side of the rainbow-arch — the side immediately adjoining the outer rim of the sun-image — while the yellow-red part lies on the outer side of the arch — the side turned away from the sun-image. What can we learn from this about the distribution of positive and negative density inside and outside the realm occupied by the sun-disk itself in the cosmos?

We will remember that along the gradient from blue to violet, negative density (Light) increases and positive density (Dark) decreases, while from yellow to red it is just the reverse — positive density increases and negative density decreases. The rainbow therefore indicates a steady increase of Dark towards the outer rim, and of Light towards the inner. The optical image of the sun in the atmosphere thus reveals a change of the ratio between Light and Dark in the radial direction, and this must be an attribute of the entire light-filled space stretching from the sun to the image. And again, the characteristics of this part of space must derive from a coincident dynamic ratio between the sun itself and the surrounding cosmic space.

The rainbow thus becomes a script in which we read the remarkable fact that the region occupied by the sun in the cosmos is a region of negative density, in relation to which the region surrounding the sun is one of positive density. *Far from being an accumulation of ponderable matter in a state of extremely high temperature, as science supposes, the sun represents the very opposite of ponderability.*

Once we realise this, our judgment of all that our terrestrially devised optical instruments, such as the telescope

and spectroscope, tell us about the nature of the sun and its
surroundings, will change accordingly. For it becomes clear that
for the interpretation of solar phenomena shown by these
instruments we cannot properly use concepts derived from observations within the earth's realm of positive density.

To compare adequately solar and terrestrial phenomena, we
must keep in mind that they are in every respect polar opposites.
For instance, the fact that the spectroscope reveals phenomena
in the sun's light which are strikingly similar to others occurring
when earthly matter is first caused to emit light — that is, brought
near the upper border of its ponderable existence — and then
studied spectroscopically, should not impose on us the illusion
that the sun consists of matter in this same condition. On the
contrary, the similarity should tell us that imponderable
substance, while on its way between sun and earth to ponderable
existence, assumes, at the point of transition, aspects exactly
like those revealed by ponderable substance at the corresponding
point in its upward transformation.

What we observe, when we study the sun through a spectroscope, is not the sun itself, but the conditions obtaining in this
border-region, where imponderable substance enters the earth-
realm.

* * * * *

The rainbow, directly we learn to see it as the border-phenomenon that it is, tells us something of itself which revives in modern
form a conception held generally in former ages, when it was
seen as a mediator between the cosmic-divine and the earthly-
human worlds. Thus the Bible speaks of it as a symbol of God's
reconciliation with the human race after the great Flood. Thus
the Greeks beheld it when they saw it as the bridge of Iris,
messenger of the Gods; and similarly the Germanic mythology
speaks of it as the pathway along which the souls of the fallen
warriors draw near to Valhalla. By recovering this old conception
in a new and scientifically grounded form we are enabled also

to rectify the misunderstanding from which the ancient bridge-conception of the rainbow has suffered in later days, when tradition had begun to replace direct insight into the truth.

When with the rise of man's onlooker-relation to the world of the senses, the rainbow could appear to him only as a form flattened against the sky, people began to think that the ancient picture of it as a bridge had been derived from its likeness to the latter's arched form. Representations of the rainbow from these times indeed show supersensible beings, such as the souls of the dead, moving upwards and downwards along the two halves of the arch. It is not in this abstract way that ancient man formed his cosmic imagery. What was seen going on between the upper and nether worlds when a rainbow appeared in the heights of the atmosphere was no traffic over the arch, but an interplay *across* the rainbow between the realm of levity, glimmering down in the rainbow's violet border, and the realm of gravity glowing up from the red. And this is how we have now learnt to see it again.

* * * * *

At one point in our optical studies (page 337) we referred to some words of Ruskin in which he deplored the influence exerted on the soul life of modern man by the world-conception of science. He illustrated this by showing how much less inspiration a man trained in the science of optics receives from the sight of a rainbow than does a 'simple peasant'. One lesson of our studies is that training in optics, if it proceeds on Goethean lines, has no such detrimental effect. There is, however, a further problem, outside Ruskin's scope, which we are now able to approach in the same healthy way.

Ruskin distinguishes between three possible stages in man's relation to the world of the senses. The first stage he calls that of 'inactive reverie'; the second — in a certain respect more advanced — that of 'useful thought', the stage of scientifically awakened man to whom all things disintegrate into countable and nothing but countable parts. Beyond this, Ruskin conceives of a third, still higher stage, in which man becomes capable of raising himself through 'higher contemplation' into an artistic-ethical relation to the content of the sense-world. Now, in the way Ruskin represents the second and third stages they seem to be exclusive of one another. That was as far as he could go, in his own day. Natural observation along Goethean lines leads to a form of higher contemplation which unites the second and third stages by nourishing man's ethical being and at the same time furnishing him with useful knowledge — knowledge, that is, which enables him to improve the conditions of the human race on earth. The following is an example of the practical possibilities that open up in the field we are discussing if we apply the knowledge gained through our new approach to the forces working in nature.

* * * * *

We shall speak here of a task of experimental research which was mentioned by Rudolf Steiner in connection with the renewal of natural science.

Rudolf Steiner felt the need for pioneers who, by advancing along the paths opened up by Goethe, would press forward into the realm of undiscovered phenomena on the upper border of nature, and this prompted him to give to those who were ready to listen various pointers towards new ways of experimental research. Among the indications given in this last field, there is one which deals with a way of influencing the spectrum by the magnet. I intended to produce an effect of the kind just indicated.

As we have seen, the spectrum is in two respects, not a complete phenomenon. There is, to begin with, the fact that the colour-band visible on the observation screen is only apparently confined to the surface of the screen. For, as we have seen, because of the differing co-ordination of levity and gravity at the two ends of the spectrum, the conditions of space prevailing at each are polarically opposite. Negative space opens up spherically behind the blue-violet colours on one side, while positive space, filled by the radially shining yellow-red colours, arises on the other. So we see that what we found earlier for the two poles of magnetism and electricity holds good also for the spectrum. That is, the two processes bringing about the relevant phenomena are not confined to the part of space which these phenomena seem to occupy; for the whole positive and negative realms of the universe share in them. Hence the spectrum, though apparently bounded at its two ends, proves by its very nature to be part of a greater whole.

In addition, the spectrum, when rightly viewed, calls for a certain completion. In following Goethe's initial observations we realised that the known spectrum, extending from red via green to violet, has a counterpart extending from violet via peach-blossom to red. With ordinary optical means it is naturally possible to produce only one type of spectrum at a time, so that each is left in need of being complemented by the other. In order to have the complete circle of colours together, it would be necessary to bring into the finite what — in one way or another — otherwise remains in the infinite. This requires a corresponding transformation of the dynamic property of space. It would be possible by making use of the magnetic force through exposing light, while forming a spectrum, to an electrically-produced magnetic field. To understand how this may be possible we have to remember what has been said about the peculiar nature of the magnetic force-field in comparison with the electric field (Chapter XIII).[4]

In order to understand the significance of this indication we must turn our attention to parts of the ordinary spectrum, well known in themselves, which we have purposely left out of our study so far. These are the regions of the ultra-violet and the infra-red, invisible in themselves, but forming part of the spectrum as a whole. The ultra-violet manifests through chemical effects, the infra-red through thermal effects. We have left them out of our considerations because these regions of the spectrum differ from the visible part not only quantitatively, as present-day science believes, but qualitatively also, and in a fundamental way. We must regard them as dynamic realms of particularly extreme

spherical and radial activities. As such they represent metamorphoses, in the Goethean sense, of the levity-gravity interaction
represented by the optically visible part of the spectrum. In this
way the spectrum discloses a threefold differentiation of that
region of force, which up to now we have called simply levity,
into activities producing chemical, optical and thermal effects.

Thus far physical investigation is able to lead us, but no
further. If, however, we let nature herself speak to us, while
holding this differentiated concept of levity in mind, she tells
us that beyond the three metamorphoses envisaged so far, there
must be a fourth.

Let us remember that it was certain phenomena of life which
first made us aware of the existence of a realm of forces with the
attributes of anti-gravity, and that these forces revealed themselves
first as creators of form. Now it is obvious that warmth, light and
chemical energy, though they all play an essential part in living
organisms, could never by themselves bring about that 'catching
from the chaos, carbon, water, lime and what not and fastening
them into a given form' which Ruskin describes as the activity
of the spirit in the plant. In order to be in this sense an instrument
of the spirit active in nature, levity must be capable of yet another
metamorphosis into an activity which controls the other three,
so that through their action, definitely shaped organic structures
may come into being.

The reason why this fourth and highest metamorphosis of
Levity does not appear in the ordinary spectrum is because it is
of too spiritual a quality to be caught by the optical apparatus. In
nature herself a creative life-process requires always the presence
of a germ already imbued with life. And so, in order to call this
fourth metamorphosis of Levity into the spectrum, stronger means
are needed than the mere optical transformation of light-filled
spaces. This stronger agent, according to Rudolf Steiner, is
magnetism. With the aid of this it will be possible to organise
together round a common spatial centre that part of the activity
of levity which escapes the optical instrument and thus remains
cosmic, and that part which appears by itself in terrestrial space.

Once this is practically carried out, we may expect a complete colour-cycle to appear as already divined by Goethe. The full circle consists of twelve discernible colours, with the Goethean *peach-blossom* diametrically opposite the green. It is in this region of the peach-blossom that — again according to Rudolf Steiner — we shall find a source of actively working life-forces, springing from the fourth metamorphosis of levity.

Our next chapter will be devoted to conveying a picture of these cosmic workings and their respective interactions.

PART THREE

TOWARDS A NEW COSMOSOPHY

Chapter XIX

THE COUNTRY IN WHICH MAN IS *NOT* A STRANGER

*I question not my Corporeal or Vegetative Eye any more than
I question a window concerning sight. I look through it and
not with it.*

WILLIAM BLAKE

INTRODUCTORY

The decision to extend this book by yet another main part was
not reached without careful consideration of the need for it.
Note the title — *Towards a new Cosmosophy*. It will have become
clear in the past pages that man is once more in need of a *sophia*
(wisdom) of himself as a *cosmic* being and therewith of the
cosmos to which he belongs, and that the road towards the
modern attainment of such wisdom was laid open by Goethe.
To arrive there, we must take this road and travel assiduously
along it. The aim of the following chapters is to give some survey
of the panorama that opens up along this road and to offer the
reader some indications for his further individual efforts in this
direction.

The attempt would not be possible without the aid of certain
results of Rudolf Steiner's investigations in the regions of the
world which are not accessible to man's physical senses. At the
end of the present chapter we will indicate how investigations
of this kind can be achieved, and what they signify for a true
continuation of the Goethean mode of research. It is enough
to say here that what one gains in this way as a widening of
one's world-picture can be described entirely on its own ground.
There will therefore be no need to relate every point in the
following account to the relevant results of Rudolf Steiner's
own investigations.

THE FOUR KINDS OF ETHER

At the end of the last chapter we found a vista opening up on certain differentiations of Levity, for we saw it capable of manifesting as Warmth, Colour, and Chemical Energy, and we came to the conclusion that these three must needs be supplemented by yet another modification, the form-creating power of Life. We will try now to convey a more distinct picture of how the action of Levity is expressed in these four modes.

As we shall see, the power of counteracting Gravity is only one of the properties of the realm of force where the four manifestations of Levity occur. It will therefore be well to find for it a name with wider implications than Levity alone would suggest. We follow Rudolf Steiner by choosing for this purpose the Greek word ETHER[1] which, however, must not be confused with the hypothetical, and as such rightly contested, 'ether' of physical science.

In connection with the fourfold differentiation of the realm of force in question, we distinguish the four modifications of Ether as 'Warmth-Ether', 'Light-Ether', 'Chemical-Ether', and 'Life-Ether'. Our observations will enable us to suggest for each of them yet another name, expressing the respective characters of their modes of action.

If we ask to what in the world of the senses the fourfold action of the Ether finally comes down, the answer must be, FORM — in its widest bearing. It is this that prompted Ruskin, when asked what Life was, to reply: 'Always stand by Form against Force'; and that made Goethe say, when he realised his growing capacity to read in the Book of Nature: 'It is a becoming aware of the *Form* with which again and again nature plays, and, in playing, brings forth manifold life.' (page 90.) While pursuing Goethe's way of plant-observation we came to see that all formative action in nature is prompted by certain archetypal (ur-) forms or images. We may now see in the Ether's fourfold activity the agent to which these ur-images and their physical reflections owe their existence. In what follows we shall therefore have to show how Warmth, Light, Chemical Action, and Life co-operate in order to beget these ur-images, first of all in the supersensible, and then to make them manifest in physical nature.

WARMTH
We start with the warmth-ether as the one relatively closest to the physical realm. For this ether manifests also directly as the physical element Fire. As the 'highest' among the four elements, and the 'lowest' among the four ethers, we may picture it as having a kind of Janus-head. Constituting as it does a border-condition between the two worlds, the warmth-ether has, on the one hand, the function of receiving the picture-weaving trans-mitted to it by the higher ethers, and, on the other, of bringing physical matter into the state where it becomes receptive to the working of the etheric forces. The warmth-ether achieves this by freeing matter from being controlled one-sidedly by the centre-bound forces of the earth. It thus calls forth, when acting physi-cally, the processes of melting of solids and of evaporation of liquids: phenomena which yielded the initial observations for our introduction of the concept of levity. In processes of this kind we now recognise the physical manifestation of a universal func-tion of the warmth-ether, namely, to divest matter of all form and to lead it over from the realm dominated by gravity into that of levity. Thus we may say that the function of the warmth-ether is to bring about at the upper border of physical nature the *chaos* — in the sense already used — which the earth needs for the ever-to-be-repeated renewal of her life. It is thus that we found chaos working in the plant, when through the union of the pollen with the seed a state of chaos is produced within the seed, which enables the *type* to impress anew its form-principle into it (page 97). Another instance of the warmth-ether's anti-gravi-tational effect, also discussed earlier, is the earth's seismic activity.

True, it appears at first sight as if little were gained by speaking of warmth-ether, instead, as we did previously, of levity in general. But it must not be forgotten that in the ether-realm, as a whole, warmth — that is, the overcoming of earthly gravity — is only one of the four modes of etheric action, albeit the one which

enables the other three to work into the physical world. We shall
see, later on, that only by taking into account the action of the
higher modifications of the ether is it possible to gain insight into
the true causes of the apparently so arbitrary occurrences of
volcanic and kindred phenomena. Here, too, it is the function of
the warmth-ether to produce in the physical sphere the chaos
which is necessary to make the physical sphere receptive to the
activities going on in higher spheres.

In view of this universal function of the warmth-ether, which
distinguishes it from the other modifications of ether, we may give
it as a second name that of 'chaoticising ether'.

LIGHT

The function of the light-ether, the second of the four modes of
ether, can best be envisaged by thinking of the difference between
a plant growing in darkness (perhaps a potato sprouting in a
cellar) and another of the same species exposed to the influence of
the light. A further striking instance of this kind is the difference
in shape between such unicellular organisms as the green algae,
which live in light and have highly differentiated forms, and the
relatively formless bacilli which grow in the dark. These things
are, of course, well-known facts. Our purpose here, however, is
not merely to record them as 'fact', but, by re-creating them
within ourselves, to use them to gain an experience of the function
of the light-ether.

The following passages from Goethe's *Metamorphosis of Plants*
are a classical example of observation of the activity of the light-
ether in the plant. They are taken from the second part of the
essay, where Goethe is describing leaf development:

'While the leaves owe their first nourishment principally to
the more or less modified watery parts, which they draw from the
stem, they are indebted for their increased perfection and refine-
ment to the light and air. The cotyledons which are formed
beneath the closed seed-sheath are charged, so to speak, with
only a crude sap; they are scarcely and but rudely organised and
quite undeveloped. In the same way the leaves are more rudely

organised in plants which grow under water than in others which are exposed to the open air. Indeed, even the same species of plant develops smoother and less intricately formed leaves when growing in low damp places, whereas, if transplanted to a higher region, it will produce leaves which are rough, hairy and more delicately finished.

'So it is also with the anastomosis of the vessels which spring forth from the larger veins, seeking each other with their ends and coalescing, and thus providing the necessary basis for the leaf-skin or cuticle. All this, if not entirely caused by subtle forms of air, is at least very much furthered by them. If the leaves of many water-plants are thread-like or assume the form of antlers, we are inclined to attribute it to lack of complete anastomosis. The growth of the water buttercup, *Ranunculus aquatilis*, shows this quite obviously, with its aquatic leaves consisting of mere thread-like veins, while in the leaves developed above water the anasto-mosis is complete and a connected plane is formed. Occasionally, indeed, in this plant, the transition may be still more definitely ob-served, in leaves which are half anastomosed and half thread-like'.

The second of these paragraphs describes the phenomenon of vascular anastomosis which, having already been more than once an object of our study, here reveals a new meaning. If, following Goethe's method, we re-create in our mind the repeated separations and reunions of the sap-vessels, while keeping in view the fact that the leaf's outer form is the result of a purposive, many times repeated anastomosis, then the picture of the activity of weaving arises before our mind's eye. (Hence the word 'tissue' for the flesh of a living being.) In truth all nature's forms are woven of light, including the crystals.[2]

How clear a picture Goethe had of the conformity of man's act of thinking with nature's way of producing her forms — both being an act of supersensible weaving — is shown by the following two verses. That on the left is a passage from *Faust*, from the scene in which Mephisto (disguised as Faust) instructs the young Scholar. The other is an altered version of it, written by Goethe at a later time to conclude an essay (*Bedenken und*

Ergebung) in which he deals with the problem of the relation between Experience and Idea:

Truly, when men their thoughts [conceive	So with a modest eye perceive
Tis as if some masterpiece they weave.	Her masterpiece Dame Nature weave.
One thread, and a thousand strands [take flight,	One thread, and a thousand strands [take flight,
Swift to and fro the shuttles going,	Swift to and fro the shuttles going,
All unseen the threads a-flowing,	Each to the other the threads [a-flowing,
One stroke, and a thousand close unite.	One stroke, and a thousand close unite.[3]

What Goethe wants to show here by applying to the activity of nature the same image which he used originally to depict the act of thinking, we can express today by saying that it is the identity of the activity of the light-ether in human thinking and in external nature which is responsible for the fact that the objective ideas operating in nature can become the content of man's consciousness in the form of thoughts.[4]

Following our previous procedure when we gave the warmth-ether a second name by calling it chaoticising ether, we can denote the light-ether also as 'weaving ether'.

*   *   *   *   *

At this point we must remember the phenomenon of the pin-hole camera, discussed in Chapter XVII. There we found one of light's faculties to consist in making present in a spaceless point an image originally expanded in space, and of letting it emerge from this point in spatial expansion (page 355), for that is exactly what the light-ether performs on a higher level of nature when with its help the spiritual archetype of a plant takes on spatial appearance. For to this end the archetype, itself without spatial limitations, imprints its image into the tiny seed, whence the growing plant organism carries it again into space. And there is in principle no limitation to the number of such seeds, each of which will bear the complete image of the archetype.

Thus the optical and the biological phenomenon supplement each other to give us a picture of the properties of the light-ether.

CHEMISM

Our procedure in discussing the chemical ether will differ from what followed previously in so far as we shall start with phenomena which give rise to this ether's second name: *sound*-ether. This name was given together with the other by Rudolf Steiner himself in view of the significance of this aspect of the third ether.

To customary scientific thinking it sounds strange, if one asserts that sound and chemical action have something to do with one another. Formerly, man was well aware that sound had power to order and re-order physical matter; we find it mentioned in the various mythologies of the peoples of old. We may recall, for example, the Greek myth of Orpheus, or the figure of the great singer-magician Väinämöinen in the Finnish epic *Kalevala*.[5] If a man of those times were to appear today and to come across the periodical system of the chemical elements and all the numerical relationships in the chemical behaviour of substances, he would at once recognise in all this a kinship with the numerical order immanent in music. And he would explain that it was this relationship between sound and matter-processes which the heroes of old still knew how to handle in actual practice.

It is known that Goethe did not make use in his poetry of things known to him merely through historical study without having himself had some experience of them. Thus, if in *Faust* we find thrice that the sun's action is accompanied by mighty sounds — in the Prologue in Heaven, at the beginning of the Second Part when 'the sun announces his approach with overwhelming noise', and in what Ariel thereupon calls to the spirits of the elements — we can infer that for Goethe the sound-nature of the cosmic ether was a matter of actual experience.

Let us in the Goethean manner look for a phenomenon through which the ordering power of sound becomes directly manifest. This we have in the so-called sound-figures, discovered in 1785 — simultaneously with Goethe's first apperception of the ur-plant — by the German physicist Chladni (1756-1827) and called after him 'Chladni's sound-figures'. They are produced with the aid of a round or square plate of glass or brass, fixed at its centre so that it can vibrate freely at its edges. It is evenly

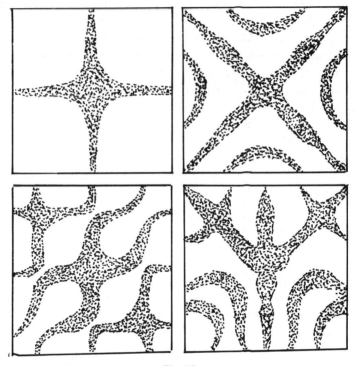

Fig. 18

and not too thickly covered with fine sand or lycopodium powder
and then caused to vibrate acoustically by the repeated drawing
of a violin-bow with some pressure across the edge of the plate
until a steady note becomes audible. Through the vibrations
thus caused within the plate, the particles of sand or powder
are set in movement and caused to collect in certain stationary
parts of the plate, thereby creating figures of very regular and
often surprising form. By stroking the plate at different points
on the edge, and at the same time damping the vibrations by
touching the edge at other points with the finger, notes of different pitch can be produced, and for each of these notes a characteristic figure will appear (Fig. 18).[6]

The significance for us of Chladni's experiment will emerge still more clearly if we modify it in the following way. Instead of directly setting the plate with the powder into vibration by stroking it with the bow, we produce a corresponding movement on a second plate and let it be transmitted to the other by resonance. For this purpose the two plates must be acoustically tuned to each other and placed not too far apart. Let us imagine, further, that the whole experiment was arranged — as it well might be — in such a way that the second plate was hidden from a spectator, who also lacked the faculty of hearing. This gives us a picture of the situation in which we find ourselves whenever the higher kinds of ether, by way of a tone-activity inaudible to our physical ear, cause shapeless matter to assume regularly ordered form.

* * * * *

This comparison of the activity of the sound-ether, as the form-endowing element in nature, with Chladni's phenomenon, is drawn correctly only if we recognise that the conception of *form*, as an expression of that which is called forth through the etheric forces in nature, comprises more than the external spatially bounded shape of an organic or inorganic entity.[7] The reason why in the case of the Chladni-figures the influence of sound causes nothing beyond the ordering of form in outer space is because on this plane of nature the only changes that can occur are changes in the positions of separate physical bodies. Where the forces of sound in ether-form are able to take hold of matter from within, they can produce changes of form of a quite different kind. This effect of the activity of sound-ether has given it its other name: chemical ether.

We have mentioned once before that our conception of 'form' in organically active nature must not be limited merely to that of a body's spatial outline. This was in connection with Ruskin's definition of the spiritual principle active in plant-formation as 'the power that catches out of chaos charcoal, water, lime and what not, and fastens them down into a given form'. Besides the external order of matter revealed in space-form, there exists also an inner qualitative order expressed in a body's chemical composition. Upon this inner chemical order is based all that we encounter as colour, smell, taste, etc., of a substance, as well as its nourishing, healing or harmful properties. Accordingly, all these parts of an organism, both in the plant kingdom and within the higher organisms, have a certain inner material order, apart from their characteristic space-structure. The one is never present without the other, and in some way they are causally connected.

In this inner order of substance we must see in the very first place the work of the sound or chemical ether. And we should be aware that by the word 'chemistry' in this connection we mean something much more far-reaching than those chemical reactions which we can bring about by the reciprocal affinity of physical substances, however complicated these reactions may be. A few examples will illustrate the difference between chemical processes caused by direct influence of the chemical ether, and others in which only the physical consequences of the ether are effective.

* * * * *

In his book, *Man the Unknown*,[8] Professor Carrel shows very impressively, by an example from the human organism, the difference of quantitative ratio in externally similar processes, one of which occurs within the domain of life, the other, outside it. He compares the quantity of liquid necessary to keep artificially alive a piece of living tissue which has been reduced to pulp, with the quantity of blood doing the same within the living organism. If all the tissues of a human body were treated in this way, it would take 45,000 gallons of circulating fluid to keep them from being poisoned in a few days by their own waste products. Within the living organism the blood achieves the same task with 1½ gallons.

Very many chemical changes within living organisms are effected by the two polar processes of oxidation and reduction.

We have discussed them repeatedly as hieroglyphs of much that occurs in nature by way of polarity. In accordance with the principle ruling the physical plane of nature, that differences of level tend to disappear, oxidation can occur by itself, whereas reduction requires the expenditure of energy. Let us from this point of view compare the transformation of oxidised into reduced iron, as it takes place inside and outside the realm of life.

An example of this process in its purely physical form is the reduction of iron-ore to metallic iron in blast-furnaces, where, with the help of high temperature and high pressure, carbon is made to combine with the oxygen ingredient of the ore and to impart to it its own imponderable energy. Precisely the same process is going on continuously and unobtrusively within the human body under normal bodily conditions of temperature and pressure, when the oxy-haemoglobin of the arterial blood changes over into the haemoglobin of the venous blood. A macrotelluric counterpart of this is the transformation of the red river-mud into the blue-black continental mud at the bottom of the sea, around the continental shores. Here, again, reduction takes place without those preliminaries that are necessary for carrying through the process by technical means.[9]

Through examples of this kind we gain insight into the nature of the chemical ether as a 'magic' force (in the sense in which we have introduced this term at the beginning of the book). What the chemical ether is capable of effecting in a gentle manner, so to speak, in co-operation with the inertness-overcoming power of the warmth-ether, can be imitated physically only by an extra-ordinary concentration of external energy and the use of masses of material substance. At the same time the imitation is never complete. For to all that happens through the action of the chemical ether there belongs the quality of cosmic youth, while everything brought about in a purely physical manner is of necess-ity cosmically old.[10]

Of all the provinces of nature towards which man's exploring eye has turned since the dawn of the onlooker-consciousness, none has furthered his purely quantitative thinking more than chemistry, ever since the discovery that the chemical reactions of the various substances are conditioned by a quite definite and constant numerical relationship. It was these relationships which impelled the rise of the atomic conception of matter and all its consequences. For since the onlooker-consciousness is quite unable to conceive the existence of numerical relationships in the physical world except as sums of computable units in space, it was natural for this type of consciousness to reduce all empirically established numerical relationships to corresponding relationships among quantities of the smallest possible material or matter-like units.

Scientific thinking, if guided by knowledge of the existence of etheric forces and their action, has no need of such an interpretation of the numerical relationships revealed in the physical world; for it knows them to be nothing but the last expression of the action of the chemical ether (hence occasionally also called 'number-ether' by Rudolf Steiner). To do justice to the appearance of measurable numerical relationships in nature, in whatever sphere, it is necessary to free ourselves from the abstract conception of number which governs modern scientific thought and to replace it by a more concrete one. We shall find that for the existence of a certain number there may be two quite different reasons, although the method of establishing the number itself is the same in each case. A simple example will illustrate this.

* * * * *

Let us look at a number of similar objects, say a group of five apples. We observe that the relation of the number five to the group of objects in front of us is purely external and accidental. In applying to it the conception 'five' we combine the single objects into a group and give it a name, or numerical label, which has nothing to do with the nature of the items making up the group. This way of thinking, we may observe, is of exactly the kind which the nominalists of the Middle Ages attributed to every conception formed by the human mind. In fact, the process of counting is a process of pure abstraction. The more differentiated are the things which we want to combine into a group through the process of counting, the further this abstraction has to go. We can count apples and pears together under the collective conception of 'fruit'; if turnips are added, we must help ourselves out with the conception 'vegetable products'; until finally we deal only with 'things', without considering any qualitative differentiation. Thus the conception of number is created solely within the human mind, which applies it to things from outside, precisely in the sense in which the Nominalists among the school-men regarded *all* conceptual activity as taking place.

From the moment when human consciousness was unable to attribute to itself any other than a purely nominalistic mode of comprehension it was inevitable that all explanations of natural phenomena would have two results: (1) the exclusion from observation of everything that could not be conceived in terms of numbers, and (2) an endeavour to find for every numerical relationship capable of empirical proof an explanation which could be interpreted as the result of taking qualitatively identical units and counting them. For this method of forming conceptions is the only one which nominalism can accept with a good conscience. The fact that in so doing it is led *ad absurdum* has only quite lately occurred to it. For if by the logical following of this path — as in modern theoretical physics — the whole universe is dissolved into units which can no longer be distinguished from each other, then it will become impossible to count these parts, for it cannot be established whether any given one of these hypothetical elemental particles has been counted or not. Nonetheless, Eddington claimed to have found the exact number of particles composing the universe — a number with 80 figures — by using a special calculus, but this number is valid only on the supposition that the particles cannot be counted because they are indistinguishable![11]

However correct the nominalistic conception of number may be in such a case as that of numbering the five apples, it is wholly incorrect to restrict the concept of number itself to one valid for this kind of occurrence. We shall see this immediately if we take one of the apples and cut it across. There we find the number five confronting us in the well-known star-like figure, represented by the fivefold pericarp in the centre of the apple. What man, restricted as he was to this mode of understanding, has completely overlooked is this: although the act of counting, by which we establish the number five, is the same in both cases, the quality of the number five is totally different. For in the case of the five pericarps this number is a quality immanent in the apple, which it shares with the whole species of Rosaceae. The apple itself is just as much 'five' as it is 'round', 'sweet', etc. In the supersensible type which creates in the plant its own organ of manifestation, the creation of a number – in the apple of the number five – is part of the form-creating activities characteristic of the type. The numerical relationships which appear between natural phenomena depend upon the way in which the chemical ether participates. This is true equally of those discovered by chemistry in the sphere of inorganic matter and used today with such great success.

Let us be quite clear that the relationship of unity to plurality in the case of the five apples is totally different from what it is in the fivefold pericarp. In the first case unity is the smallest quantity represented by each of the five apples. There, the step from one to two is made by joining together two units from outside. The path from one to many is by way of continuous addition. In the second case the unity is represented by the pericarp – i.e. by the one comprising the many, the latter appearing as parts of the whole. In such a case two is part of one and so are three, four, five, etc. Plurality arises from a continuous process of division of unity.

The ancient world knew the idea of number only in the last-mentioned form. There unity appeared as an all-embracing quantity, revealed through the Universe. The world's manifoldness was felt to be not a juxtaposition of single things, externally connected, but the content of this unity, and therefore derived from it. This was expressed by the pre-Socratic Greek philosophers in the formula ἕν καὶ πᾶν (the One and the All).

With the appearance of the Arabs on the scene of history, human thought turned to the additive concept of number, and the original distributive concept receded gradually into oblivion. The acceptance of the new concept made it possible for the first time to conceive the zero. It is clear that by a continuous division of unity one is carried to a constantly growing number of constantly diminishing parts, but without ever reaching the nothing represented by the number zero. Today we should say that in this way we can reach zero only by an infinite series of steps. Yet the idea of the infinite did not exist in this form for ancient man. On the other hand, in the arabic conception of number the steps necessary to reach zero are finite. For just as by the external addition of unities we can step forward from one number to the next, so we can also step back on the same path by repeated subtractions of unities. Having thus reached One, nothing can stop us from going beyond it by one more such step. The arabic numerical system, therefore, is the only one to possess its own symbol for zero.

It has been correctly noted that the penetration into European thought of this additive concept of number was responsible for developing the idea of the machine; for it accustomed human beings to think calmly of zero as a quantity existing side by side with the others. In ancient man the idea of nothingness, the absolute void, created fear; he judged nature's relation to the void accordingly, as the phrase 'natura abhorret vacuum' indicates. His capacity to think fearlessly of this vacuum and to handle it thus had to be developed in order to bring about the Machine Age, and particularly the development of efficient steam engines. Consider also the decisive part played by the vacuum in Crookes's researches, through which the path to the sub-physical realm of nature was laid open.

Nature herself, however, makes use of number as a regulating factor not only in the electrical and gravitational connections of inorganic matter, but as a quality among qualities wherever sound-ether from the upper boundary of nature so regulates the dynamic of material processes that the manifold sense-qualities appear in their time-and-space order.

When we discussed in Chapter XII the discovery of the mechanical equivalent of heat by J.R. Mayer, we pointed out that the existence of a definite numerical relationship between disappearing and appearing energies did not by any means prompt Mayer to establish a kinetic theory of heat, as Helmholtz later did on the ground of Mayer's discovery, but in complete contrast to Mayer's own conception. Mayer himself felt no need to form a picture of a multitude of discrete particles in a state of motion in order to bring to his understanding the fact of a certain constant numerical relationship. For he experienced in the number itself the revelation of a creative reality. In the same chapter, when discussing the atomistic conception of matter, we pointed to Faraday's refusal of Dalton's theory. He, too, felt no need to picture amounts of discrete particles in order to explain the existence of the definite proportions, etc., in chemistry. For him, *the proportions themselves* were the only actual facts, in comparison with which he regarded the atom as a mere word (page 278). By their capacity for conceiving number as a phenomenon in itself, Mayer and Faraday showed that they had an inkling of the existence of the chemical (sound-) or number-ether.

At this point in our discussion it becomes possible to supplement in an essential manner the picture of electricity and magnetism given in Chapter XIII.

We have learnt to conceive of electricity and magnetism as polarities of the second order – effects of a polarically differentiated interaction of the primary polarity, Levity-Gravity, with the difference that on both sides of the electrical polarity the stress lies more on levity, whereas with magnetism it lies more on gravity (page 307). We have now come to see that levity itself may be differentiated by the various modifications of ether. Naturally this brings up the question of how far the various secondary polarities are the outcome of a particular interaction of one or other kind of ether with gravity.

An indication of this became noticeable in the ordinary spectrum, with its threefold quality as 'infra-red' (heat), visual (colour) and 'ultra-violet' (chemical) spectrum. In extending the general statement that colours are the effect of an interaction — in Goethe's sense — of Light and Dark, or — if we carry Goethe's approach further — of Levity (negative density) and Gravity (positive density), we can now say: In the visual part of the spectrum the working of light-ether becomes manifest; in the ultra-violet part that of chemical ether; and in the infra-red part that of warmth-ether. Now, as a result of its two-sided nature, the warmth-ether is capable of manifesting directly as measurable heat, whereas the two other ethers become phenomenal through their intermingling with positive density. In all three instances, however, the relevant ethers maintain their intrinsic natures, gravity providing only the means whereby they manifest and act physically.

Besides this form of interrelation of the light-ether and the chemical ether with gravity, in which they maintain their original etheric character, there exists another form of interrelation in which they are, as it were, overpowered by gravity. *What we designate as electricity is light-ether thus mastered by gravity, and magnetism is chemical (sound-) ether in a corresponding condition.* By thus getting to know the deeper nature of these two forces we are enabled to understand many things in modern physical observation and theory which resist comprehension within the boundaries of physical thought. For instance, we can now see how it could happen that light was conceived of as merely a particular form of electro-magnetic vibrations. This idea received particular confirmation from the observations of Heinrich Hertz, who found that the electro-magnetic vibrations arising from spark-discharges follow the same laws of spatial propagation as 'light' was known to do. (We are compelled to put here the word *light* between inverted commas because, as we have learnt, it is not the light itself that appears in the optical phenomenon, but light interacting with gravity — i.e. 'colour' in Goethe's sense.) The fact, then, that light in its space-bound condition and electricity show certain similarities in their spatial behaviour, is only to be expected in view of their etheric kinship. If, however, we follow the correct genetic order, we shall not regard light as a form of electricity, but electricity as an offspring of light.[12]

This insight into the cosmic position of electricity also enables us to obtain an appropriate conception of the so-called quantum theory — essential for modern physics — through which atomistic thinking became extended to pure energy-processes. It was the physicist Max Planck who, because of the unexpected results of certain physical measurements concerning the radiation of heat, first had the idea that energy when being emitted or absorbed by a physical body, cannot increase or diminish continuously, but only by discrete amounts, the so-called quanta.[13] Let us apply to this what we have already learnt.

We must remember that it is characteristic of centrally orientated field-actions to tend towards multiplication of field-centres (all-relating points), the property 'dry' of the element Earth thereby coming to expression. There is one ur-plant, but innumerable physical plants, each springing from a centre-bound seed and itself in turn producing many such seeds. The same rule holds good in all other domains of nature; the tendency of physical matter to turn into dust is a special instance of it. In this sense we discussed, in Chapter XII, the process of friction, whose occurrence we found always to be connected with some process of disintegration, natural or artificial. In line with this, physical research has found that when energy is captured by inert matter, or when matter is stimulated by some means to emit energy, the energy appears to have the form of discrete energy — 'particles', or 'quanta'.

Let us look in this sense at the photo-electric effect, which has done so much to confirm the quantum theory. It occurs when light meets a metal plate. The plate gives off electrical energy which stands to the incident light-energy in a relation that can be understood only by supposing the electrical energy to be set free in discrete quanta, as well as by supposing that the incident light-energy is itself quantised. But when it came to explaining this phenomenon theoretically, Eddington's question, 'Discovery or Manufacture?', was not put. For while the physicists thought that some basic fact concerning the nature of light was 'discovered', they were actually faced — as in all cases of this kind — with 'manufactured' phenomena. These are without exception the outcome of a process of decomposition to which the light-ether is exposed, if it is captured by gravity and, as a result, appears as electricity. Rudolf Steiner, accordingly, described electricity as 'disintegrated light'. To this, and this alone, the quantum theory applies here.

The phenomena which gave rise to the quantum theory were believed to have disproved for the first time the conception that 'nature does nothing by jumps'. In reality this could have been noticed long before, directly the quantitative facts of the chemical behaviour of physical substances became known. For there, too, in the combination of chemical elements, she admits only stepwise changes. (For example, a certain quantity of carbon combines only with a definite quantity of oxygen to make carbon monoxide, or with twice that quantity to make carbon dioxide, with nothing in between.) The same facts characterise quite another domain, already mentioned as being akin to chemistry, foreign to it though it may seem to be. This is music. For a characteristic of music is that it exhibits quite definite numerical laws with regard to the relationships between the rates of vibration which determine pitch — a fact common to whatever scales have been used by different peoples during various historical periods. In this fact we recognise a peculiarity of the sound ether. And again, something very similar is shown in the realm of quantum theory by the fact that certain 'invariants' prevail in the energy-'jumps', just as they do in macroscopic chemistry and in music. (Note in this respect the Balmer-series of the lines of the hydrogen-spectrum, with their astonishing algebraic proportions.)

In all these phenomena we meet symptoms of sound-ether action, in a form which is related to its original existence as electricity is to light-ether — namely in its gravity-captured form. In the self-contained fields of magnetism we enounter the same thing in manifest form.

Two facts may be brought in here from the realm of the

intra-material processes disclosed by modern nuclear research, for they prove that the forces at work there are gravity-captured forces of sound-ether, and therefore magnetic forces.

No sooner was it discovered that the element Radium disintegrates spontaneously into the elements Helium and Lead, than the question arose whether the customary derision of medieval alchemy was really justified. The question was heard again when it became possible by means of electrical bombardment to transform one chemical element into another, and even to create elements not found in nature. Sometimes these techniques are spoken of as 'modern alchemy'. Although this way of regarding modern nuclear research as akin to what the alchemists strove for (and achieved), represents a typical confusion of nature's nether and upper borders, still the 'magic' of which the true alchemist tried to become worthy, and the 'magic' which modern atomic physics sets going, issue ultimately from one and the same source: the chemical or sound-ether, the first magic ether, as we have had reason to call it. The only difference between the two methods is that by the first method this ether was brought into action in its original cosmic form, helping to produce life-affirming substances – the great alchemists were always active physicians – while by the second method it is being made use of as a captive of gravity – that is, in the form of magnetism – resulting in the production of life-denying substances. What is set free through atomic fission as well as fusion is levity in the form of heat, light and chemical action which, as a result of having been age-long captives of gravity, have become alienated from their cosmic origin.

Further, a peculiarity of the happenings within matter is that they are accessible to scientific thinking only if they are conceived of as vibratory processes. And these vibrations are found to stand in such numerical relations that, if one looks for some analogue in the macroscopic realm, one is again directed to music. Today it is no scientific heresy to speak of a 'reflection of the harmonies of the spheres within matter'. What physical research now needs to do is to recognise the spiritual implications of its own attainments and to take the path of modern Goetheanism. For anyone who is convinced of the cosmic-etheric origin of electricity and magnetism can have no doubt that researchers guided by such a conception would learn to employ both forces in a manner which would have a cosmically fertilising effect on the earth (as indicated at the end of the previous chapter), instead, as today, in a manner that threatens the earth and its population with cosmic death.

* * * * *

These considerations naturally suggest that in speaking of the life-ether, the next and last kind of ether in the series, something similar will have to be said about its two forms of occurrence: in its original cosmic form, and when it is captured by gravity. In other words, one must expect that, besides electricity and magnetism, there exists a third force which is related to life-ether as the other two forces are related to light- and sound-ether respectively. This force is still unknown to us. However, in view of all the danger man has already brought on the earth by means of his matter-bound thinking and his manipulations divorced from the cosmos in the fields of electricity and magnetism, one can only hope that until the new cognitional morality has been sufficiently developed and spread to prevent still greater peril from being brought on by the application of this force, it will remain unknown.

LIFE

As already mentioned, the three kinds of ether, warmth, light and sound, are not sufficient in themselves to bring into existence what in its proper sense we call 'life' in nature, i.e. the formation of single living organisms. This requires the action of a fourth kind of ether, the life-ether, ranged above the other three. We can best comprehend the life-ether's contribution to the total activity of the ether in nature by considering the interaction of the four kinds of ether with the four physical elements.

We have seen that the warmth-ether has the double function

of being at once the lowest ether and the highest physical element,
thus acting as a sphere of reflection for the other kinds of ether
and the elements respectively. Each stage in the etheric has its
reflection in the physical, as the table below shows. Thus to the

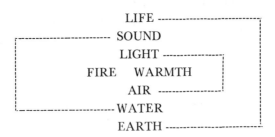

physical air the etheric light is related. (The affinity of light and
air is best seen in the plant and its leaf-formation.) To bring about
real changes in the material composition of the physical world
requires the stronger powers of the chemical ether. Therefore it
is also the first ether of which we had to speak as 'magical' ether.
Its effects reach into the watery element which is already bound
up with gravity, but by its own strength it cannot penetrate
beyond that. The causation of material changes in the liquid
sphere would in fact be all that these three kinds of ether could
achieve together.

Only when the power of the life-ether is added to the three
others can etheric action reach as far as the sphere of solid matter.
Thus the life-ether is responsible for all solid formation in nature,
both in her organic and inorganic fields (the latter — crystal-
formation — being the effect of external ether-action).[14] It is to
the action of the life-ether that nature owes the existence in her
different realms of multitudes of separate solid forms. To mention
an instance from our previous studies: in the same way as volcanic
phenomena manifest the warmth-ether's gravity-overcoming power
on a macrotelluric scale, so snow-formation illustrates the life-
ether's matter-shaping might.

Through its power to bind flowing action into solid form, the life-ether is related to the sound-ether in the same way as the articulated word formed by human speaking is related to the mere musical tone. The latter by itself is as it were fluid. In human speech this fluidity is represented by the vowels. With a language consisting only of vowels man would be able to express feelings, but not thoughts. To let the word as carrier of thought arise out of sound, human speech possesses the consonants, which represent the solid element in it.

The emergence of the sense-bearing word from the merely ringing sound is an exact counterpart to what takes place in nature when the play of organic liquids, regulated by the chemical ether, is caused by the life-ether to solidify into outwardly percep-tible form. By reading in this way the special function of the life-ether among the other three, we are led to the term 'Word-ether' as an appropriate second name for it, corresponding to the term sound-ether coined by Rudolf Steiner himself for the chemical ether.

Chaoticising, Weaving, Sounding, and, lastly, Speaking the form-creative Word into the realm of Gravity — these are the four activities through which the dynamic realm which we first designated comprehensively as Levity brings forth nature's manifold entities of which we finally become aware through our corporeal senses.

* * * * *

In the introduction to this chapter we said that at the end of it we would give some information as to the mode of cognition that enabled Rudolf Steiner to have direct insight into the sphere of the supersensible ether, and out of it to pass on the teachings from which the observations of this chapter derive. For it is to his spiritual-scientific research that we owe the possibility of discerning in the world of the senses the action of the fourfold ether. In a way, this applies even to some of our earlier obser-vations, at the very beginning of this book, on the development of the picture of man's threefold psycho-physical organism. Still, it is only the observations in the present part of the book, that make it necessary to explain in some detail the justification for employing for scientific research the results of supersensible investigation. For it might be plausibly asked whether, by proceeding in this way, we are not abandoning the pure method of Goethe. Our description of the character of Rudolf Steiner's investigations, and how such investigations become possible, will show that this is not so.

* * * * *

We will remember from our optical studies the two forms of vision arising from the activity of the eye's inner light – the dream-vision and the seeing of after-images. Of these two, seeing in dream is in a certain sense the purer form of inner seeing in that it arises without any outer stimulus exercised upon the physical organ of sight. On the other hand, it lacks that objective conformity to law characteristic of the after-images which mirror the order of the external world. There is an arbitrary, enigmatic element in dream-pictures, and their logic often seems to run counter to that of waking consciousness. A further characteristic of dream-perception is that we are tied to the level of consciousness prevailing in the dream. While we are dreaming we cannot awaken to the extent of being able to make the pictures the object of conscious observation.

With the after-images it is different. Although to begin with they are present in our consciousness with a clarity no greater than that of the dream-pictures, nevertheless we are able so to enhance our consciousness of them as to bring them under observation like any external phenomenon. As previously shown, it is possible, even while the eye is riveted on an impression from outside, to develop such awareness in the activity of the inner light called forth by this impression, that together with the results of the deeds and sufferings of the light we can perceive something of these deeds and sufferings themselves. Perception of the after-images thus turns into what we may call perception of simultaneous images. This activity of the eye corresponds with what Goethe, in a different connection, called an 'alliance of the eyes of spirit with the eyes of the body'.

These two forms of visual perception — which we may briefly call: (1) perception of *post*-images, and (2) perception of *co*-images — represent successive rungs on a 'spiritual ladder' pointing beyond themselves to a further rung. By the logic of succession this may be expected to consist in some sort of seeing of *pre*-images, with the characteristic of being a still less physical mode of seeing than the two others. This seeing must be based on an activity of the inner light which will be similar to that in dream by its arising without any stimulus from external light-impressions, yet at the same time there must be no arbitrariness in the contents of this perception. Further, our consciousness in this perceptive activity must be such as to allow us to be in full control of it, as we are of ordinary day-waking seeing.

This kind of pure sense-free perception does indeed exist, and it can be aroused by means of a well-ordered training from the dormant state in which it is present in every human being. Anyone who learns to see in this way gains perception of the activity of cosmic light, contacting it directly with his own inner light — that is to say, without mediation of his corporeal eye which is subject to gravity. So this eye-of-the-spirit becomes capable of perceiving the levity-woven archetypes (ur-images), which underlie all that the physical eye discerns in the world of ordinary space.

In respect of the intrinsic character of the world-content thus perceived, Rudolf Steiner called this mode of perception, Imaginative perception, or, simply, Imagination. By so doing he invested this word with its due and rightful meaning.[15]

From what we found in our optical studies concerning the nature of after-images (Chapter XV), it is clear that the acquisition of Imaginative perception rests on a re-awakening in the eye (and thus in the total organism behind the eye) of certain 'infant' forces which have grown dormant in the course of the growing up of the human being. It thus represents a fulfilment of Thomas Reid's philosophic demand. Consequently we find among the descriptions which Traherne gives of the mode of perception peculiar to man when the inner light, brought into this world at birth, is not yet absorbed by the physical eye, many helpful characterisations of the nature of Imaginative perception, some of which may be quoted here.

Consider, in this respect, the following passage from Traherne's poem *The Praeparative*, quoted earlier. In describing the state of soul at a time when the physical senses are not yet in operation, Traherne says:

> 'Then was my Soul my only All to me,
>   A living, endless Ey,
> Whose Power, and Act, and Essence was to see:
>   I was an inward Sphere of Light
> Or an interminable Orb of Sight,
>   Exceeding that which makes the Days,
>   A *vital* sun that shed abroad its Rays:
>   All Life, all Sense,
> A naked, simple, pure Intelligence.'

This is the condition of soul of which Traherne says in the same poem that through it a man is still a recipient of the 'true Ideas of all things'. In this condition the object of sight is not the corporeal world which reflects the light, but light itself, engaged in the weaving of the archetypal images. In a later passage of the same poem Traherne expresses this by saying:

> 'Tis not the Object, but the Light
> That maketh Hev'n ....'

And more clearly still in the following part of his poem *An Infant Eye*:

> 'A simple Light from all Contagion free,
> A Beam that's purely Spiritual, an Ey
> That's altogether Virgin, Things doth see

Ev'n like unto the Deity;
That is, it shineth in an hevenly Sense,
And round about (Unmov'd) its Light dispense.
'The visiv Rays are Beams of Light indeed,
Refined, subtil, piercing, quick and pure;
And as they do the sprightly winds exceed,
Are worthy longer to endure;
They far out-shoot the Reach of Grosser Air,
With which such Excellence may not compare.
But being once debas'd, they soon becom
Less activ than they were before.'

How at this stage the soul experiences the act of perception in itself is shown in the following passage from the poem *Wonder*:

'A Nativ Health and Innocence
Within my Bones did grow
And while my God did all his Glories show
I felt a vigour in my Sense
That was all SPIRIT: I within did flow
With seas of Life like Wine.'

Utterances of this kind show that the faculty of Imagination, in the sense of perceiving the ur-images of the world with an eye-of-the-spirit which has been made strong enough to require no support from the physical eye, is the metamorphosis of a faculty possessed by all men before birth and still in early childhood. If we look at the matter in this light, we see that to acquire the faculty of Imagination means carrying through consistently the training inaugurated by Goethe.

* * * * *

The characterisation of spiritual Imagination seems to contradict, at least partly, the foregoing description of the ether. For since Imagination as a means of investigating the etheric realm

had to be explained as a heightening of the power of the spirit-
eye, it must seem surprising to learn that a certain mode of activity
of the ether has a quality which makes appeal to aural experiences. The full answer to this question must await the discussion
that follows this chapter. Two points, however, may be brought
forward at once. First, where gravity with its tendency to indi-
vidualise, is absent, no such sharp distinctions exist between one
form of perception and another as are found in the sphere of the
physical senses. Secondly, even in ordinary sense-perception a
certain overlapping of visual and aural experiences is known to
us. We need only think how common it is to give musical attributes, such as 'consonant' and 'dissonant', to colours, and to
describe tones as 'light' and 'dark'. The reason is that subcon-
sciously we accompany visual experiences with tone-sensations,
and vice versa. Cases are even known of human beings in whom
the secondary sensation occurs with such intensity as to equal the
primary one. Such people say that they 'see' sounds and 'hear'
colours.

What we are thus dimly aware of in physical sense-perception
becomes fully conscious experience once the supersensible part
of a particular sense can work unimpeded by the corporeal organ.
In this respect we find Traherne again an eloquent witness to the
corresponding experience from a period of man's life when the
physical senses do not yet exist, or when the soul is not yet fully
absorbed into them. We remember from his poem *Dumbness*
the lines:

> 'No ear,
> But Eys themselves were all the Hearers there;
> And evry Stone and evry Star a Tongue,
> And every Gale of Wind a Psalm or Song:
> The Hevens were an Oracle and Spake
> Divinity....'

and similarly from his poem *Wonder* that 'evry thing that I did
see did with me talk'.

* * * * *

It remains to show that the acceptance of information obtained through spiritual Imagination, without ourselves being as yet in actual command of it, is not in contradiction with the Goethean principle of pure reading in the phenomena of the world.

Let us, to this end, think of reading in the ordinary sense of this word, calling to mind that for the acquisition of this faculty we depend on someone who can teach it because he already has it. Exactly the same holds good for the reading with which we are here concerned. Here, too, a teacher already possessing this faculty is required. Thus Goethe became for us a teacher of reading, and it would be a mistake to imagine that he, for his part, needed no teacher. In his case this function was fulfilled partly by what he learned through his studies of the earlier fruits of man's spiritual activity, that is, from an epoch when vestiges at least of the original, instinctive faculty of spiritual imagination were still extant. A similar function on our own path of study was performed by our occupation with the old doctrine of the four elements and the basic concepts of alchemy.

Although such a training in reading, as gained through Goethe himself, is indispensable, it does not suffice to meet the present-day demands of a scientific understanding of the universe. For this, we need a 'technique' of reading that cannot be attained along these lines alone. Awareness of this fact led Rudolf Steiner to pursue his spiritual-scientific investigations and to communicate the results in such a way that they can be a 'school of reading' for those who study them. Hence it is a misunderstanding of the whole meaning of his teachings when its contents are quoted — as they sometimes are even by adherents — in such a way as to suggest that by their help a better 'explanation' may be gained of matters for which there is otherwise no, or at least no satisfactory explanation. The question: 'How does spiritual science (anthroposophy) explain this or that?', is quite wrongly put. We ought rather to ask: 'How does spiritual science help us to read more clearly this or that otherwise enigmatical chapter of the script of existence?'

In this sense we have tried to conduct all our past observations, including those of the present chapter, and we shall continue to do so. Our aim is not to produce 'explanations' of the world's phenomena which claim to be 'better' than those hitherto available, but to decipher the script which the spirit is always writing through these phenomena.

Chapter XX

PRO ANIMA

Thy functions are ethereal,
As if within thee dwelt a glancing mind,
Organ of vision! And a Spirit aëreal
Informs the cell of Hearing, dark and blind.

WILLIAM WORDSWORTH

THE WELL-SPRINGS OF NATURE'S DEEDS AND
SUFFERINGS

As our observations of nature from the point of view of levity-gravity effects have shown, these two forces, which represent a primary polarity, are able to interact in various ways, thereby giving rise to manifold secondary polarities. The question, therefore, arises as to the cause of these interactions. Obviously, this must be a further kind of force, to which both gravity and levity are subordinate.

In what follows we shall try, so far as is possible within the scope of this book, to throw light on the nature of this force. Since the direct experience of the dynamic realm constituted by it is based on faculties of the mind other than those needed for the Imaginative perception of the etheric realm, we shall have to examine also the nature and origin of these faculties. This will lead us again to the study of one of man's higher senses, this time his sense of hearing, with the aim of finding the spiritual function that is hidden in it. Again our order of procedure will have to be the one followed in the last chapter, in that it will be necessary first to make ourselves acquainted with the nature of the force in question and then to turn to an examination of the sense-activity concerned.

* * * * *

Among the secondary polarities which we have previously met, and which have now to be considered as an outcome of the action of the third force, there was in the first place our own psycho-physical organisation. We found our mental activity based on the nervous system, representing the salt-pole, our volition based on the metabolic processes, representing the sulphur-pole, and our feeling life based on the rhythmic system, representing the mercurial mean between the two. These three can now be characterised as follows.

Man's body as a life-bearing organism evidently consists of a physical organisation permeated by etheric force. Their interaction, however, is not uniform throughout the body, each of the three systems shows a different interrelation between them. In the metabolic region, they are linked together in the 'sulphur' way. Here, therefore, the warmth-ether takes the lead and acts in such a way that the higher kinds of ether are able to work magically into the material processes of the body. On the side of the nerves and senses system, the life-ether has the lead, bringing about fixed forms in a 'salt'-like manner. These provide a foundation for the activity of the other ether-forces, without, however, being actually permeated by them. Psychologically, these two kinds of relationship come to expression in the various degrees of consciousness: unconsciousness at the lower pole, consciousness at the upper pole, and a medium degree of consciousness in the middle as a result of a continuous alternation between the two conditions.

This description now helps us to realise that the third type of force, in so far as it is active in man, has the capacity, by co-ordinating the physical and etheric parts of the organism in one way or another, to promote happenings either of a more corporeal or a more psychical nature — namely, motion at one pole, sensation at the other, and feeling in the middle between them.[1] Remembering Goethe's formula, 'colours are *deeds* and *sufferings* of light', we realise how deeply true were the concepts to which he was led by his way of developing observation and thought.

What we have now brought to our awareness by studying man, holds good in some sense also for the animal. The animal, too, is polarised into motion and sensation. (What makes the animal differ from man need not concern us here, for it belongs to a dynamic realm other than the one we are now studying. This other realm will come under consideration in the next chapter.) A similar and at the same time a different picture arises when we turn to the plant. The plant, too, is characterised by a threefold structure, root, stem with leaves, and florescence, which in turn represent the 'saline', 'mercurial', and 'sulphurous' functions of the alchemical triad. Yet, compared with man and animal, respiration serves here the opposite purpose (reduction of carbon instead of oxidation); motion — even in the form of those rare outer movements effecting a change in the position of single parts of the plant' body — occurs as a mere inner movement of the saps in the service of the plant's processes of growth and formation; and as the plant's 'doing' is confined to purely inward organic happenings, so is that which in the higher beings makes for inner sensation shown by the plant purely outwardly as corporeal quality. This last fact was given a most apt expression by Ruskin in his *The Queen of the Air*, where, in describing the forming of blossom in the plant as the climax of the 'spirit' active in it, he says: 'Its (the plant's) form becomes invested with aspects that are chiefly delightful to our own human passions; namely, first, with the loveliest outlines of shape and, secondly, with the most brilliant phases of the primary colours, blue, yellow, red or white, the unison of all; and to make it more strange, this time of peculiar and perfect glory is associated with relations of the plants or blossoms to each other, correspondent to the joy of love in human creatures and having the same object in the continuance of the race.'[2]

If we wish to understand why the same dynamic action working on the physical and etheric organisms of the plant, on the one hand, and of man and the animal, on the other, brings about effects so different, we must turn to the realm whence this action originates in both cases. For the animal and for man it is their own body which, in addition to its individual physical and etheric organisation, is also fitted with an individual organisation of the higher kind. Not so with the plant. For the rhythms of its growth, the successive formation of its various organs, the production of its colours, etc., the plant depends on outer conditions.

What strikes us first in this respect is the plant's dependence on the succession of the seasons which, in turn, are an outcome of the changing mutual positions of earth and sun. That which forms part of the individual organism in higher living beings is located in the cosmic surroundings of the plant. In fact, it is our planetary system which provides the impulses that stir the etheric and physical forces — either from without or from within — to their various interactions, thus bringing about all the manifold secondary polarities. This prompted Rudolf Steiner to give this type of dynamic action the name 'astral', whereby he also restored this expression to its true, original, meaning.

We shall now enter into a closer study of the astral realm of the universe.

* * * * *

When contemplating nature and man from the viewpoint of the world's astrality, one is led to a picture of our cosmic system in which the earth appears in the centre of a number of force-fields which penetrate each other and in their peripheral region extend beyond one another in accordance with the respective orbits of the various planetary bodies. This picture is indeed one which seems to be incompatible with the heliocentric conception of the universe, first taught in modern times by Copernicus, and which, through the work of Kepler and Newton, has established itself in the modern mind as the only valid one. Now it is true that the heliocentric viewpoint cannot be denied a certain justification. There is, after all, the fact that the orbits which the heavenly bodies appear to follow when viewed in this way, assume a particular geometrical character which cannot be accidental.

And more than that, when the heliocentric aspect is seen in its true setting, it forms (as will be shown later) an extremely revealing part of the script which tells us of the nature of the astral forces. Still, this is not enough to justify the claim of exclusive validity for this aspect. The fact that we have to abandon it when we wish to gain insight into the true *dynamic* order of the world cannot be brought home to us more clearly than through the following statement by Professor Max Plank in a lecture on theoretical physics given in 1909 at the Columbia University, New York:

'Only the hypothesis of the general value of the principle of Relativity in mechanics could admit the Copernican system into physics since this principle guarantees the independence of all processes on the earth from the progressive motion of the earth. For, if we had to make allowance for this motion, then I should, for instance, have to reckon with the fact that the piece of chalk in my hand possesses the enormous kinetic energy corresponding to a velocity of about 30 km/sec.' [3]

The implications for us of these remarks by an eminent physicist can be expressed as follows:

In a science which deals with movement as an event of absolute dynamic reality, the Copernican aspect loses its significance as the only valid aspect of our cosmic system. For its application as a means of describing the dynamic happenings within this system presupposes the acceptance of a relativistic conception of motion. Indeed, for the building up of a picture of the dynamic structure of our system, the Copernican viewpoint is inadequate. Consequently, there is nothing to prevent us from taking the geocentric standpoint, since this appears to be the right one for gaining insight into the astral realm of the universe.

* * * * *

From our preceding observations we may expect the astral realm to be as little uniform as is the etheric. In fact, just as the etheric realm was found to be subdivided into four different

modes of etheric action, so we shall now find that the astral
realm subdivides into a number of different modes of astral
action.

As the originator of the secondary polarities in earthly nature
the astral realm must undoubtedly itself be structured polarically,
one part of it forming the cause of all the happenings by which
levity is brought into interaction with gravity, the other of all
the happenings by which gravity is brought into interaction with
levity. There must be a further part which is responsible for the
establishment of the 'mercurial' mean between the two poles of
the secondary polarity. This leads us to a threefold aspect of the
astral realm.

Closer inspection reveals a repetition of this threefold order
within each of the two polar regions. Earlier observations have
taught us to distinguish the material happenings at the two poles
of the secondary polarity as 'sulphurous' and 'saline'. Of the
former process, by which matter is carried from its gravity-bound
to its gravity-free condition, we know that it takes place in three
stages, of which the first implies the lifting of matter from the
solid to the liquid condition, the second from the liquid to the
aeriform condition, and the third to the condition of pure heat.
There are three corresponding stages by which ether becomes
susceptible to gravity. It is in their nature that they are not in
the same degree manifest as are their polar opposites. Still,
properly guided observation is able to detect them and enables us
to describe them as follows. At the first stage, ether, which in
itself has a purely peripheral orientation, becomes linked to some
all-relating point; at the second stage, the various ether activities,
already point-related, are brought into some characteristic interrelationship so as to become the cause of a particular formative
action in the material realm; at the third stage, the etheric aggregate
thus organised receives the impulse to link itself with some particular portion of ponderable matter.

Each of these six forms of astral activity springs from a cosmic
source of its own which, with reference to the particular visible
planet related to it, can be designated as 'Moon', 'Mercury',

'Venus', on the one hand, 'Saturn', 'Jupiter', 'Mars', on the other. There is a seventh sphere which functions as a mediator between these two groups and which, for a similar reason, can be termed 'Sun'. (Note that in the names given here those of Mercury and Venus appear in reversed order. This is how they were used in former times. In a cosmology which aspires at a qualitative understanding of the universe, it is necessary to return to this usage in view of the qualities represented by these names.)

Before we embark upon a description of some effects of the seven astral activities, let it be stressed that the true picture of the relationship between the apparent effect and the relevant sphere of causation should not be lost sight of. While it is justified from the point of view we have here developed to say simply that 'Saturn', 'Mercury', etc., have this or that effect, this must not be taken to mean that the effect in question has its cause in the visible planet. As we shall see, there are rhythms in earthly nature which coincide with the recurring constellation of some particular planet. But this does not mean that the observable cosmic motion is itself the cause of the observable terrestrial event. Both must rather be conceived as effects of a common cause, which itself consists in certain changes in the dynamic condition of the particular astral force-sphere. This, then, brings us to the question of the role of a planet's physical body within the totality of its astral being.

Strange though the picture of the universe we have here arrived at may appear, if compared with the customary one, it would be wrong to regard it as incompatible with modern scientific thought. For in another field of observation a very similar picture has already imposed itself on the human mind as a result of modern scientific research. It is the picture of glandular action in the human body. Observation has taught to distinguish between the gland as a spatially limited physical organ and the gland as a functional sphere, and to conceive of the latter as the essential gland. Seen thus, 'the spatial and temporal dimensions of each gland are equal to those of the entire organism' (A. Carrel). In this way we come to see the human organism as a realm of interpenetrating spheres of distinctive physiological activities. Each of these activities is anchored somewhere in the physical body by the anatomically discernible gland-body, and the latter's relationship to the functional sphere is such that a gland's 'physiological individuality is far more comprehensive than its anatomical individuality'.

We need only translate this statement into its macrocosmic counterpart to obtain another statement which expresses fittingly the relationship of the visible body of a planet to the functional (astral) sphere indicated by its orbit. Then we shall say that 'a planet's astral individuality is far more comprehensive than its astronomical individuality'.

It should be observed that the step we have here taken, by using a conception obtained through microcosmic observation to help us to find the answer to a question put to us by the macrocosm, complies with one of the fundamentals of our method of research, namely, to allow 'the heavens to explain the earth, and the earth the heavens' (Rudolf Steiner).

* * * * *

With these preparatory remarks in mind, we can now enter on a description of some selected phenomena with the aim of recognising them as manifestations of various astral activities, and so of becoming more familiar with the characteristics of these activities themselves.

Let us call to mind once more the three stages in the process of sublimation at the sulphuric pole of the alchemical polarity, as it manifests itself biologically in the successive stages of plant formation, and meteorologically in the order of cloud forms. We can now say that the sap-bearing parts of the plant are predominantly under the sway of the Moon-forces, the happenings in the leaves, where the air is particularly at work, under that of Mercury, and the inflorescence, where the element of fire plays so predominant a role, under that of Venus. In this last respect, Ruskin's description of the plant's stage of flowering (page 421), with its unmistakable Venus-character, is a fine example of the certainty of qualitative experience of cosmic properties to which artistically enlivened seeing leads, because it is a 'seeing with the eyes of the body in living interconnection with the eyes of the spirit'. Moreover, the fact that cosmic quality becomes so conspicuous just at this stage of the plant's life-cycle, shows us that the plant here passes over from the stage of its 'doing' to the stage of its 'suffering' as a result of the incipient action of the opposite astral forces. Similarly, in the meteorological sphere, we can read in the Stratus-formation the working of the Moon, in the Cumuli that of Mercury – where in fact the ancients saw the god Mercurius (Hermes) as particularly active – and in the Cirri that of Venus. Here the same things happen between the elements of Air and Fire as when below on the sea, through the power of the wind, the water foams up, thus forming the traditional birth-place of Venus (Aphrodite).

The same succession of stages is found in the human organism in the transformation of food to the point where it passes into Chaos. As with the functional spheres of the endocrine glands, which have already presented themselves to us as a replica of the astral organisation of the universe, we discover in the special power of the digestive juices, such as ptyalin, pepsin, etc., another type of the body's astral activity.

As the three sub-solar planetary spheres are responsible for events of a 'sulphurous' character, so are the three supra-solar spheres responsible for those of a 'saline' character. From the realm of plant life we may take the woody and barklike formation of the trees as representing the operation of Saturn-forces. Similarly, all that goes on in the organising of the single leaf, and particularly in the organisation of the countless separate leaves which make up the foliage of a tree into a unified whole, the characteristic crown of a tree, is an example of the work of Jupiter. Both activities are assisted by the force of Mars, which directs them from the cosmic periphery toward the single physical object, as in the formation of starch-grains from the carbon of the surrounding air with the assistance of light and water, and in general in all processes of 'spiritual assimilation'. In the earth's meteorological sphere we find a happening characteristic of Mars-activity in the transition of imponderable matter into the ponderable condition through snow and rain, and in particular through lightning.

In man himself, the activity of the Saturn-force is most clearly manifest in the formation of the hard skull, that of Jupiter, the planet of 'Wisdom', in the formation of the complicated structure of the brain, which enables it to co-ordinate the bodily and psychic functions of the entire man. Mars is active in the blood, endowing it with the power to solidify the various formative processes into discrete organic formations.

In order that Form should come about, the forces of Saturn are required; for the formative process to take place in Wisdom-filled order, Jupiter's forces are necessary. If form and order are to become manifest in the realm of earthly substance, both require the assistance of Mars. We can best form an idea of the part which Mars contributes to the coming into being of the world of Form in nature if we observe what takes place when we make use of speech as a medium for expressing our thoughts. In order to be able to shape a thought we have to participate in the formative force of Saturn. We depend upon Jupiter to bring about logical connection between the single thoughts. To announce them to the world, we need the motive force of Mars, which enables us so to set external matter in motion that it becomes a carrier and relayer of our thoughts. (We here touch upon the connection of the acoustic movements of the air with the astral forces which will occupy us more closely in the next part of this chapter.)

Between the two groups of astral force operating in this manner, the Sun acts as a mediating element through its double function of supporting the activity of the three lower planets by means of its heat and of conveying to the earth, through its light, the forces of the three higher planets. In the human micro-cosm the Sun-forces accomplish a corresponding task by means of the influences which radiate from the heart through the body along the paths taken by the blood.

* * * * *

When we discussed the relationship between the visible plan-etary body and its force-sphere, we hinted at the existence of certain rhythms in earthly nature which coincide with the periods of rotation of these bodies, while emphasising that both were to be regarded as effects of a common dynamic cause. That hap-penings of a rhythmic nature should be particularly characteristic effects of astral activities will be readily understood when one considers the function of the rhythmic system in man as a mediator between the two polarically opposite systems. Wherever two poles meet, there oscillation arises, because the process, thus generated, assumes alternately the character more of one pole or of the other. On this fact all mechanical oscillation depends; similarly the oscillating property of certain electrical circuits, and so also any other rhythmical happening. Among those shown by the earth on a large scale, a few may here be mentioned.

There is, above all, the regular growing and withering process of the earth's vegetable cover in its interconnection with the changing positions of sun and earth. Another such rhythm of a similarly striking character is that of the tides, running parallel with the changing positions of moon and earth. Scientific thought in the past was naturally driven to picture the regular change between ebb and flow in the sea as an effect of the moon's gravitational influence on the earth. Now, ebb and flow do not alternate only once during a single revolution of the earth, but twice, which means that there is a second elevation of the water diametrically opposite that which arises below the body of the moon. Mechanistic thought has taken pains to remove this apparent contradiction of the gravitational explanation by apply-ing various hypotheses, all naturally of a mechanical kind. A way of thinking which does not aim at 'explaining' nature, but at 'reading' it, is not in need of such hypotheses. For, prompted by such a way of thinking to look for other phenomena which form a further letter in the same word in nature's script, we notice, besides the phenomenon of the rising and falling surface of the liquid cover of the earth, a similar happening in her vegetable cover in the form of a rising and falling of the organic saps, again in unison with the phases of the moon. Evidently, this cannot be ascribed to a gravitational pull of the moon. Rather do both events inform us of an alternating process of interconnecting and disconnecting levity and gravity which is in resonance with the astral rhythm peculiar to the moon-sphere.[4]

Among the processes in the human body which happen in a rhythmic way, that of the female fertility period is known to follow, not in phase but in duration, the lunar rhythm. Here, too, it is in the first place the liquid element which is subject to this rhythm. Once again it is the human microcosm which allows us to recognise especially clearly the specific quality of the dynamic in question, in this case of the lunar astrality. In order that the substance of the germ-cell may be in a receptive condition for the higher formative forces which, from out of the cosmic environment, bring forth the new human form, this substance must be withdrawn from its domination by the earth. This indeed is the function of the Moon. The germ-cell is joined through the act of fertilisation by the forces of Mercury and Venus, which help it to enter into the state of chaos suitable for creative interaction.

On the other hand, the Saturn-rhythm can be found in the formation of the human skeleton. Observation has shown that, even if the skeleton, as usually happens, stops growing in the early twenties, it nevertheless reaches its final shape and its final hardening only between the twenty-eighth and thirtieth years. This is the time in man's life when Saturn returns for the first time to the position in which it stood relatively to the earth at his birth, or, more correctly, at his conception.

* * * * *

Even among the mineral substances of the earth there are some that are under the sway of the planetary rhythms. In connection with our discussion of electricity in Chapter XIII we spoke of the special function of the metals as the representatives of the middle alchemical quality. As one of the characteristics which reveal this function we mentioned the peculiar capacity of metals to behave as 'solid fluids'. This exceptional place among the mineral substances of the earth, the metals owe to their close association with the extra-terrestrial astral forces of the universe.

In this field, too, we owe to Rudolf Steiner the timely renewal of an ancient knowledge concerning the distinctive characters of seven metals, each of which stands in a special relation to one of the seven planetary force-spheres, as shown in the following table:

Saturn	Lead
Jupiter	Tin
Mars	Iron
Sun	Gold
Venus	Copper
Mercury	Quicksilver
Moon	Silver

Observations of the behaviour of these metals in connection with the positions of the corresponding planets have been carried out by L. Kolisko over many years. Their salts were submitted, singly and in combination, to certain capillary effects, and the results have shown that the earth bears in her womb substances whose dynamic condition follows exactly the events in the planetary realm of the universe.[5]

If we survey what up to this point our observation has taught us about the nature of the astral forces, we realise that they are the generators of what — in its widest implication — we can term as 'soul', both inside single living beings and outside in nature and in the whole universe. For to the activity of these forces is due all that exists and happens in one form or another as nature's 'deeds' and 'sufferings', and so has some relation to our own volitional and sensational being.

To see the world in this way as endowed with *soul* is an aspect which was by no means unfamiliar to man in former times.

It was naturally lost when the onlooker-consciousness awoke. In this respect it is of historical significance that the same man, G.A. Borelli (1608-79), a member of the Florentine Academy, who was the first to inquire into the movements of the animal and human body from a purely mechanical point of view, made the first attempt to deduce the planetary movements from a purely physical cause.[6] Through this fact an impulse comes to expression which, in analogy with the *Contra Levitatem* of the Florentine Academicians, we may term *Contra Animam*. And just as we set against the former our present-day *Pro Levitate* by extending scientific inquiry to the etheric realm so do we have now set against the latter, by extending our observations to the astral realm of the universe, the required *Pro Anima*.

HEARING AS DEED

In the last part of Chapter XIX we said that we have the right to employ results of investigation carried out by higher faculties of spiritual perception without contradicting our principle of seeking to understand the phenomenal world by reading it, provided our doing so helps to enhance our own reading activity, and provided it can be shown that the acquisition of the higher faculties of perception is a direct continuation of the training we have to apply to our mind and senses to make them capable of such reading. As regards the forces of astral character, the first of these two conditions has been fulfilled by the observations we have already worked through in this chapter. We have still to show that the second condition is equally fulfilled.

The faculty of the mind which permits direct investigation of the astral realm was called (spiritual) Inspiration by Rudolf Steiner, who thereby restored to this term, also, its proper meaning. We have already indicated that this faculty resides in the sense of hearing in the same way that the faculty of Imagination — as we have found — resides in the sense of seeing. In order to understand why it is this particular sense which comes into consideration here, we have to consider that the phenomena through which the astral world manifests most directly are all of a

rhythmic nature. Now, the sense through which our soul penetrates with direct experience into some outer rhythmic activity
is the sense of hearing, our aural perceptions being conveyed
by certain rhythmic movements of the air. In what follows we
shall see how the study of both the outer acoustic phenomena
and our own psycho-physical make-up in the region of the
acoustic sense, leads to an understanding of the nature of Inspiration and of how it can be trained.

* * * * *

Among all our sense-perceptions, sound is unique in making
itself perceptible in two quite different ways — via the ear as a
direct sense experience and via the eye (potentially also via the
senses of touch and movement) in the form of certain mechanical
movements, such as those of a string or a tuning fork. Hence the
world-spectator, as soon as he began to investigate acoustic
phenomena scientifically, found himself in a unique position. In
all other fields of perception, with the exception of the purely
mechanical processes, the transition to non-stereoscopic colourless
observation had the effect that the world-content of the naive
consciousness simply ceased to exist, leaving the ensuing hiatus
to be filled in by a pattern of imagined kinematic happenings —
for example, colour by 'ether'-vibrations, heat by molecular
movements. Not so in the sphere of acoustics. For here a part of
the entire event, on account of its genuine kinetic character,
remains a content of actual observation.

In consequence, the science of acoustics became for the
scientific mind of man a model of the required division between
the 'subjective' (that is, for scientific considerations non-existent)
and the 'objective' (that is, the purely kinematic) part of observation. The field of aural perception seemed to justify the procedure of collecting a mass of phenomena, stripped of all that is
experienced by man's soul in meeting them, and of assembling
them under a purely abstract concept, 'sound'.

Professor Heisenberg, in his lecture (quoted at the beginning of Chapter I) on the way in which the scientific interrogation of nature has deliberately limited itself, draws attention to the fact that a full knowledge of the science of optics in its present form might be acquired merely through theoretical study by one born blind, yet without his ever getting to know what *light* is. Heisenberg could, of course, have said the same of the science of acoustics in regard to one born deaf. But we can go a step further by asking how far a deaf and a blind person could get towards *establishing* the respective science. The answer must be that, whereas the person lacking sight would not of himself be in a position to establish a science of optics, it would be well within the scope of the deaf man to establish a science of acoustics. For all the processes essential to a physical acoustics are accessible to the eye and other senses.

In order to make our experience of hearing a finger-post pointing the way to an understanding of the faculty of Inspiration innate in man, we must first of all seek to transform acoustics from a 'deaf' into a 'hearing' science, just as Goethe turned the theory of colour from a colour-blind into a colour-seeing science.

*   *   *   *   *

Following our procedure in the case of optics, we select from the total field of acoustic phenomena a defined realm specially suited to our purpose. As it was then the spectrum, so it will be now the so-called *quality* of sound, or *tone-colour*.

By this term in acoustics is understood a property possessed by sound apart from pitch and volume, and dependent on the nature of the source from which a tone is derived. It is the tone-colour by which the tone of a violin, for instance, is distinguished from a tone of equal intensity and pitch produced by a flute. Similarly, two musical instruments of the same kind are distinguished from each other by tone-colour.

Tone-colour plays a specially significant part in human and animal voices. Not only has each individual voice its unique colour, but the colour varies in one and the same person or animal, according to the prevailing mood. Moreover, by uttering the various vowels of his language, man is able to impart varying colour to the sounds of his speech. For the difference we experience when a tone is sung on the vowel 'a' or the vowel 'e', etc., derives from the particular colour given by the vowel to that tone.

Among the discoveries of the last century in the realm of acoustics, there is one which especially helped to establish a purely kinematic conception of sound. Helmholtz showed that tones which to our ears seem to have a clear and definite pitch may be split up by a series of resonators into a number of different tones, each of them sounding at a different pitch. The lowest of these has the pitch which our ears attach to the entire tone. Thus in any ordinary tone there may be distinguished a 'fundamental' tone and a series of 'overtones'. Helmholtz further showed that the particular series of overtones into which a tone can be resolved is responsible for the colour of that tone as a whole. Naturally, this meant for the prevailing mode of thinking that the experience of the colour of a tone had to be interpreted as the effect of a kind of acoustical adding together of a number of single tone perceptions (very much as Newton had interpreted 'white' light as the outcome of an optical adding together of a certain number of single colour perceptions).

The picture becomes different if we apply to the aural experience Goethe's theorem that, in so far as we are deluded, it is not by our senses but by our own reasoning. For we then realise that sounds never occur of themselves without some tone-colour, whilst physically 'pure' tones − those that represent simple harmonic motions − exist only as an artificial laboratory product. The colour of a tone, therefore, is an integral part of it, and must not be conceived of as an additional attribute resulting from a summing up of a number of colourless tone experiences.

Further, if we compare our experiences of the two kinds of tone, they tell us that through the quality or colour of the natural tone something of a soul-nature, pleasant or unpleasant, speaks to us, whereas 'pure' tones have a soulless character.

Resolving normal tones by Helmholtz's method (useful as it

is for certain purposes) amounts to something like dissecting a living, ensouled organism into its members; only the parts of the corpse remain in our hands.

* * * * *

Having thus established that the psychic content of aural experience forms an integral part of the tone-phenomenon as such, we must seek to understand how the kinetic process which is indispensable for its appearance comes to be the vehicle for the manifestation of 'soul' in the manner described.

To this end we must first of all heed the fact that the movement which mediates aural sensation is one of alternating expansion and contraction. Expressed in the language of the four Elements, this means that the air thus set in vibration approaches alternately the condition of the watery element beneath it and of the element of fire (heat) above it. Thus, in a regular rhythm, the air comes near the border of its ponderable existence. Purely physical considerations make us realise that this entails another rhythmic occurrence in the realm of heat. For with each expansion of the air heat is absorbed by it and thereby rendered space-bound, while with every contraction of the air heat is set free and returns to its indigenous condition — that is, it becomes free from spatial limitations.

This picture of the complete happenings during an acoustic event enables us to understand how such a process can be the vehicle for conveying certain astral impulses in such a way that, when met by them, we grow aware of them in the form of a direct sensation. Taking as a model the expression 'transparent' for the perviousness of a substance to light, we may say that the air, when in a state of acoustic vibration, becomes 'trans-audient' for astral impulses, and that the nature of these vibrations determines which particular impulses are let through.

What we have here found to be the true role of the kinetic part of the acoustic process applies equally to sounds which are emitted by living beings, and to those that arise when lifeless material is set mechanically in motion, as in the case of ordinary noises or the musical production of tone. There is only this difference: in the first instance the vibrations of the sound-producing organs have their origin in the activity of the astral part of the living being, and it is this activity which comes to the recipient's direct experience in the form of aural impressions; in the second instance the air, by being brought externally into a state of vibration, exerts a kind of suction on the astral realm which pervades the air, with the result that parts of this realm become physically audible. For we are constantly surrounded by supersensible sounds, and the state of motion of the air determines which of them become perceptible to us in our present state of consciousness.

* * * * *

At this point our mind turns to a happening in the macro-telluric sphere of the earth, already considered in another connection, which now assumes the significance of an ur-phenomenon revealing the astral generation of sound. This is the thunderstorm, constituted for our external perception by the two events: lightning and thunder.

Remembering what we have found earlier (Chapter XII) to be the nature of lightning, we are now in a position to say: a supra-terrestrial astral impulse obtains control of the earth's etheric and physical spheres of force in such a way that etheric substance is thrown into the condition of space-bound physical matter. This substance is converted by stages from the state of light and heat via that of air into the liquid and, in certain cases, into the solid state (hail). To this we now add that, while in lightning the first effect of the etheric-physical interference of the astral impulse appears before our eyes, our ears give us direct awareness of this impulse in the form of thunder. It is this fact which accounts for the awe-inspiring character of thunderstorms.

* * * * *

The picture we have thus received of the outer part of the acoustic process has a counterpart in the processes inside the organ of hearing. Hearing, like seeing, depends upon the co-operation of both poles of the human organism – nerve and blood. In the case of hearing, however, they play a reversed role. In the eye, the primary effect of light-impressions is on the nervous part; a secondary response to them comes from the blood organisation. In the ear, the receptive organ for the astral impulses pressing in upon it is a part which belongs to the body's limb system, while it is the nervous organisation which functions as the organ of response. For in the ear the sound-waves are first of all taken over by the so-called ossicles, three small bones in the middle ear which, when examined with the Goethean eye, appear to be a complete metamorphosis of an arm or a leg. They are instrumental in transferring the outer acoustic movements to the fluid contained in the inner ear, whence these are communicated to the entire fluid system of the body and lastly to the muscular system.[7] We shall speak of this in detail later on. Let it be stated here that the peculiar role played by the larynx in hearing, already referred to by us in Chapter XVI, is one of the symptoms which tells of the participation of the muscular system in the internal acoustic process.

Psychologically, the difference between ear and eye is that aural perceptions work much more directly on the human will – that is, on the part of our astral organisation connected with the limb system. Whereas eye-impressions stimulate us in the first place to think, ear-impressions stimulate us to ... dance. The whole art of dancing, from its original sacred character up to its degenerate modern forms, is based upon the limb system being the recipient of acoustic impressions.

In order to understand how the muscles respond to the outer astral impulses which reach us through our ear, we must first understand what happens in the muscles when our will makes use of them for bodily motion. In this case, too, the muscular system is the organ through which certain astral impulses, this time arising out of the body's own astral member, come to expression. Moreover, the movement of the muscles, though not outwardly perceptible, is quite similar to acoustic movements outside the body. For whenever a muscle is caused to alter its length, it will perform some kind of vibration — a vibration characterised even by a definite pitch, which differs in different people. Since throughout life our body is never entirely without movement, we are thus in a constant state of inward sounding. The muscular system is capable of this vibration because during the body's initial period of growth the bones increase in length to a much greater extent than do the sinews and muscles. Hence the latter arrive at a condition of elastic tension not unlike that of the strings of a musical instrument.[8]

In the case of bodily movement, therefore, the muscles are tone-producers, whereas in acoustic perceptions they are tone-receivers. What, then, is it that prevents an acoustic perception from actually setting the limbs in motion, and, instead, enables our sentient being to take hold of the astral impulse invading our muscles?

This impediment comes from the contribution made by the nervous system to the auditory process. In order to understand the nature of this contribution we must remember the role played by the blood in seeing. It was found by us to consist in the bringing about of that state of equilibrium without which we should experience light merely as a pain-producing agent. Similarly, the perception of sound requires the presence of a certain state of equilibrium between the nerve system and the limb system. In this case, however, a lack of equilibrium would result not in pain, but in ecstasy. For if acoustic impressions played directly into our limb-system, with nothing to hold them in check, every tone we encounter would compel us to an outward manifestation of astral activity. We should become part of the tone-process itself, forced to transform it by the volitional part of our astral organisation into spatial movement. That this does not happen is because the participation of the nervous system serves to damp

down the potential ecstasy. Hence it is more or less left to the
sentient part of the astral organisation — that is, the part free from
the physical body — to partake in the astral processes underlying
the tone occurrences.

Our picture of the particular interaction of the two polar
bodily systems in the acts of seeing and hearing now enables us
to understand more clearly how these two spheres of perception
overlap in man — a phenomenon to which we had to refer when
discussing in the previous chapter the characteristics of sound-
ether. For we have seen how the system which in seeing is the
receiving organ, works in hearing as the responding one, and
vice versa. As a result, optical impressions are accompanied by dim
sensations of sound, and aural impressions by dim sensations of
colour.

* * * * *

We have obtained a sufficiently clear picture of the organisation of our sense of hearing to see where the way lies that leads
from hearing with the ears of the body to hearing with the ears
of the spirit, that is, to the inspirative perception of the astral
world.

In the psycho-physical condition which is characteristic of
our present-day consciousness, the participation of our astral
organisation in any happenings of the outer astral world depends
on our corporeal motor system being stimulated by the acoustic
motions of the air, or of some other suitable medium contacting
our body. For it is only in this way that our astral organisation
is brought into the sympathetic vibrations necessary for perceiving
outer astral happenings. In order that astral events other than
those manifesting acoustically may become accessible to our
consciousness, our own astral being must become capable of
vibrating in tune with them, just as if we were hearing them — that
is, we must be able to rouse our astral forces to an activity similar
to that of hearing, yet without any physical stimulus. The way to
this consists in training ourselves to experience the deeds and

sufferings of nature as if they were the deeds and sufferings of a beloved friend.

It is thus that we shall learn to hear the soul of the universe directly speaking to us, as Lorenzo divined it, when his love for Jessica made him feel in love with all the world, and he exclaimed:

'There's not the smallest orb which thou behold'st
But in his motion like an angel sings,
Still quiring to the young-eyed cherubins, —
Such harmony is in immortal souls;
But whilst this muddy vesture of decay
Doth grossly close it in, we cannot hear it.'

KEPLER AND THE 'MUSIC OF THE SPHERES'

'One must choose one's saints ... and so I have chosen mine, and before all others, Kepler. In my ante-room he has ever a niche of his own, with his bust in it.'

This opinion of Goethe's must surprise us in view of the fact that Kepler was the discoverer of the three laws called after him, one of which is supposed to have laid the foundation for Newton's mechanical conception of the universe. In what follows it will be shown how wrong it is to see in Kepler a forerunner of the mechanistic conception of the world; how near, in reality, his world-picture is to the one to which we are led by working along Goetheanistic lines; and how right therefore Goethe was in his judgment on Kepler.

Goethe possessed a sensitive organ for the historical appropriateness of human ideas. As an illustration of this it may be mentioned how he reacted when someone suggested to him that Joachim Jungius — an outstanding German thinker, contemporary of Bacon, van Helmont, etc. — had anticipated his idea of the metamorphosis of the plant. This remark worried Goethe, not because he could not endure the thought of being anticipated (see his treatment of K.F. Wolff,) but because this would have run counter to the meaning of man's historical development as he saw it. 'Why do I regard as essential the question whether

Jungius conceived the idea of metamorphosis as we know it? My answer is, that it is most significant in the history of the sciences, *when* a penetrating and vitalising maxim comes to be uttered. Therefore it is not only of importance that Jungius has not expressed this maxim; but it is of highest significance that he was positively unable to express it — as we boldly assert.'[9]

For the same reason Goethe knew it would be historically unjustified to expect that Kepler could have conceived an aspect of the universe implicit in his own conception of nature. Hence it did not disturb him in his admiration for Kepler, that through him the Copernican aspect of the universe had become finally established in the modern mind — that is, an aspect which, as we have seen, is invalid as a means of forming a truly dynamic conception of the world.

In forming his picture of the universe, it is true, Copernicus was concerned with nothing but the spatial movements of the luminous entities discernible in the sky, without any regard to their actual nature and dynamic interrelationships. Hence his world-picture — as befits the spectator-form of human consciousness which was coming to birth in his own time — is a purely kinematic one. As such it has validity for a certain sphere of human observation.

When Kepler, against the hopes of his forerunner and friend, Tycho Brahe, accepted the heliocentric standpoint and made it the basis of his observations, he did so out of his understanding of what was the truth for his own time. And his own time required a conception of the universe in correspondence with man's spectator-relationship to it. This is what prompted him to accept the Copernican system. His observations, however, based on this acceptance, enabled him to improve Copernicus's picture considerably by recognising the planetary orbits as being not cyclical but elliptical, and by discovering the basic laws that govern the rate of the single planet's motion and the ratio of the planets' respective times of revolution round the sun: the three Keplerian Laws. In keeping with the outlook of the genuine spectator, these laws are of purely kinematic character: i.e. they contain no statement of the dynamic cause of the motions. Kepler also spoke of the universe dynamically, but where he did so we find him speaking out of an entirely different conceptual background; in fact one which shows that he had some deep intuitive knowledge of the world's astrality.

It was left to Newton to conceive of the planetary movements as caused by the same force that causes physical bodies on the earth to assume the smallest possible distance from the earth's centre. We have seen in Chapter XI (p. 191) how Ruskin turned against Newton in this respect by pointing out that the upward-acting process on which depends the formation of the apple, high up on the tree, must be regarded as no less fundamental for forming a picture of the universe than the downward-acting process which causes the apple to fall. Although no explicit statement by Goethe concerning this part of Newton's ideas is known, Faust's dispute with Mephistopheles over the origin of the earth's mountains, quoted in Chapter II, and Goethe's general outlook on nature, leave no doubt as to how he would have expressed himself on this problem.

It has been found that through a simple mathematical transformation, the equation which represents Kepler's third law can be transformed into the formula representing Newton's law of gravitation, and vice versa. This has given rise to the conviction, held universally ever since, that Kepler was a forerunner of Newton's mechanistic conception of the universe. Yet, something that can be proved mathematically need not coincide with objective reality. And reality, if properly read, speaks a different language. To see this, let us discuss Kepler's third law in a truly Keplerian manner.[10]

In textbooks and encyclopaedias it is usually said that the discovery of the third law was the surprising result of Kepler's fantastic attempt to prove by external observation what was once taught in the school of Pythagoras, namely, that (in Wordsworth's language):

'By one pervading spirit
Of tones and numbers all things are controlled.'

Actually, Kepler's great work, *Harmonices Mundi*,[11] in the last part
of which he announces his third law, is entirely devoted to proving
the truth of the Pythagorean doctrine that the universe is ordered
according to the laws of music. This doctrine sprang from the
gift of spiritual hearing still possessed by Pythagoras, by which
he could perceive the harmonies of the spheres. It was the aim of
his school to keep this faculty alive as long as possible, and with
its aid to establish a communicable world-conception. The
Pythagorean teaching became the foundation of all later cosmo-
logical thinking, right up to the age which was destined to bring
to birth the spectator-relationship of man's consciousness with the
world. Thus it was left to Copernicus to give mankind the first
truly non-Pythagorean picture of the universe.

When Kepler declared himself in favour of the heliocentric
aspect, as indicated by Copernicus, he acknowledged that the
universe had grown dumb for man's inner ear. Yet, besides his
strong impulse to meet the true needs of his time, there were
inner voices telling him of secrets that were hidden behind the
veil woven by man's physical perceptions. One of these secrets
was the musical order of the world. Such knowledge, however,
could not induce him to turn to older world-conceptions in his
search for truth. He had no need of them, because there was yet
another voice in him which told him that the spiritual order of
the world must somehow manifest itself in the body of the world
as it lay open to physical perception. Just as a musical instrument,
if it is to be a perfect means of bringing forth music, must bear in
its build the very laws of music, so must the body of the universe,
as the instrument on which the harmonies of the spheres play
their spiritual music, bear in its proportions a reflection of these
harmonies. Kepler was sure that investigation of the world's
body, provided it was carried out by means of pure observation
and intuitive judgment, must needs lead to a re-establishment of
the ancient truth in a form appropriate to the modern mind.
Thus Kepler, guided by an ancient spiritual conception of the
world, could devote himself to confirming its truth by the most
up-to-date methods of research. That his search was not in vain,

the following examination of his third law will show.

Through this law a certain relation is expressed between the spatial dimensions of the different planetary spheres and the time needed by the relevant planet to circle once round the circumference of its own sphere. It says: 'The squares of the periodic times of the planets are always in the same proportion as the cubes of their mean distances from the sun.'

In mathematical symbols this reads: $\dfrac{t_1^2}{t_2^2} = \dfrac{r_1^3}{r_2^3}$

In this formula the spatial entities in the form in which they appear express something that is directly conceivable — r^3 representing the measure of a volume in three-dimensional space. The same cannot be said of the entities which have to do with time. For 'squared time' is something with which our conception of time is unable to connect any concrete idea. We are therefore called upon to find out what form we can give this side of the equation so as to express the time-factor in a manner which is in accord with our conception of time, that is, in linear form.[12] This form readily suggests itself if we consider that we have here to do with a ratio of squares. For such a ratio may be resolved into a ratio of two simple ratios.

In this way the equation — $\dfrac{r_1^3}{r_1^3} = \dfrac{t_1^2}{t_2^2}$

assumes the form — $\dfrac{r_1^3}{r_2^3} = \dfrac{t_1/t_2}{t_2/t_1}$

The right-hand side of the equation is now constituted by the double ratio of the linear values of the periods of two planets, and this is something with which we can connect a quite concrete idea.

To see this, let us choose the periods of two definite planets — say, Earth and Jupiter. For these the equation assumes the following form ('J' and 'E' indicating 'Jupiter' and 'Earth' respectively):

$$\frac{r_J^3}{r_E^3} = \frac{t_J/t_E}{t_E/t_J}$$

Let us now see what meaning we can attach to the two expressions $\dfrac{t_J}{t_E}$ and $\dfrac{t_E}{t_J}$.

During one revolution of Jupiter round the sun the earth goes round the sun 12 times. This we are wont to express by saying that Jupiter needs 12 earth-years for one such revolution; in symbols:

$$\frac{t_J}{t_E} = \frac{12}{1}$$

To find the analogous expression for the reciprocal ratio:

$$\frac{t_E}{t_J} = \frac{1}{12}$$

we must obviously form the concept 'Jupiter-year', which covers one revolution of Jupiter, just as the concept 'earth-year' covers one revolution of the earth (always round the sun). Measured in this time-scale, the earth needs for one of its revolutions $\frac{1}{12}$ of a Jupiter year.

With the help of these concepts we are now able to express the double ratio of the planetary periods in the following simplified way. If we suppose the measuring of the two planetary periods to be carried out not by the same time-scale, but *each by the time-scale of the other*, the formula becomes:

$$\frac{r_J^3}{r_E^3} = \frac{t_J/t_E}{t_E/t_J} = \frac{period\ of\ Jupiter\ measured\ in\ Earth\ years}{period\ of\ Earth\ measured\ in\ Jupiter\ years}$$

Interpreted in this manner, Kepler's third law discloses an intimate interrelatedness of each planet to all the others as co-members of the same cosmic whole. For the equation now tells us that the solar times of the various planets are regulated in such a way that for any two of them the ratio of these times, *measured in their mutual time-units*, is the same as the ratio of the spaces swept out by their (solar) orbits.

Further, by having the various times of its members thus tuned to one another, our cosmic system shows itself to be ordered on a principle which is essentially musical. To see this, we need only recall that the musical value of a given note is determined by its relation to other notes, whether they sound together in a chord, or in succession as melody. A 'C' alone is *musically* undefined. It receives its musical character from its interval-relation to some other note, say, 'G', together with which it forms a Fifth. As the lower note of this interval, 'C' bears a definite character; and so does 'G' as the upper note.

Now we know that each interval represents a definite ratio between the periodicities of its two notes. In the case of the Fifth the ratio is 2 : 3 (in the natural scale). This means that the lower note receives its character from being related to the upper note by the ratio 2 : 3. Similarly, the upper note receives its character from the ratio 3 : 2. The specific character of an interval arising out of the merging of its two notes, therefore is determined by the ratio of their ratios. In the case of the Fifth this is 4 : 9. It is this ratio, in fact, which underlies our experience of a Fifth.

The cosmic factor corresponding to the periodicity of the single note in music is the orbital period of the single planet. To the musical interval formed by two notes corresponds the double ratio of the periods of any two planets. Regarded thus, Kepler's law can be expressed as follows: *The spatial ordering of our planetary system is determined by the interval-relation in which the different planets stand to each other.*

By thus unlocking the ideal content hidden in Kepler's third law, we are at the same time enabled to do justice to the way in which he himself announced his discovery. At first sight it may certainly seem surprising that Kepler announced his discovery in the form in which it has henceforth engraved itself in the modern mind, while refraining from that analysis of it which we have applied to it here. Yet, in this respect also Kepler proves to have remained true to himself. There is on the one hand, the form in which Kepler pronounced his discovery; there is, on the other, the context in which he made his pronouncement. We have already pointed out that the third law forms part of Kepler's comprehensive work, *Harmonices Mundi*. To the modern critic's understanding it appears there like an erratic block. For Kepler this was different. While publishing his discovery in precisely the form in which it is conceived by a mind bent on pure observation, he gave it a setting by which he left no doubt as to his own conception of its ideal content. And as a warning to the future reader not to overlook the message conveyed by this arrangement, he introduced the section of his book which contains the announcement of the law, with the mysterious words about himself: 'I have stolen the golden vessels of the Egyptians from which to furnish for my God a holy shrine far from Egypt's confines.'

Chapter XXI

KNOW THYSELF

Our inquiries have led us to a picture of man as a sensible-super-
physical organism composed of three dynamic aggregates —
physical, etheric, astral. As three rungs of a spiritual ladder they
point to a fourth, which represents that particular power in man
by which he distinguishes himself from all other beings in nature.
For what makes man differ from all these is that he is not only
fitted, as they are, with a once-for-all given mode of spiritual-
physical existence peculiar to himself, but that he is endowed with
the possibility of transforming his existence by dint of his free
will — that indeed his manhood is based on this capacity for
self-willed Becoming.

To this fourth principle in man we can give no better name
than that which every human being can apply to himself alone
and to no other, and which no other can apply to him. This is
the name, 'I'. In truth, we describe man in his entirety only if
we ascribe to him in addition to a physical, etheric and astral
organism, the possession, of an I (Ego).

Naturally, our previous studies have afforded many opportunities for observing the nature and mode of activity of the I.
Still, at the conclusion of these studies it is not redundant to form
a concise picture of this part of man's being, with particular
regard to how it works within the three other principles as its
sheaths. For in modern psychology, not excluding the branch
of it where efforts are made to penetrate into deeper regions of
man's being, nothing is less well understood than the true nature
of man's egoity.

* * * * *

In order to recognise the peculiar function of the I in man, we must first be clear as to how he differs from the other kingdoms of nature, and how they differ from one another with respect to the mode of action of the physical, etheric and astral forces.

The beings of all the kingdoms of nature are endowed with an aggregate of physical forces in the form of a material body subject to gravity. The same cannot be said of the etheric forces. Only where life is present as an inherent principle – that is, in plant, animal and man – is ether at work in the form of an individual etheric organisation, while the mineral is formed by the universal ether from outside. Where life prevails, we are met by the phenomena of birth and death. When a living organism comes to birth, an individual ether-organism is formed out of the general etheric substance of the universe. The death of such an organism consists in the separation of the etheric from the physical part and the dissolution of both in their respective mother-realms. So long as an organism is alive, its physical form is maintained by the ether-body present in it.

Our studies have shown that the plant is not devoid of the operation of astral forces. In the plant's life-cycle this comes to clearest expression in its florescence, but it is a working of the astral forces from outside, very much as the ether works on the mineral. As a symptom of this fact we may recall the dependence of the plant on the various outer astronomical rhythms.

It is only in animal and man that we find the astral forces working in the form of separate astral bodies. This accounts for their capacity for sensation and volition. Besides the alternation of birth and death, they experience the rhythm of sleeping and waking. Sleep occurs when the astral body leaves the physical and etheric bodies in order to expand into its planetary mother-sphere, whence it gathers new energy. During this time its action on the physical-etheric aggregate remaining upon earth is similar to that of the astral cosmos upon the plant.

Again, in the animal kingdom the ego-principle works as an external force in the form of various 'group-soul' activities — as we have already called them — which control and regulate the life of the different animal species. It is in the group-ego of the species that we have to look for the source of the wisdom-filled instincts which we meet in the single animals.

Only in man does the ego-principle enter as an individual entity into the single physico-etheric-astral organism. Here, however, the succession of stages we have outlined comes to a conclusion. For with the appearance of the I as an individual principle, the preceding evolutionary process — or, more correctly, the involutionary process — begins to be reversed. In moving up from one kingdom to the next, we find always one more dynamic principle appearing in a state of separation from its mother-sphere; this continues to the point where the I, through uniting itself with a thus emancipated physico-etheric-astral organism, arrives at the stage of self-consciousness. Once this stage has been reached, however, it falls to the I to reverse the process of isolation, temporarily sanctioned by the cosmos for the sake of man.

That it is in the very nature of the I not to leave its sheaths in the condition in which it finds them when entering them at the beginning of life, can be seen from the activities it performs in them during the first period after birth. Indeed, in man's early childhood we meet a number of events in which we can perceive something like ur-deeds of the I. They are the acquisition of the faculties of walking, speaking and thinking. What we shall here say about them has, in essentials, already been touched upon in earlier pages. Here, however, we are putting it forward in a new light.

Once again we find our attention directed to the threefold structure of man's physical organism. For the faculty of upright walking is a result of the I's activity in the limb-system of the body; the acquisition of speech takes place in the rhythmic system; and thinking is a faculty based on the nerve-system. Consequently, each of the three achievements comes to pass at a different level of consciousness — sleeping, dreaming, waking.

All through the struggle of erecting the body against the pull of gravity, the child is entirely unaware of the activities of his own I. In the course of acquiring speech he gains a dim awareness, as though in dream, of his efforts. Some capacity of thinking has to unfold before the first glimmer of true self-consciousness is kindled. (Note that the word 'I' is the only one that is not added to the child's vocabulary by way of imitation. Otherwise he would, as some mentally inhibited children do, call all other people 'I' and himself 'you'.)

This picture of the three ur-deeds of the I can now be amplified in the following way. We have seen that the region of the bodily limbs is that in which physical, etheric and astral forces interpenetrate most deeply. Consequently, the I can here press forward most powerfully into the physical body and on into the dynamic sphere to which the body is subject. Here the I is active in a way that is 'magic' in the highest degree. Moreover, there is no other action for which the I receives so little stimulus from outside. For, in comparison, the activity that leads to the acquisition of speech is much more of the nature of a *re*action to stimuli coming from outside — the sounds reaching the child from his environment. And it is also with the first words of the language that the first thoughts enter the child's mind. Nothing of the kind happens at the first stage. On the contrary: everything that confronts the I here is of the nature of an obstacle that is to be overcome.

There is no learning to speak without the hearing of uttered sounds. As these sounds approach the human being they set the astral body in movement, as we have seen. The movements of the astral body flow towards the larynx, where they are seized by the I; through their help the I imbues the larynx with the faculty of producing these sounds itself. Here, therefore, the I is active essentially within the astral body which has received its stimulus from outside. In order to understand what impels the I to such action, we must remember the role played by speech in human life: without speech there would be no community among human individuals on earth.

An illustration of what the I accomplishes as it enters upon the third stage is provided by the following episode, actually observed. Whilst all the members of a family were sitting at table taking their soup, the youngest member suddenly cried out: 'Daddy spoon ... mummy spoon.... ' (everyone in turn spoon) '... all spoon!' At this moment, from merely designating single objects by names learnt through imitation, the child's consciousness had awakened to connective thinking. That this achievement was a cause of inner satisfaction could be heard in the joyful crescendo with which these ejaculations were made.

We have seen that the presence of waking consciousness within the nerve-and-senses organism rests upon the fact that the connection between physical body and etheric body is there the most external of all. But precisely because this is so, the etheric body is dominated very strongly by the *forces* to which the physical head owes its formation. This, too, is not fundamentally new to us. What can now be added is that, in consequence, the physical brain and the part of the etheric body belonging to it – the etheric brain – assume a function comparable with that of a mirror, the physical organ representing the reflecting mass and the etheric organ its metallic gloss. When, within the head, the etheric body reflects back the impressions received from the astral body, the I becomes aware of them in the form of mental images (the 'ideas' of the onlooker-philosopher). It is also by way of such reflection that the I first grows aware of itself – but as nothing more than an image among images. Here, therefore, it is itself least active.

If, once again, we compare the three happenings of learning to walk, to speak and to think, we find ourselves faced with the remarkable fact that the progressive lighting up of consciousness from one stage to the next, goes hand in hand with a retrogression in the activity of the I itself. At the first stage, where the I knows least of itself, it is alive in the most direct sense out of its own being; at the second stage, where it is in the dreaming state, it receives the impetus of action through the astral body; at the third stage, where the I wakens to clear self-consciousness, it assumes merely the role of onlooker at the pictures moving within the etheric body.

Compare with this the paths to higher faculties of knowledge, Imagination and Inspiration, as we learnt to know them in our previous studies. The comparison shows that exactly the same forces come into play at the beginning of life, when the I endeavours to descend from its pre-earthly, cosmic environment to its earthly existence, as have to be made use of for the ascending of the I from earthly to cosmic consciousness. Only, as is natural, the sequence of steps is reversed. For on the upward way the first deed of the I is that which leads to a wakening in the etheric world: it is a learning to set in motion the etheric forces in the region of the head in such a way that the usual isolation of this part of the etheric body is overcome. Regarded thus, the activity of the I at this stage reveals a striking similarity to the activity applied in the earliest period of childhood at the opposite pole of the organism. To be capable of imaginative sight actually means to be able to move about in etheric space by means of the etheric limbs of the eyes just as one moves about in physical space by means of the physical limbs.

Similarly, the acquisition of Inspiration is a resuming on a higher level of the activity exercised by the I with the help of the astral body when learning to speak. And here, too, the functions are reversed. For while the child is stimulated by the spoken sounds he hears to bring his own organ of speech into corresponding movements, and so gradually learns to produce speech, the acquisition of Inspiration, as we have seen, depends on learning to bring the supersensible forces of the speech-organ into movement in such a way that these forces become the organ for hearing the supersensible language of the universe.

* * * * *

Our knowledge of the threefold structure of man's organism leads us to seek, besides the stages of Imagination and Inspiration, a third stage which is as much germinally present in the body's region of movement, as the two others are in the regions of thought and speech. After what we have learnt in regard to these three, we may assume that the path leading to this third stage consists in producing a condition of wide-awake, tranquil contemplation in the very region where the I is wont to unfold its highest degree of initiative on the lowest level of consciousness.

In an elementary manner this attitude of soul was practised by us when, in our earlier studies, we endeavoured to become inner observers of the activity of our own limbs, with the aim of discovering the origin of our concept of mass. It was in this way that a line of observation opened up to us which led to the recognition of the physical substances of the earth as congealed spiritual functions or , we may say, congealed utterances of cosmic will.

Cosmic Will, however, does not work into our existence only in such a way that, in the form of old and therefore rigid Will, it puts up resistance against the young will-power of the I, so that in overcoming this resistance the I may waken to self-activity. Cosmic Will is also present in us in an active form. We point here to the penetration by the higher powers of the universe into the forming of the destiny of humanity and of individual man. And here Rudolf Steiner has shown that to a man who succeeds in becoming a completely objective observer of his own existence while actively functioning within it (as in an elementary way we endeavoured to become observers of our limb actions while engaged in performing them) the world begins to reveal itself as an arena of the activities of spiritual Beings, both lower and higher than man, whose reality and acts he is now able to apprehend through inner awareness. Herewith a third stage of man's faculty of cognition is added to the stages of Imagination and Inspiration. When Rudolf Steiner chose for it the word Intuition, in its most comprehensive sense, he applied this word, also, in its truest meaning.

* * * * *

While through Imagination man comes to know of his ether-

MAN OR MATTER

body as part of his make-up, and correspondingly through Inspiration of his astral body, and thereby recognises himself as participant in the supersensible forces of the universe, it is through Intuition that he grows into full awareness of his I as a spirit-being among spirit-beings –

God-begotten, God-companioned,
for ever God-ward striving.

Prospect

THE CREATIVE POWERS IN NATURE

Our considerations have reached the stage where it is possible to express something which was only referred to in the first part of this book and then, for definite reasons, not expressly touched upon again.

We have discussed in these pages varied types of forces, after having cleared the way for a legitimate conception of force. This consisted in turning to that region in ourselves, beyond the boundaries of the spectator-consciousness, where we experience ourselves as a being exercising force: the region of our own will. From this point on, our path was, step by step, an appeal to will-potentialities slumbering in us. Our unprejudiced self-observation tells us that the manifestation of physical forces in our body presupposes the presence of will. It tells us further that will is a power the carrier of which is our Self.

What in this way is valid for us as human beings, is correspondingly true for all expressions of force outside man. 'Force', Rudolf Steiner once said, 'is the one-sidedly spatial manifestation of the spirit'. Now that we have come to the end of the book, we shall present some observations on the concrete spiritual beings whose one-sidedly spatial manifestations we encountered in the various expressions of force in nature.

* * * * *

To speak of forces, without experiencing them as meaningful expressions of the will of spiritual beings, would have been quite impossible to man before his entry into the mere onlooker-relationship to the world. Originally he had experienced himself entirely and only as a being among beings. At that time, indeed, he knew no self-originated impulses, but felt himself as a mere member or organ of divine-cosmic beings superior to him. With the passage of time this experience of beings faded out, and he began to recognise only forces. Finally, as we have seen, even the concept of force became for him problematic.

It is characteristic that along with the new awakening of the active relationship of the Spiritual in man to the Spiritual in the universe (witnessed, as we have seen, in Goethe and others) an awareness of the *beingness* of the world also awakens. In the case of Traherne and of Reid this does not, indeed, come to clear expression, for a reason we will discuss later. But when Luke Howard speaks of the 'countenance of the sky' and says of its phenomena that they are, in this field, the equivalent of the changing expressions of man's face revealing 'a person's state of mind and body', this can be for us a token of the dawning relationship meant here. The same is true of Ruskin. To him 'Queen of the Air' is a definite being — the one whom the Greeks called Athena — whose activities in the heavens, in the earth, and in the heart, as he conceives them, he describes in the book bearing this title. Similarly, in his *Ethics of the Dust*, he denotes the generation of the crystals in their various forms and colours as the activity of various spirit-beings to whom he gives names which the Egyptians used for them. That such spirit-beings were not for him a mere product of his poetic imagination, however, he shows clearly enough. We may see here an attempt to follow his progress from 'force' to 'form' by taking a further step from 'form' to 'being'.

Goethe shows us the same thing when, in his meteorological comments, he says to Eckermann that he represents the earth to himself as a great, living being endowed with the process of breathing. We are also thinking particularly here of the dispute between Faust and Mephistopheles concerning the origin of the mountains, to which we referred in Chapter IV. That Goethe was in earnest about the words he put into the mouth of Mephistopheles is shown by his secretary's notes referring to various passages in the Bible. We cited one of these, from Paul's

Epistle to the Ephesians, as pointing in its very wording to the spiritual strife to which mankind in our time is to the highest degree exposed.

This was the point in our opening considerations when already something had appeared of *beingness* as the true background of the world of forces. (See the closing part of Chapter IV.) What came before us there was part of a comprehensive picture which now, at the end of our considerations, we shall present in its entirety. But it will be easier to understand the present-day significance of this world-picture if we first indicate its historical background.

* * * * *

In Chapter VII we referred to the significance of the Church Father, Augustine, with regard to establishing a relationship of man to Divine Guidance for the era in which man had to live without knowledge of the source and origin of his soul before birth. The historical function which Augustine had, in this sense, to perform also comes to expression through his making the Old Testament the sole source of the developing ecclesiastical doctrine of salvation. As a result, the Christian religion became monotheistic in the sense of the Mosaic Law, through which the Deity who spiritually led the Hebrew people commanded them to have 'no other gods before Me'. Among the Apostles it was in particular Peter who represented this impulse, and it was from him as its first Bishop that the Church derived its authority.

Besides Peter, however, there were also in early Christianity Apostles such as Paul and John, through whom another impulse was working. This impulse, too, we have encountered in the preceding pages, when we discussed (in Chapter VII) Traherne's conception of Childhood in contrast to Augustine's. The biographical sketch in the Appendix to this book includes a description of the crisis encountered by Traherne during his youth in his relation to the Bible. One sees how his studies of the Greek philosophers, above all Plato and Plotinus, helped him to overcome this crisis; and how, as a result of this, the Gospel according to St. John and the Epistles of Paul became the most inspiring for him of all the writings of the New Testament. What set him free from his doubts was his encounter with the essence of the pre-Christian Mysteries, and his realisation that there existed for the soul in those times a way to a direct apprehension of the Divine World. Yet whoever attained, on the pathways of the Mysteries, to this degree of vision, experienced the universe as populated by a multitude of spiritual beings of higher than human degree. The so-called polytheistic religions of the ancient peoples are a reflection of this. In entire correspondence with it, the writings of John, above all his Apocalypse, and the Letters of Paul, show both these early teachers of Christendom as bearing in their souls a polytheistic experience of the Divine-Spiritual World.

The fact that we do not encounter this in the case of Traherne — the same is true of Reid — despite the attitude to Christianity that they both had, is based on something else. Both, through their professional education as servants of the Church, were so impregnated with the monotheistic form of Christianity that they were unable to overcome its one-sidedness, although they would have done so if they had held consistently to their own experience. But of what else is Plato speaking, when he talks of the IDEAS, than of individual spiritual beings — in fact, beings of a very high degree of divinity? Traherne, however, was at least able to say of himself that he had personally seen the 'true Ideas of all things'.

Much that never became clear and distinct to Traherne, or at any rate was not clearly expressed by him, was stated in full clarity — though in a traditional form — by an earlier writer who belongs to the same stream. We refer to John Colet, the remarkable Dean of St. Paul's Cathedral in London, who lived from 1466 to 1519 and founded St. Paul's School. The impulses which inspired Colet's work as a Christian teacher become evident when we find that he wrote down in an independent form, the Christian teaching concerning the nine Divine Hierarchies, first developed under the instruction of St. Paul by one of his pupils and thus implanted in Christian doctrine.

In the Acts of the Apostles (Chapter 17) we read of a sermon by Paul on the Areopagus in Athens, and how 'certain men clave unto him and believed'. One of them was Dionysius, surnamed the Areopagite. This was the title of the highest judge in the Athenian State, who carried out his functions on that hilltop. Now under the signature of this Dionysius there came down to later times a series of writings, one of which deals with the Celestial Hierarchies. There has been much dispute as to whether these writings, and above all the one cited here, really originated with that pupil of Paul, and thus whether their content has or has not the authority of the Apostle behind it.

One can understand that those who feel themselves called to represent the purely Augustinian-monotheistic form of Christian belief, shall at all times find it necessary to dispute the authenticity of this document. And to do this, using simply the means of philological research, is not difficult. For the conceptual form in which this document is cast clearly has the colouring of the Neoplatonist Proclus, who lived in the fifth century A.D. This, too, is the period when the writings of Dionysius are mentioned for the first time. In the form in which they are known to us they can, in fact, have come into being only at that late date. Yet this is no proof that their content does not stem from the one whose name they bear, if we recall how people in those times thought regarding the identity of the authors of such writings.

For reasons mentioned before, the Dionysian teachings could not at first be embodied in the Christianity that was spreading far and wide. They remained, to borrow an expression from the language of the Greek Mysteries, 'esoteric' teachings. The usual way of protecting such a teaching was to keep it unwritten and to pass it on by word of mouth from teacher to pupil through the generations. One of the facts of the spiritual awakening acquired in the Mystery schools was a strengthening of the pupil's memory to such an extent that throughout his life he retained the content of the teaching given him. While the old Mystery wisdom was dying away gradually, the Greek philosopher Plotinus, in the third century, penetrated to it once more by a philosophic path, and gave it out openly. This made it feasible to infuse such a teaching as that of the Divine Hierarchies also into the general spiritual life, and to do so in a universally understandable conceptual form. The teaching was not written down, however, until about three hundred years later, after the lifetime of Proclus, the last representative of Neoplatonism established by Plotinus. Naturally this was done in the conceptual language of Neoplatonism. Which member of the School fostering the teachings of Dionysius did the writing was of no significance for the spirit of that age. The essential teaching was that of Dionysius the Areopagite, and so it was transmitted to the contemporary and later world under his name. Moreover, it was the custom in the Mystery schools that successive teachers took the name of the founder of the school. 'Dionysius the Areopagite' was the title of an office based on certain capacities which were acquired on the path the first Dionysius had travelled under the guidance of St. Paul.

Anyone seeking proof that behind this teaching there stands the authority of Paul can find it at many places in the latter's own writings, among them the passage quoted in Chapter IV. True, this has to do with cosmic-spiritual Beings of Evil. But these Beings are only the shadow, as it were, of the Beings of the Good, having originally been in the same rank and standing in a definite connection with them. In so far Paul speaks of them in his Letter to the Ephesians, he gives them exactly the names borne by the corresponding Beings in the teaching of Dionysius. In fact, it is through the knowledge of the latter's teaching that it first becomes possible to read correctly such passages in Paul, as well as certain expressions in the Gospels. Many misunderstandings have arisen because later translators and expounders no longer recognised the words written there as the names of definite Hierarchies. Thus the writings of the New Testament, and among them the Epistles of Paul, if read correctly, testify to the recognition on the part of the Apostles and their pupils of the existence of a heaven populated by many spiritual beings, ordered according to definite ranks.

Noteworthy in connection with the further fate of the teaching concerning the Hierarchies is what John Colet did for the continued knowledge of them. Among his writings there is a dissertation on the teaching of Dionysius. This is mainly a somewhat condensed translation of the Dionysian writing itself, interspersed only here and there with Colet's own ideas. It is known that, when he wrote this, he had available nothing more than his recollection of the writings of Dionysius; but he was noted for his wonderful memory. It is reported of him that in his youth he was visited by a strange personality, who exercised upon him an influence that resulted in an enhancement of his powers of memory for the rest of his life. However this may have happened, the important thing for us is that we find in Colet a personality in whom an interest in the writings of Dionysius was combined with an extraordinary enhancement of certain mental capacities. Indeed, it was to these that he owed the possibility of reproducing the writings. Naturally, for someone like him there could exist no doubt as to their authenticity.

The writings of Colet were first made known in wider circles by J.H. Lupton, master at St. Paul's School from 1864 till 1899, who published them in the Latin original and in English translation.[1] To him we also owe the knowledge of how Colet met the writings of the Areopagite. What follows, based on Lupton's introductory remarks, is part of the necessary basis for a true estimation of the Hierarchy teaching in our time.

The period in which John Colet lived is distinguished by the sudden appearance of Hellenistic culture in Florence, and its spread from there into the spiritual life of the century. In Florence itself this led to the founding of a Platonic Academy by Cosimo de' Medici. Leading figures in this Hellenistic Renaissance were Pico de Mirandola and Marsiglio Ficino. Both, in their thinking, found themselves led by Plato to the spiritual source that they craved for. From Plato they went to Plotinus, and from Plotinus to Dionysius, and thus, after a temporary turning away from Christianity, they came back to it again. Spirits such as these, and many others in their time, needed the discovery of the extra-Hebraic, that is, the ancient Mystery roots of Christianity in order to be able to be Christians. It was the same with John Colet. J. H. Lupton investigated the various channels through which Colet came into contact with the Neoplatonic stream in Florence. One of his sources was the biographical sketch of Colet, which Erasmus of Rotterdam wrote shortly after Colet's death. According to this, Colet's first encounter with the writings of Plato came during his student days at Oxford. We may recall how a similar encounter took place at Oxford for Traherne. Along the same path on which he came to Paul, there came 200 years earlier the Florentines and Colet. They came, that is, to the Apostle who, in contrast to the original Disciples, knew only through his own spiritual vision of the existence of the God who had become man and, as such, had overcome death.

The way in which Colet comments for his contemporaries on the writing of Dionysius shows that he was particularly concerned to make it understood that such a work does not seek to transmit mere knowledge — even though this be of a higher sort — but to bring the reader on the path to a personal experiencing of its content. In other words, he wanted it to be realised that the work was intended as a book of training, to be used for meditation. Lupton, too, in his introduction, gave special emphasis to this. Beyond that, he was too much a child of the Christian monotheism of his time to recognise that for Dionysius — and also for Colet — the Hierarchies were not, as he puts it, mere impersonal emanations of God, the various qualities of which Dionysius had simply furnished with names which he found at hand in tradition.

The task of again comprehending the world, both above and beneath man, as filled and interwoven with *beings*, is in fact first given again to human thinking in our century. It was Rudolf Steiner who opened the way to this. His teaching concerning the Hierarchies naturally coincides in its characteristic features with the Areopagite's, for it has the same array of facts as its essence. Yet it is not a mere reiteration of the earlier, but is considerably more extensive. Hence we shall deal with it here only in this contemporary form.

* * * * *

The teaching of spiritual science concerning the Hierarchies, like the older teaching, does not aim at transmitting mere knowledge, but at opening the way towards actual experiencing. This is true of everything that Rudolf Steiner expressed in written or verbal form, whether it was concerned with advice on inner training or with the results of his own spiritual investigations. Hence his work comes into connection with the Paul-Dionysius stream, as we have characterised it. His first book with a spiritual-scientific content, *Christianity as Mystical Fact*, also testifies to this.[2] There he presented the events of Palestine in their relationship to the essence of the ancient Mysteries. His connection with the above-mentioned stream is shown also by the fact that he always spoke as a personal seer. For he never expressed anything concerning spiritual facts or relationships without having investigated these with the means of modern spiritual cognition. This applies equally to the discussion of teachings which have been, since more or less ancient times, the common property of human culture — such as the teachings of Zarathustra and Buddha, the content of the Egyptian and Greek Mythologies, the Old and New Testament, etc., concerning all of which he wrote and spoke in detail.

In addition to all this, however, Rudolf Steiner dealt also with details of the spiritual history of mankind which at the time were generally unknown because there was no written document concerning them. In such a case he would say that if a document were discovered, it would confirm the correctness of his communications. Such an event actually occurred not long before these lines were written; we will therefore mention it briefly here.

There has been much discussion concerning a collection of ancient writings (The Dead Sea Scrolls), discovered in 1947-8 in some caves near the Dead Sea and generally attributed to an esoteric order which had played a role in the spiritual life of Palestine during the century before the appearance of Christ. Much that has now been learnt from the Scrolls had been

communicated more than thirty-five years previously in all essential detail by Rudolf Steiner, in lectures on the Matthew Gospel.
Thus an objective event has confirmed the character of spiritual
science, as always claimed by its founder.³ Rudolf Steiner would
have been able to lecture in a similar way concerning the Hierarchy
teaching of the Areopagite, even if these writings had remained
unknown and there had existed no information about their
content.

As we have already mentioned, Rudolf Steiner went far
beyond Dionysius in the presentation of particulars. The information he gave has to do with the activity of the various grades
of Hierarchies in the creation and maintaining of Nature on her
various levels, including the physical organisation of man. It
further concerns their activity in the shaping of the fate of the
individual man, in the spiritual guidance of the peoples of the
earth and of the successive periods of time, and still other matters.
It deals with the coming forth, from specific hierarchical Beings,
of opposition to the realisation of the original Divine Plan, both
in the cosmos and in human beings, in other words with the
origin of Evil. Out of the wealth of Rudolf Steiner's communications concerning all this, let us take some of the basic material.

Rudolf Steiner first published information concerning the
nature and activity of the Hierarchies in 1909 in his book *Occult
Science – an Outline*.⁴ This work is mainly devoted to describing
the evolution of the earth as part of the planetary system, and
with it that of man, from their creation up to the present, along
with a survey of coming stages of this evolution. Detailed information is given concerning four great cosmic periods, designated
as 'Old Saturn', 'Old Sun', 'Old Moon' and 'Earth'. Each of these
periods, in sequence, served, as far as man is concerned, for the
creation and initial development of his physical body, his etheric
body, his astral body, and the implanting of the germ of his
Ego. At the beginning of each period, a specific Hierarchy is
active in the emanation of the substance in question, while other
Hierarchies approach in order to organise and shape the vehicles
we wear today as the various bodily organisations. In describing

these activities, Rudolf Steiner calls the Hierarchies by definite names formulated by himself, but he always also joins to these the names which have been customary in 'esoteric Christology'. The latter are the names which Dionysius, going partly back to older nomenclatures, had given them. As the following synopsis shows, the nine Hierarchies form three groups, generally designated in spiritual science as the First, Second, and Third Hierarchy. On a certain occasion Rudolf Steiner gave expression, through particular names, to the common characteristics shared by each of the three groups. These are shown in the first column. The synopsis also shows, alongside the spiritual-scientific and esoteric Christian names for the various ranks, the customary translations of the names into present-day language. Finally it shows the creative contributions made by the Hierarchies, out of their own substance, to the building up of the world and of the human being.

I. HIERARCHY

Spirits of	Spirits of Love	Seraphim	Seraphim	
Strength	Spirits of Harmony	Cherubim	Cherubim	
	Spirits of Will	Thrones	Thrones	Donors of the Physical[5]

II. HEIRARCHY

Spirits of	Spirits of Wisdom	Kyriotetes	Dominions	Donors of the Etheric
Light	Spirits of Motion	Dynameis	Powers	Donors of the Astral
	Spirits of Form	Exusiai	Mights [6]	Donors of the Ego

III. HEIRARCHY

Spirits of	Spirits of Personality	Archai	Principalities
Soul	Spirits of Fire	Archangeloi	Archangels
	Sons of Life	Angeloi	Angels

As we shall hear in more detail, the Beings of the two lowest ranks of the Third Hierarchy — the Spirits of Fire and the Sons of Life — had not yet, during the first great period of evolution, Old Saturn, taken part in the common work of creation. This was because they had not yet attained, in their own evolution, to the stage necessary for such activity. They were still objects of the creative activity of Higher Beings — the Seraphim and Cherubim. All of this is set forth in detail in *Occult Science* and in other works by Rudolf Steiner.

The activity of all the Hierarchies in Nature and man, at the present stage of the Earth's evolution is arranged as follows:

As 'Spirits of Strength', those belonging to the First Hierarchy are carriers and manifesters of the basic forces of the universe, and therewith of the earth. When we speak, in the language of the Four Elements, of Fire and Air, we are in reality speaking of the earthly realm of activity of the Seraphim and Cherubim. Next to these, the element Water, and from out of it the element Earth, represent the realm of activity of the Thrones. When, in Chapter IX, we discussed the conception of the Four Elements at first in its historic aspect, we found that for a van Helmont the two lower Elements still appeared as essentially different from the two upper ones in that the lower formed the realm of the 'created', and the upper that of 'uncreated', things. We can now see how in this there is expressed a lingering experience of the fact that the creation of our universe began with an activity of those Beings, the Thrones, whose present-day field of work is the sphere of the two lower Elements.

As 'Spirits of Light', those belonging to the middle Triad have their realm of activity in the present etheric sphere. When we described, in Chapter XIX, the Light Ether, we were really speaking of the field of activity of the Spirits of Form (Exusiai); of the Spirits of Motion (Dynameis) in describing the Sound Ether, and of the Spirits of Wisdom (Kyriotetes) when we spoke of the Life Ether.

Let us now go somewhat more closely into the activity of the Spirits of Form. They are, as the preceding synopsis shows, the original givers of the human Ego, whose essential distinguishing mark is the capacity for thought. They have their macrotelluric field of work, as just indicated, in everything which appears in Nature as form woven from light. In the chapter 'Always Stand by Form' we cited, in order to characterise Ruskin's way of perception, a section from his *Queen of the Air* which shows that, for him, 'Form' is active Being; on the other hand these Beings have reference in their action, or nature, to 'the human intelligence that perceives them'. Here we see how Ruskin came to the identity of the hierarchical beings in both realms.

It was no different with Goethe. We are thinking first of the two excerpts from his *Metamorphose der Pflanzen*, which we quoted in connection with our discussion of the Light Ether. But we would especially recall the verse quoted on page 394, in which Goethe describes the weaving activity of Nature and the weaving activity of human thinking in closely corresponding words, in order, since he could not find a valid philosophical foundation for it, at least to express in poetic form the spiritual identity of the two.

Details similar to those presented concerning the Spirits of Form with regard to the activity of the Light Ether could be given about the spirits of Motion and of Wisdom and the Ethers with which they are connected. We will leave the interested reader to follow this up.

In contrast to the two upper hierarchical Triads, the third Triad has the soul sphere of man, of individuals as well as human groups, as its field of work, hence the name, 'Spirits of Soul'. To every individual human being there is apportioned a particular Angel. Similarly, an entire nation has an Archangel as its leading and impulse-giving Spirit. Reaching beyond the nations and peoples, the Archai are active; they give the character to whole periods of time; hence spiritual science also speaks of them as of 'Time Spirits'. In the soul-structure of the individual man the Angels work primarily in his thinking; the Archangels in his feeling, and the Archai in his willing. (All this will be found presented in full detail by Rudolf Steiner in lectures given in Christiania (Oslo) in 1910 in a cycle called *The Mission of the Individual Folk Souls*.) [7]

For us human beings, the physical as well as the etheric and astral bodies are fields of activity of our Ego. The same is true, correspondingly, of the Hierarchies, who are active equally in the various physical elements, etheric force-fields and in the astral realm of the universe. We learnt in Chapter XX that there are seven modifications of cosmic astrality — outwardly noticeable in the existence and the movements of the various bodies of our planetary system. We therefore used for them simply the names of the corresponding planets. We found there a polarity between the three inner and the three outer planetary spheres of force, with the Sun as a realm of mediating forces between them. This arrangement is in fact a mirroring of the order of the Hierarchies. For the sphere of the three inner planets is that of the three lowest ranks: Angels-Moon, Archangels-Mercury, Archai-Venus.[8] The three planetary spheres beyond the Sun are the domain of the three highest ranks: Thrones-Mars, Cherubim-Jupiter, Saturn-Seraphim; while the entire middle group — Spirits of Wisdom, of Motion and of Form — is active from out of the Sun sphere.

We must still refer to an aspect of the modern Hierarchy teaching which will help us to understand the origin of Evil among the Higher Beings of the Universe. As we have seen, it was Goethe's merit to have found that in order to arrive at a true knowledge of what anything *is*, one must put the question, 'How does it *become*?' We were able to show that he became, in this fashion, the true founder of a teaching of evolution in Nature. Rudolf Steiner carried on Goethe's method of investigation by accomplishing the same thing with regard to knowledge of the Spiritual Beings of the Universe. In this realm, also, earlier ages were able only to put the question, 'What *are* the Hierarchies?' Hence the answer was the Hierarchy teaching in the form given it by Dionysius the Areopagite. Our own time is the first to be faced with the need to comprehend the cosmos, penetrating even into its spiritual realms, from the aspect of evolution, in order that the 'I' of man, which has awakened to itself, may find its own organic place therein. This demand is met by the Hierarchy teaching of Rudolf Steiner, in that he discloses for the first time the facts of the gradual upward evolution of the Spiritual Beings who stand above man.

As Rudolf Steiner shows in *Occult Science*, the Spirits of Will, of Wisdom, of Motion and of Form become, one after another, the Givers of a specific world-substance, the three last ones after having previously helped to work on substance given by the Spirits of higher rank. Spiritual science tells us little more than that about the progress of these High Hierarchies; this is because the subject cannot be laid hold of in concepts we can

comprehend. It is different with the members of the Third Hierarchy: the Archai, Archangels, Angels. They are forerunners of an
evolution of consciousness that is also our own. We have already
pointed out that on Old Saturn the two ranks standing just above
us had not yet risen to the stage of being able to act from out of
themselves. They do so first during the subsequent periods of
creation. We will try now to give an outline of the whole process.

The path of all Spiritual beings leads from being a creation of
God to becoming co-creator with Him. The transition from the
first stage to the second takes place through the Spiritual Being
attaining to a consciousness of his Self. One may call this the
Ego-stage of the Hierarchy in question. It is on this level that we
human beings now find ourselves, and the whole fourth period of
creation is there in order that we gradually awaken to our Ego
and attain to the full use of it. Other beings have preceded us in
gaining the ego-capacity; still others will follow us. All are subject
to evolution, marked always by a development of consciousness
from pre-ego conditions, through the ego-state, to such conditions
as lie above it.

These stages are, for all the Hierarchies named, the same as
for mankind, though every Hierarchy passes through them in a
different way, for each has a different cosmic task. Goethe's
concept of metamorphosis applies here. With this qualification,
the following successive stages of consciousness are true for all
these Hierarchies: Trance, Sleep-Consciousness, Dream-Conscious-
ness, Ego-Consciousness, Imaginative, Inspirational, Intuitive
Consciousness. At present the four lower stages of consciousness
exist alongside of one another on earth in the mineral, plant,
animal and human kingdoms. Three of them belong normally
to man; it is only in exceptional, pathological conditions that he
falls below the condition of sleep into catalepsy and trance.

At the present stage of our development we can only to a
certain degree attain to the three higher levels of consciousness.
They will become our full capacities in future cosmic periods
of evolution. Today they are the normal state of consciousness
of the three Hierarchies which have preceded us in evolution: the

Angels, Archangels and Archai. Out of this comes the following picture of the stages of these Hierarchies, including our own — i.e. the one which it is our task to become:

	Old Saturn	Old Sun	Old Moon	Earth
Archhai	Ego-	Imaginative	Inspirational	Intuitive Consciousness
Archangels	Dream-	Ego-	Imaginative	Inspirational "
Angels	Sleep-	Dream-	Ego-	Imaginative- "
Men	Trance-	Sleep-	Dream-	Ego- "

Now it is this evolutionary aspect that makes it possible to see the so-called Evil, in terms of its origin and actual nature, as a reasonable part of the Divine Plan of Creation. The Areopagite naturally knew, as did his teacher Paul, about the existence of hierarchical Beings who oppose the Divine Plan. Absolute Evil, however, does not exist for him; but what appears as such has as its cause, in the Beings in question, a 'weakness in respect of their natural energy'. The weakness is a lack, an insufficiency, in these Beings, who in themselves are of like origin with the good Beings of the same rank. In contrast to Dionysius, Colet shows himself as a characteristic spirit of the late Middle Ages, no longer able to think in terms of such concepts. For him the opposing Beings are evil Spirits, and for ever, and go towards eternal damnation.

In accord with Dionysius, and yet going beyond him, Rudolf Steiner has shown that in each of the great cosmic periods there are Beings who fail to reach the evolutionary goal assigned to them, and who are, since then, Beings 'that have remained behind'. Thus they have dropped out of the tempo of the cosmic process of becoming, and have become 'abnormal'. As a result, they develop in such a way that they try to retard the cosmic process or to hurry it unduly. It was to this that we pointed at the end of Chapter IV, when we spoke of Luciferic and Ahrimanic Beings. The former are those that work retardingly, the latter, precipitately. We may recall what was said there about the two ways of not keeping 'Knowing' and 'Doing' in step with one another. We find this back here as the tendencies in the two kinds of 'abnormal' Beings.

Essential to the picture of the abnormal Hierarchies, transmitted to us by Rudolf Steiner, is the fact that the dropping out from the normal course of evolution rests originally upon a sacrificial renunciation by the Beings concerned. They have brought this offering in order that Man may, through them, experience those forms of opposition which he needs in order to gain the forces without which he could not reach the goal of his evolution. By the same token, every step man makes towards this goal becomes at the same time a step towards redemption for these Beings.

In the light of what was discussed in Chapter I, and of everything that has been dealt with in the course of this book, it will be clear to the reader that in our dealings with Nature, and in the results of this for civilisation, we are today exposed above all to Beings of an Ahrimanic kind, and must come to terms with them. They have their positive task in giving the Earth its necessary density, so that it can exist as an independent planetary body. Therefore they have gravitation for their domain, as the previously noted 'normal' Hierarchies have the various cosmic domains of energy. Along with gravitation, we have learnt to know electricity and magnetism as etheric forces that have been laid hold of by gravitation. Now we are able to say that their existence is indebted to Ahrimanic activity, for it is through this that the ethers in question have been to a greater or lesser degree overcome by gravitation and made similar to it. Thus out of Light-ether came electricity, and out of Sound-ether magnetism. Their 'ahrimanic' character is indeed made clear in all that we have been able to say about them in this book: as a result of man's contact with them his Doing has far outstripped his Knowing, and in the same way he has incurred the temptation to achieve power for himself over Nature and over his fellow-men. Goethe, indeed, already saw this in his time, and therefore allowed Faust to be tempted by Ahriman-Mephistopheles. Concerning man's necessary struggle with such beings, we have already seen it referred to by Paul in his Letter to the Ephesians. So it is that man's tasks in seeking to understand nature are bound up with his ethical aspirations.

We said that although basically the same stages of consciousness apply to the beings of the Third Hierarchy as to ourselves,

474

yet they differ for the different Hierarchies in the sense of the Goethean concept of Metamorphosis. Here the question arises as to what this difference is, and what is the meaning that underlies the succession of Hierarchies. The essential fact is that each Hierarchy is called into being by the Creator in order to enrich the World with one essential quality. In Wisdom, Beauty and Strength, in Harmony and Love, the Higher Beings are superior to us in a way that demands our reverence. Man is intended to bring into the world a new attribute – Freedom. This is what makes necessary the forces of Opposition to which we are exposed through the existence of Evil. When man has attained to Freedom in the sense meant here, he will have become the Tenth Hierarchy. A teaching of the Hierarchies valid at that time will therefore have to speak of ten Hierarchies, and will call the tenth Hierarchy the 'Spirits of Freedom'.

* * * * *

We have found as a distinguishing mark of the Goethean method of research that a true knowledge of nature cannot be achieved without making oneself – in Goethe's words – worthy of it; that is, not without ethical striving by the investigator. We can now add that such an endeavour is destined to bring about consequences for Nature. For becoming a Hierarchy means, as we saw, growing from creature to co-creator. Concerning this, also, Paul bore witness in a passage in his Letter to the Romans (8, 19-21). So may the words that he uses there form the conclusion of this book, complementing those quoted earlier from his Letter to the Ephesians. The words run, again in a translation that tries to accord as far as may be with the sense of the original text:

'The whole creation waits anxiously for the becoming manifest in man of that in him which springs from the Divine.

'For the kingdoms of the creatures are subjected to illusion, not of their own will, but by the Subjector; yet partaking in hope, for the whole creation will be liberated from the bondage of corruption and taken up into the freedom which grows for the Children of God out of the light of revelation.'

APPENDICES AND NOTES

Appendix I

THOMAS TRAHERNE

The events that led to the discovery of Traherne's writings and the identification of the author are a model of the workings of the destiny-forming powers in the cultural evolution of mankind. Let us first, then, tell the story.

One day in the year 1895 a certain bibliophile, while turning over the contents of a secondhand book barrow in London's East End, pulled from the bottom of one of the piles two anonymous manuscript volumes of the seventeenth century, both in perfect preservation. He bought them for a few pence. What he found in one of them made him think of Henry Vaughan, the well-known religious poet of the seventeenth century, as the probable author. A friend of his, a connoisseur of the literature of that period, shared his view. The latter purchased the volumes from the finder with the idea of surprising the circle of readers interested in subjects of this kind by publishing some hitherto unknown poems by Vaughan. His death in 1899 prevented the publication, which he had already started to prepare. In this way an error which it would have been difficult to discover and rectify never saw the light of day. With the sale of his library, the manuscripts went to a well-known London bookseller, who showed them to a friend, Bertram Dobell, to get his opinion concerning the authorship. Dobell was a self-made man who had worked his way up from a poor errand boy to become the owner of a famous bookshop in London's Charing Cross Road. He soon noticed the fundamental difference between the spiritual temper of these poems, with their lively, joyous ring, from the quiet, restrained, slow-moving verse of Vaughan. But if not Vaughan, who was the author?

When Dobell reported his doubts to the original finder, the

latter could not deny that they were justified. And more than that: he now remembered having himself once been struck by a poem with just that same joyous ring. This was when, many years before in the British Museum Library, he had been looking through an anonymous little book of just that period. So he went to the Library and copied out the entire volume for his friend. What Dobell found there left him in no doubt that these poems and the two manuscripts were by the same author. But, alas, the little book bore no author's name. Its foreword, however, mentions that the author had been private chaplain to Sir Orlando Bridgeman, Lord Keeper under King Charles II. It was not difficult to find out the chaplain's name — Thomas Traherne. A contemporary biographical dictionary gave some information about Traherne's origin and academic career. Further research brought to light two prose volumes bearing his name, which had been lying unknown in libraries. In one of them Dobell found in the midst of the prose a verse passage identical with one in his manuscripts. Traherne's authorship of these was thus finally established. For all further knowledge of his life and personality, Traherne himself unintentionally provided the essential material by his way of using, as illustrations for what he wanted to convey spiritually, concrete experiences of his soul in its encounter with its natural and social environments.

* * * * *

Traherne was born in 1638 at Hereford, the capital of the county with the same name, which lies in the west of England bordering on Wales, and is itself partly English, partly Welsh. His parents were very poor. His mother seems to have died when he was still very young. His father appears to have been a person of low moral standards. Vice and quarrels and tears, so he tells us, were a frequent part of the little boy's early impressions. Fortunately, he was removed fairly soon from his parental home to the house of an uncle, a well-to-do innkeeper in the town, who was held in great esteem by his fellow citizens. He was a kindly man, full of personal vigour, who saw to it that young

Thomas was well looked after and given a good education. He died when Traherne was eight years of age, but this brought no change in the boy's circumstances. It seems that his foster brothers continued to care for him, as their father had done. The uncle also seems to have left him some money, for we find him later as a student at Oxford without the aid of a scholarship.

According to the custom of the time, Traherne joined the university at the age of sixteen, and stayed there, with one interruption, for eight years. At the end of the first four years he left with his first degree in order to take up practical work for about a year with a minister in his home town. At the close of this period he was ordained, and given the living of the little parish church of Credenhill, near Hereford. Since, at the age of twenty, he was not yet old enough to act as rector, he went back to Oxford for a further four years of intensive studies. At the age of twenty-four, with an M.A. degree, he left for Credenhill. During this second period at Oxford his personality had already begun to attract the attention of others through the high qualities of his soul and the width and depth of his learning. This may have prompted Sir Orlando Bridgeman, six years after Traherne's move to Credenhill, to invite him to join his London household as private chaplain. There Traherne came into touch with the wider life of his time. After five years this period came to an end with the dismissal of Bridgeman from his post by the King. Disappointed by the King's failure to behave as a responsible sovereign, Bridgeman had refused to carry out a certain royal order. He left London with his household to spend the rest of his life at his villa in Teddington, near London, where he died two years later in the summer of 1674, Traherne survived him by only three months. The exact date of Traherne's death is uncertain: we know only that he made his will on September 27th, and was buried on October 10th beneath the reading desk in Teddington Church.

* * * * *

The outer events in Traherne's life are at the same time milestones of his inner development — a development which one cannot but reckon among the great events in mankind's history.

Traherne was fortunate in having been spared the torture of the petrified form of medieval eduation, commonly practised in those days. It seems that he was taught at home by teachers who had been touched by the new educational current flowing especially from the endeavours of Amos Commenius, the great Bohemian reformer. The new trend aimed at breaking with the formalistic, classical instruction, and at bringing to the child's knowledge, instead, the actual content of the world of the senses in its manifold aspects. In his *Centuries of Meditations* Traherne tells us with what jubilation his mind absorbed all that was presented to him in this way. Soon, however, another note begins to sound. 'When any curious cabinet or secret in chemistry or physic' was offered him, he diligently looked into it, but 'when I saw to the bottom, I despised it'. The following three utterances of his will explain the reason for this ever-recurring disappointment. From his childhood days he remembered having experienced that 'all things abided eternally as they were *in their proper places'*. Later in life, when he had achieved the consummation of his spiritual endeavours, he could once again say, in describing his beatific vision: 'This spectacle, once seen, will never be forgotten.... It puts a lustre upon God and all His creatures and makes us to see them in a Divine and Eternal Light. I no sooner discerned this, but I was seated in a throne of repose and perfect rest. All things were well *in their proper places.'* But now we hear him saying: 'Everything in its place is admirable, deep and glorious; out of its place it is like a wandering bird, is desolate and good for nothing.' It was the disrupted way in which the contents of this world were conveyed to him that caused his mind, so convinced of the underlying unity and innate order of all things, to suffer. He felt himself enriched, but on closer inspection he found these riches to be unco-ordinated bits of knowledge which he himself had not the power to co-ordinate.

This disappointment, recurring repeatedly through those years, was one of three experiences that were destined to lead young Traherne's soul into a shattering crisis. The second came with the onset of puberty. Disappointed with the subjects he was taught, he began to avoid them and to surrender to sports and all sorts of physical activities, and to indulge in fine garments and amusements, not always of an innocent character. During the moments when he emerged from this 'limpid stream, fouled with mud', he was shocked to realise how he had lost his former chaste relationship with the world around.

The third shock, partly caused by the other two, came from his experience of the loss of his original faith in God, and in the revelation of God through Holy Scriptures. Remembering his early years, stricken with poverty and family quarrels, he cries rebelliously: 'How can I believe that He gave His Son to die for me Who, having power to do otherwise, gave me nothing but rags?' At first he still feels the peace-bestowing power flowing from the contents of the Bible. But soon he begins to question – who can give him certainty that they are true? He feels torn between his experience of the subject matter of the biblical accounts – 'I was very sure that Angels and Cherubim could not bring unto me better tidings' – and his doubts of their divine authority. For the Bible itself offered no secure proof of this to his inquiring mind, stirred as it was by the 'new philosophy' that was implied in what he had been taught by his teachers. 'I could not think that God being Love would neglect His Son, and therefore surely I was not His son, nor He Love: because He had not ascertained me more carefully that the Bible was His book from Heaven.... Many other inquiries I had considering the manner of His revealing Himself.'

Until the day of the great crisis appeared; he was away from home, having been sent to the country to be spared the turbulent social conditions caused in town by the Civil War. It happened during an evening walk when night was drawing on. He was alone among quiet country fields. The sky was overcast, with a threat of storm. Everything around seemed to lie in a stupor of death. Suddenly he felt bursting on him a flood of utter desperation and abysmal horror:

'No Earth, nor Woods, nor Hills, nor Brooks, nor Skies
Would tell me where the hidden Good,
Which I did long for, lies....'

So he says in a poem called *Solitude*, in which he describes this hour of trial.

Thus we find Traherne, not yet sixteen, exposed to a most real threshold-experience, surely one of symptomatic character. Insanity, criminality or suicide are in wait for the soul that falls into the abyss opening at this threshold — a danger to be observed more and more frequently among the younger generations of today. With a tremendous effort of will, Traherne succeeded in finding the way back to himself. He decided to set out in the search of Truth. The road seemed to lie open through his forthcoming studies at Oxford.

Into these studies he now plunged with all his capacity for enthusiasm. We notice the peculiar character of this time of transition from the Middle Ages to the Modern Age when we read that he imbibed with gratitude 'the secrets of nature with Albertus Magnus, or the motions of the Heavens with Galileo, or the cosmography of the moon with Hevelius, or the body of man with Galen, or the nature of diseases with Hippocrates .... or of poesy with Homer, or of Grammar with Lilly'. Yet there is also that other note of dissatisfaction experienced once before in the midst of his delight with what he was learning from his earlier teachers. What troubled him is again a lack of *ideal* interconnection between the many details of knowledge. 'There was never a tutor that did professly teach Felicity, though that be the mistress of all other sciences. Nor did any of us study these things but as *aliena*, which we ought to have studied as our own enjoyments. We studied to inform our knowledge, but knew not for what end we so studied.' And again the same complaint we know from earlier quotations: 'He knoweth nothing as he ought to know, who thinks he knoweth anything without seeing its place, and the manner how it relateth to God, Angels and Men, and to all the creatures in Earth, Heaven, and Hell, Time and

Eternity.' Astounding words in view of the time they were written, reminding one of Faust's desperation in the opening scene of Goethe's drama, as well as of many a present-day student's sighs — including the present author's. (See the introductory chapter.) There can be felicity for the soul only through finding her relationship with the world as God's creation in every single detail. But God, as Traherne saw Him, could not be encountered through the 'mere lazy dream' with which he found most men contenting themselves. For him, this was merely a form of atheism! A true God must satisfy man's highest reason. To acquire this standard of reason, however, called for the highest ethical endeavour.

A decisive help in regaining his inner certainty came to him from his studies of pre-Christian wisdom. He read Plato, Plotinus and the writings whose author went under the name of Hermes Trismegistus. These writings, widely circulated at that time, were actually a fruit of ancient Egyptian initiated knowledge. Plato, above all, became important for Traherne as the philosopher of creatively working IDEAS and as a guide to the cognition of them. The significance of all these writings was that in them he found what the Bible had concealed from him — namely, that there had existed a path of training by which the human mind could attain to actual insight into the mysteries of the universe. Here was shown to him the source whence in olden times wisdom had flowed into humanity, and it became clear to him that the wisdom of the Bible had a similar origin. Hence there was no longer any need to accept the Biblical revelations on mere outer authority. It was only natural that, as a result, the Epistles of St. Paul and the writings of St. John became for him the guiding parts of the New Testament.

After the year when his studies were interrupted, he was again involved in a severe battle with himself. His writings indicate that he had the opportunity of entering on a career that would entail great 'care and labour', but which promised considerable financial rewards — 'many thousands per annum' in his own words. From various utterances of his we can surmise that he had a legal career in view. The definite offer of patronage which is implied in his words, his own intellectual gifts, so noticeably developed in the meantime, and the prospect of a successful career in the public life of his country — all this pointed him strongly in this direction. His spiritual experiences pointed in another. He finally listened to them, which meant keeping to his intended career as a clergyman, and therefore continuing his study of Divinity. For him, it also meant entering on a path of strict spiritual discipline. During the next four years at Oxford he seems to have advanced so far along this path that his personality attracted attention. For a fellow student wrote of him some time later: 'I have known one, and indeed a great friend of Christ, who I verily believe enjoyed more of Christ and his gracious presence in civil employments and creature enjoyments than many (yea, may I not say than most) Christians do in their most spiritual duties and ordinances. O, what might we enjoy Christ in the visible Book of Nature, and creature comforts, had we but spiritual hearts!'

As rector and curator of souls at Credenhill, he became for others a guide along the path he was himself following. Since his activities there belong to a particular field of the spiritual life of England in those days, it will be well to give a brief account of this. Little attention is paid to it in our day, and yet it is of particular historical importance as a forerunner of modern spiritual striving.

In the cultural history of recent centuries, though not on the surface of civilisation, an essential role has been played by certain brotherhoods which, while resembling the monastic orders in a certain sense, yet differed from them significantly. Their members followed certain strict rules of outer and inner life, but at the same time shared the life of other people by having families, carrying on an ordinary profession, etc. The impulse for this kind of life had come from a personality who, in the fourteenth century, had lived in southern central Europe under the name of the 'Friend of God'. Among his pupils there arose the idea which led to the foundation of the Community of the Brethren of Modern Devotion.

On the other hand, there had come into existence in the fifteenth century the Brotherhood of the Rosicrucians, whose members were enjoined to occupy themselves with the world of the senses in a manner that would lead to an apperception of the spirit in nature. Their striving was thus in the sense of true alchemy. They used to speak of the *Book of Nature* as one of the sources of Divine revelation – an expression well known to us from Goethe's endeavours, and significantly applied to Traherne's spiritual relation to nature by his former fellow student (in the last quotation). The members of this Brotherhood also shared in the ordinary life of other people, while leading a strictly regulated inner life. Both these movements were inspired by the impulse to do justice to the dawning age, which was to develop a mighty external civilisation, but in such a way that the human soul would be safeguarded from losing itself in this civilisation.

There can be no doubt that during his second period at Oxford, Traherne received some essential advice in line with these spiritual movements. For at Credenhill we find him forming the spiritual centre of a religious community of a kind not unfamiliar in England at that time. These communities called themselves 'Families', and their members were enjoined to lead exactly the kind of life that was characteristic of the Brotherhoods just mentioned. From a contemporary account we know of an outstanding member of the Credenhill Family, Mrs Susanna Hopton, a well-to-do woman who was active in outer life, being engaged through her husband's prominent position in many social activities, yet throughout the week she withdrew five times a day for periods of contemplation and meditation, and would not allow herself to be diverted from this rule except by some exceptionally urgent business. This was the person for whom Traherne, after having left Credenhill, wrote his *Centuries of Meditations* as an aid for her devotions. We have an anthology of prayers from her hand in the midst of which are a few words of thanksgiving for her spiritual friendship with Traherne: 'I praise Thee, for the super-exalted love of a redeemed person.'

The testimony quoted earlier by Traherne's fellow student is proof enough that no overestimation prompted Susanna Hopton to use these words of her friend and spiritual guide.

Appendix II

ARISTOTLE AND GALILEO

With the help of the geometrical considerations in Chapter X we came a certain distance in our attempt to compose a picture of levity as an autonomous force in polar relationship to gravity. This enables us to dispose of a centuries-old error in regard to Aristotle's conception of the behaviour of freely-falling bodies. For a method of research such as is practised in this book it becomes a matter of what might be termed historical conscience not to omit such a rectification once it has become possible.

In Galileo's day and for quite a time previously, the notion was firmly established that the speed with which a body falls to earth varies according to its weight or mass. In order to demolish this view, derived, so it was said, from a dictum of Aristotle's, Galileo is reputed to have carried out his experiment from the leaning tower of Pisa.[1] Aristotle's supposed doctrines had continued through the centuries entirely unopposed, so that Galileo's proof that all bodies fall to the ground with equal acceleration and therefore, when dropped from the same height, reach the bottom after the same time, signified a resounding victory over Aristotelian dogma. We are now in a position to show, however, that what Galileo disproved as an error was in fact a false interpretation of Aristotle's real opinion. The historic change in the relationship of human consciousness to the outside world had brought it about that what Aristotle had actually taught could no longer be understood in Aristotle's sense.

We drew attention in Chapter VII to the difference between the world-views of Plato and Aristotle, a difference due to Plato's retention, and Aristotle's loss, of a knowledge of the pre-existence of the soul. So long as the human being on earth possessed this knowledge, he felt that with his soul he belonged by nature to the element of levity. Aristotle, however, was aware that the human spirit was entering on a path which was destined to lead it downwards into gravity, and he felt impelled to provide the coming age with a conception of nature wherein levity and gravity held the balance between them. We find all his writings, including even his *Ethics*, penetrated through and through with this principle of balance. What he has to say about the behaviour of bodies subject to gravity, therefore, can be judged properly only if we set it alongside what he says in connection with levity. Actually, he himself always treats both aspects together, usually in one and the same sentence. But in the time when the kind of consciousness that was to lead to the *Contra-Levitatem maxim* began to emerge, such a fact was no longer taken into account; with the result that many misinterpretations of Aristotle's teachings arose, similar to the one challenged by Galileo.

Aristotle approached nature not with the spectator-consciousness used perforce by Galileo, as a child of his age, but with a consciousness that was still to a high degree participatory. Accordingly, we should expect his conception of levity to match what we have ourselves been seeking anew through the overcoming of the spectator-consciousness. And this is just what we find. Since our own incursion into geometry we know exactly that in levitational space there are no point-to-point connections, and that the upward-directed effect of levity always manifests in plane-formations. We know, too, that in the sphere of levity corporeal existence does not extend from an interior point to a delimiting outer surface, but from the all-embracing plane to a delimiting inner surface. When, therefore, Aristotle speaks of 'light bodies', and says that they travel upwards in following levity, just as heavy bodies travel downwards in following gravity, we must not interpret this as if it referred to bodies subject to gravity but with a specific weight less than that of their surroundings, nor imagine their movement as analogous to the movement of a centrally-determined body through Euclidean space, comparable, let us say, to ascending air-bubbles in water, as has been done by modern commentators.[2]

Furthermore, we must not overlook the fact that Aristotle still had a living conception of the Four Elements, which he elaborated in a manner that remained valid throughout the ensuing centuries up to van Helmont. We ourselves felt it necessary in Chapter IX, before developing the new conception of levity, to renew the doctrine of the Four Elements, the reason being that the two conceptions are organically interrelated. It is in accordance with this relationship that Aristotle deals with the whole subject. Thus, for example, he comes to speak of light and heavy bodies also in terms of 'fire-bodies' and 'earth-bodies' respectively. This may suffice to show that even on the side of gravity Aristotle's descriptions must not be read as if his concepts coincided with those of the Contra-Levitatem age.

In this sense we must pay particular attention to the word used by Aristotle – and, be it reiterated, always with regard to both aspects – where we today would speak in connection with gravity of the 'mass' or 'weight' of a body, so that his word has been equated with these two concepts. This word is ῥοπή (*rhopē*) from the Greek verb ῥέπω (*rhepō*) 'to incline', 'to dip'. As such it originally denoted the inclination of a pair of scales, and was also used in a metaphorical sense to express the 'weightiness' of a person or affair. Thus it is true that in the first place it had to do only with the kind of dynamic which the earthward pull of gravity brings into play. Aristotle, however, expressly uses the word also in regard to levity, which shows that for the Greek this word as originally used had a different shade of meaning from what we understand in our way by the weight or mass of a physical body.

Recent translators and commentators have indeed noticed the difficulty involved in translating ῥοπή adequately; certainly all their attempts so far have come to grief, and this through always approaching the problem, without hesitation, from the standpoint of post-Galilean physics. The solution is found as soon as one abandons this procedure, and, resorting to re-creative imagination, puts oneself deliberately into the mode of experiencing the world which in Aristotle's day was the natural one.

Let us now look at the statement in the Fourth Book of Aristotle's *Physics*, which contains the alleged error refuted by

Galileo. We shall leave the word ῥοπή untranslated, and in addition put the term 'more quickly' in inverted commas, so as to indicate that this word also must be looked at again; it cannot without more ado be made to carry the meaning given to 'velocity' by the spectator-mind. Aristotle says:

'Thus we see that the things which possess the greater ῥοπή, in regard to gravity or levity alike – provided that other conditions are equal – move 'more quickly' in relation to the same area, in fact, proportionally to its (i.e. the *rhopē*'s) respective quantity.'

In order to attain to a correct understanding of the experience which the Greek expressed by the attribute 'quick' (*tachys*), we must consider two more words in the above quotation. The one is χωριον (*chōrion*), which we have translated as 'area'. It comes from the same root χερ (*cher-*) as the word χειρ (*cheir*, hand) which means 'to grasp', 'to encompass'. (In the initial sounds 'gr' in 'grasp' we can recognise the Greek 'ch-r'.) All the words derived from this root, such as χωρα (*chōra*, land), χωριον above and others, signify in various ways something that is spatially extended and can be grasped or encompassed. When Aristotle applies χωριον to the spatial domain traversed by bodies of varying ῥοπή with varying 'quickness', it is evident that nothing could be further from his thought than the idea of a straight line such as Galileo with his kind of consciousness envisaged – meaningless as it would have been in any case with reference to levity.

The other word to be commented on is the verb that in Greek expresses movement. The directness with which the ancient Greek experienced in himself such external happenings is shown by the fact that he said – in using the so-called 'middle' voice of the verb, halfway in signification between the active and the passive – 'the body carries itself' (φερεται, *pheretai*) for 'the body moves'; it is as if a body in a state of motion were in each case the bearer of a volitional being experienced as we experience ourselves when moving our own body.[3]

We now come to the term 'quick', which denotes the intensity of the body's motion.

For someone like Aristotle it was not yet possible to form a purely *kinematic* concept of velocity as the expression of a purely spatial happening irrespective of the moving mass, nor to form a purely static concept of mass independent of the state of motion. For, in reality, there is no mass which is not in a state of some velocity, and there is no velocity except as the property of some definite mass. Still, modern physical science includes among its concepts one which covers in its own way both a mass and its state of motion. This is the concept *quantity of motion*, or *momentum*, determined by the product of mass and its velocity. The greater the velocity of a certain mass, the greater its momentum, and again, the greater the mass of a body moving with a certain speed, the greater is its momentum. Expressed in symbols this reads: M = mv. Since the spectator-thinking was compelled to start for its measurements from 'distance', 'time', and 'mass', the momentum appears in a certain sense as a derived quantity, namely as the product of the mass and the quotient of distance-divided-by-time (the velocity). However, the expressions 'quantity-of-motion' and 'momentum' already reveal quite clearly that even the scientific observer who was confined to an onlooker-relation to the world could not help feeling the fundamental character of this dynamic property of physical bodies.

It is this property of bodies which is first of all experienced by a soul in the state of participating consciousness, and of which the Greek, therefore, spoke when using his word for 'quick'. (Note the range of meaning of this word in English!) It is in this sense, therefore, that Aristotle uses the word when stating that bodies with a greater ῥοπη move 'more quickly' across a given area.

If it is asserted, as is done in modern editions of his works, that Aristotle committed the blunder of regarding levity as a positive force alongside gravity, and if it is then ignored that in the above-quoted passage something is being said not only about gravity but about levity as well; and if, further, the gravity-*rhopē* is interpreted as the gravity-determined mass of the body, and the *chōrion* within which the movement occurs, as the one-dimensional line along which the centre of gravity of a falling body moves; and if, finally, the 'quickness' with which the body moves is interpreted as the rate of the spatial displacement of the body along this line, then one arrives unfailingly at that interpretation which Galileo so successfully disposed of with his observations. There is nothing in Aristotle's statement, however, to call for such refutation. His experience was that bodies with a different intensity of 'inclination' towards the force-field to which they are akin, assume across equal areas different momenta, and he even knew that proportionality exists between the inclination and the momentum.

If Aristotle could have been present at the tower of Pisa, watching Galileo's experiment, he might have been inclined to demonstrate his meaning by dropping stones of unequal weight from the top of the tower on to Galileo's head, but actually such an argument would not have been necessary, for on this point Aristotle and Galileo would have been in complete agreement.

Appendix III

GOETHE, FARADAY, AND MATHEMATICS

In recent centuries there have been two great men who have shown, in their approach to scientific research, that man is capable of proceeding like a true mathematician even though he is not using mathematics in the accepted sense. These two men were Goethe and Faraday. They had this ability because all their lives they were able to draw on the forces of childhood, forces to which man, in the early part of his life, owes the organic growth and development of his body and soul. Goethe and Faraday worked in quite different fields and had different spheres of influence. They differed also in the external course of their lives and in the inner paths followed by their souls. Yet it is possible to discern a deep-down relationship between them, in the way in which they let the contents of the external world become experience, and then grasped the Idea inherent within the empirical knowledge they had gained. Both were equally strangers to mathematics in the narrower sense, and yet these two men proceeded to treat the world of experience in a way that was entirely mathematical. Thus they were the first in our time to bear witness to the fact that the human mind has the capacity for proceeding mathematically, in a sense wider than is usually applied to the term 'mathematics'. This agrees with the original meaning of the word, which is well worth considering.

'Mathematics' derives from the Greek verb *manthanein* which was used to describe all activities of acquiring contents of consciousness, i.e. to learn, to experience, to perceive, to note, to perform an act of cognition, to grasp and so forth. The stem consonants of the verb are *m-n*, a sequence found in its most basic form in the Greek *menos* (Latin *mens*, mind). For the Greeks, this covered a wide range of meanings, but always related to a very specific dynamic process in the soul which has been described, quite rightly, as 'power striving to become active', be it more at the physical level, as life instinct or vital energy and hence life as such, or in the sphere of the soul, as courage, heroism, and finally in heated emotional reactions such as vehemence and anger. In the latter sense, the word could also be used to describe the power of fire. (The Romans, too, used the word *mens* to describe a number of emotive reactions.) However varied the range of meaning, the underlying idea: power striving to become active, was always there. The people of earlier times felt that at the heart of any activity of learning, grasping, and cognition, lay the very force to which they also owed their life instinct. They knew that it had not originated on earth, and with its help they were able to rise, in the experience of life, to the world of their own origins. On the other hand they knew themselves to have been brought into earth-existence by this force, and felt it pulsing through them in the process of cognition.

The original meaning of the word mathematics thus relates to the very point we arrived at in Chapter VIII, when it became obvious that the soul owes its ability to think mathematically, in this case in the narrower sense now generally accepted, to the forces of our origin which are at work in the child. Goethe owed to them his ability to work creatively, something immediately obvious from the introduction to his method. They continued to well up fresh as spring water even when he had reached an advanced age, and he owed this to what he himself referred to as his 'recurrent puberty' or also 'temporary rejuvenation'. In the case of Faraday, these forces remained alive and continued at the same level throughout his life. It is this which made it possible for these two men to be 'mathematicians' in the sense we are concerned with here.

To appreciate Goethe's achievement in the light of this concept, let us recall once more the moment which marked the birth of present-day science — Galileo's discovery that nature was 'written in mathematical language'. Whence did the impetus come, we must ask ourselves, for modern consciousness to develop a view of nature that is based entirely on quantitative, mathematical concepts? (Our investigation of the underlying principles has already shown that none other would suit an onlooker-consciousness; here the question is as to the *impetus.*) And furthermore, what made the enquiring mind of man feel so secure in the knowledge acquired by such means?

When man assumed the role of world-onlooker, the effect of this for him was that he first of all came to experience the whole of nature around him as something alien in substance to his own essential nature. On the other hand there was his mathematical cognition, an objective, constructive activity carried out wholly within himself, in which he was able to experience himself as being wholly within it with his soul. It became apparent to him – as it had originally to Galileo – that he was able to enter right into things which initially were alien to him in substance, to become immersed in them, as it were, with what he had constructed in his own mind, i.e. that a mathematical formula may be used to express things which otherwise present themselves to him only in their outer aspect. Thus something which initially is outside us can become inner. And the feeling of inner certainty and security which goes with this arises from the exactness inherent in mathematics.[1]

The price which the human spirit had to pay for this faculty was that the scope of his enquiry into nature was narrowed down. This is what Heisenberg referred to in the address mentioned at the beginning of this book.[2] The resulting image of the world no longer includes anything of the reality perceived by the soul as it experiences the qualitative contents of nature. This was where Goethe came in and took the next significant step. He gained the faculty to take in and make *inward* something initially outside himself, doing this in qualitative terms with the same exactitude as the 'exact' scientists have managed to do in quantitative terms. In his argument with Kant's definition of the limits set to man's powers of cognition, he was able to say of himself that looking upon ever-creative nature had helped him to attain a state where in his mind he was *taking part* in her productions. He knew that in doing so he was just as much a 'mathematician' as were those who were exploring the purely quantitative aspects of nature. He was quite unambiguous about this. He was able to be so definite about it because, though he did not himself have the gifts to be creatively active in the field of pure mathematics, he nevertheless clearly understood its nature. This is evident from various statements he made, some of which are given below.

In his collection *Sprüche in Prosa* (Aphorisms in Prose) (also known as *Maximen und Reflexionen* — Maxims and Reflections), a whole section is devoted to mathematics. The following passages are taken from this.

'Like dialectics, the science of mathematics is an organ of the higher inner perception; in its application it is an art, like the art of rhetoric. For both, only the form is of value, with the content of no significance. It simply does not matter to them whether calculations are done in pennies or in guineas, or a speech is made in defence of truth or falsehood. It is the essential character of the person which counts, as he conducts his business, or performs his art. A defence lawyer carrying the day in a just cause, a penetrating mathematician looking upon the starry heavens, will both appear equally god-like.'

In Goethe's experience, it had first been necessary to fit himself for the task if true cognition was to be achieved in his particular sphere of research. He demands the same of the true mathematician:

'The mathematician is perfect only in so far as he is perfect as a human being, as he is aware within himself of the beauty of truth; only then will his work be thorough, lucid, circumspect, pure, clear, graceful and indeed elegant. It needs all this to come close to Lagrange.'

Reading these words, it seems strange that the opinion can have arisen that Goethe did not appreciate mathematics. They show quite clearly that he was fully au fait with research done in mathematics in his day. When we came to consider how Goethe learnt of Howard's study of cloud formations, it was noted that in coming across this significant work he became immediately interested in the ethical character of the man who made those discoveries. It is unlikely that Goethe was able to take in the whole content of the creative work of the great French mathematician Lagrange (1736-1813), but his intuitive perception certainly led him to grasp its significance. And, as in the case of Howard, he obviously endeavoured to learn about Lagrange as a person, to get a picture of the whole personality.

Yet Goethe also felt constrained to be critical of mathematicians — especially the 'physico-mathematical guild':

'Mathematicians are peculiar people; on the basis of the great things they have achieved, they have now set themselves up as the guild of guilds, unwilling to give recognition to anything that does not come within their compass, that their organ is unable to handle. On one occasion, a leading mathematician, being urged to consider a chapter on physics, said: "But can none of it be reduced to calculus?" '

Among his collection of essays entitled *Zur Naturwissenschaft im Allgemeinen* (On Science in General), there is one with the title *Über Mathematik und deren Missbrauch* (Mathematics and its Misuse). In this, he mainly gives the word to other scientists, men of standing like the great mathematician, physicist and encyclopaedist d'Alembert, giving them considerable space, and merely sums up and interprets their statements at the end. He gives his reasons for this in the introduction: 'It pleased me not to find that my intentions were falsely interpreted. I have heard accusations against me as though I were an opponent, an enemy of mathematics altogether; yet there is none who holds it in greater esteem than I do, for it is able to do the very thing which to perform has been totally denied me.' He had chosen his own way of declaring himself on this point, by making use of the words of others, men of greatness and renown.

As Goethe was nobly and humbly admitting, it was denied to him to move in the sphere of formal concepts of pure mathematics. Yet he certainly was a 'mathematician', in the wider sense we are concerned with here. He tells us this himself, in an essay *Der Versuch als Vermittler von Objcht und Subjekt* (The Experiment as Mediator between Object and Subject). He had found that the way to grasp the Ideas pertaining in nature as they reveal themselves to sense perception, was to put together a number of related phenomena in such a way that they declare to the mind of man the natural laws that are common to them. What he learned in this way he referred to as 'higher perception'.

'Perception of this kind, based on a number of other perceptions, is obviously of a higher kind. It is like the formula used in arithmetic to express countless examples of a calculation. To work towards gaining this type of higher perception is, I believe, the scientist's highest obligation.... This deliberation, carefully taking first one thing, then the next, and the next, or rather to draw inferences only step by step, is something we can learn from the mathematicians, and even if we are not doing calculations, we should proceed always as if we were accountable to the strictest of geometricians.'

Goethe therefore considers scientific work that is in accord with nature to consist in applying the mathematical approach to one's treatment of the phenomena as they are revealed to the senses. Goethe's archetypal phenomena are, within the sphere of what may be known and experienced in terms of quality, what axioms are to the mathematician in the sphere of what may be known and experienced in terms of quantity.

It is characteristic of the very nature of Faraday that contemporary references permitting us to picture the man and the scientist are uncommonly numerous. Added to this are his own careful records, many volumes of them, in which throughout his working life he was in the habit of putting down his thoughts on the subject of his studies and every detail of his experimental work. The details given below come from the rich biographical material available in published form.[3]

In Faraday's time, what was completely new and surprising in his concept of the influences exerted upon each other by bodies that were vehicles for the forces of electricity or magnetism, was that those effects were due to the state produced in

the whole of space by the presence of such bodies. It was Faraday
who established the now familiar concepts of a field of force and
of lines of force. Instead of an effect produced at a distance, by
one body inexplicably influencing another across the space
between them, Faraday spoke of a potential effect existing
throughout the whole field, with the body responding to it
wherever it might be within that field. He was able to do this
because he abstained completely from evolving any hypotheses by
merely thinking about things, and instead approached the events
as they presented themselves to him with a mental activity wholly
of the type described as 'intuitive judgment', though its origins in
his case differed from those of Goethe's. The difference was due
to the fact that destiny led the two men to the exploration of
different fields of knowledge.

The areas of knowledge and experience explored by Goethe
were in spheres of nature for which the human organism is
equipped with specific sense organs. Electricity and magnetism,
on the other hand, the field in which Faraday made his great
discoveries, belong to a sphere of forces not open to direct perception. Faraday therefore needed quite different qualifications from
those of Goethe to attain similar achievements in his field. As
already stated, Goethe, looking back at a later date to his
botanical studies, was able to say of himself that he had achieved
his results ('finally', he adds) 'not through being unusually gifted,
nor by a moment of inspiration, unexpected and sudden, but by
consistent endeavour'. For Faraday, one might say almost word
for word the opposite. To understand what was needed here, it
will be necessary to give at least a brief intimation of where
electricity and magnetism have their place within the total order
of nature. A more detailed treatment of the subject will be found
in Chapter XIII.

Again it is necessary to return to the concept of man as it
arises from the analysis presented in Chapter II, a concept which
has already proved its usefulness in providing further insights on
a number of occasions. It is the concept of man in his trinal
psycho-physical constitution, with the system of nerves and
senses providing the physical basis for his conceptual thinking

in waking awareness, the rhythmic system the basis for his feeling, in dream-like awareness, and the system of metabolism and limbs the basis for his activities of will, which take place at the sleep-level of awareness. Corresponding to this, man encounters nature at three levels of activity. To everything that is luminous and produces sound, we relate through the part of our soul which is awake in awareness; our response to heat effects is more dream-like; and our relationship to electrical and similar processes is the same as what happens within us when we perform an act of will. (Transitional stages occurring both without and within may be ignored at this point.)

This encounter between nature and man at three different levels is not a subjective experience merely arising on the basis of man's constitution, but something based on an actual corre-spondence between man and nature, as already referred to else-where. There is a sphere outside in nature that represents in nature what the sphere of metabolism and will is in man, etc. To achieve conscious awareness of this sphere, the mind has to be trained, and this was discussed earlier in this book. It certainly is inappropriate to ask how one would perceive electricity, if one had the physical sense to do so, for it is in the very nature of this sphere, outside as well as within man, that the possibility of direct sense percep-tion of it, of any kind whatever, is not to be thought of. The sensory perceptions made when electricity is in action, of phenomena such as light, sound, and so on, or the physical sensation one may have if it enters into the organism, are con-comitant phenomena, which may be compared to the concepts accompanying an act of will.

There is a word for the process by which awareness may be attained of factual realities in spheres not directly accessible to sense perception. This word is Intuition. It is what Goethe had in mind when he spoke of 'intuitive judgment'. It has already been shown that it was this which led Galileo to make his fundamental discoveries, in his case – using the word in its best possible sense – intuition acting instinctively. And it was this also, though more penetrating in nature, which helped Faraday to form a concept of the electric and magnetic states and the changes in them. This concept, the accepted one today, was at first rejected by some of his contemporaries, whilst others quite rightly admired him greatly for it. Let me quote some of the latter:

The first person to be quoted is James Clerk Maxwell, the man to whom scientists are indebted for the final, mathematical form of electromagnetic theory. He formulated in mathematical terms what Faraday, as Maxwell himself put it, saw 'in the mind's eye'. (Note how the phrase familiar to us from Goethe is here used spontaneously by Maxwell, in his accurate assessment of Faraday.) Studying Faraday's records, it was immediately obvious to him that in the way the former used the concept of electric and magnetic lines of force in his phenomenological description of the processes of electromagnetic induction, he showed himself to be 'a first-class mathematician', having 'an approach which mathematicians may use to develop valuable and fruitful methods'. This is what Maxwell himself did, and because the method he created in this way was rather different from that generally used till then in applying mathematical concepts to electric processes, he prefaced his treatise on *Electricity and Magnetism* with a special explanation (Apologia), setting forth the differences between his own work and the approach used by the German mathematicians also working in this field. There he states that prior to embarking on the study of electricity, he had deliberately refrained from looking at the mathematics of the subject until he had read Faraday's *Experimental Researches on Electricity*. He continues:

'As I proceeded with the study of Faraday, I perceived that his method of conceiving the phenomena was also a mathematical one, though not exhibited in the conventional form of mathematical symbols. I also found that these methods were capable of being expressed in the ordinary mathematical forms, and thus compared with those of the professed mathematicians.

'For instance, Faraday in his mind's eye saw lines of force traversing all space where the mathematicians saw centres of force attracting at a distance: Faraday saw a medium where they

saw nothing but distance. Faraday sought the seat of the phenomena in real actions going on in the medium, they were satisfied
that they had found it in a power of action at a distance impressed
on the electric fluids.'

Maxwell found that both methods would in fact lead to the
same result, but Faraday's approach proved to be one where 'we
being with the whole and arrive at the parts by analysis, while the
ordinary mathematical methods were founded on the principle of
beginning with the parts and building up the whole by synthesis.'
Does this not remind one of the conversation between Goethe and
Schiller — totally unknown to Maxwell — on the question of
whether nature should not be studied by going from the whole to
the parts rather than from the parts to the whole? And indeed,
Maxwell found that several of the most fruitful methods developed by mathematicians could be expressed very much better with
the aid of Faraday's ideas than in the manner used theretofore. He
actually called the purely mathematical method he had developed,
of starting from the 'potential' as a quantity that will satisfy a
particular partial differential equation, the 'Faraday method'.

Maxwell's report — and this is typical — contains the following
personal comment, very much like the comments one finds so
frequently in the writings of others who have made the acquaintance of Faraday himself or of his work: 'If by anything I have
written I may assist any student in understanding Faraday's
modes of thought and expression, I shall regard it as the accomplishment of one of my principal aims — to communicate to others
the same delight which I have found myself in reading Faraday's
Researches.'

Among the physicists on the Continent, it was Helmholtz who
first came to recognise the fundamental significance of the
concept of electrodynamic processes produced by Faraday and
formulated in mathematical terms by Maxwell. From the various
references he made to this in lectures and talks, the following
may be quoted. Helmholtz, too, acknowledges Faraday's achievement to be '...the work of a great mathematician without using
a single mathematical formula.' Later, he speaks of the 'mar-

vellously clear and lively intuition' which Faraday was able to form, of the processes in an electric or magnetic field, and that it was this which enabled him to develop a concept of these processes where it was no longer necessary to refer to forces producing a direct effect at a distance. It needed James Clerk Maxwell, another personality capable of that depth and independence of thought, to use the established forms of systematic thought and erect that great edifice, the plan of which Faraday had conceived in his mind, seeing it so clearly before his own eyes and endeavouring to make it visible also to the eyes of his contemporaries.

Elsewhere Helmholtz said: 'Nevertheless, the fundamental conceptions by which Faraday was led to the much-admired discoveries have not received an equal amount of consideration. They were very divergent from the trodden path of scientific theory, and appeared rather startling to his contemporaries. His principal aim was to express in his new conceptions only facts, with the least possible use of hypothetical substances and forces. This was really an advance in general scientific method, destined to purify science from the last remnants of metaphysics.'

Again one notes clear indications of a Goethean approach. It has to be added, however, that Helmholtz did not use this himself in his further investigations, being in fact one of the major proponents of the mechanistic approach to all natural processes, starting with those of heat. It is the same role which he played in taking up the discovery of J.R. Mayer, a spirit akin to that of Faraday, and giving his own interpretation to the laws Mayer had found pertaining to the relationship between work done and heat generated.

Let us also quote the words of another contemporary scientist, Justus Liebig, one of the great chemists of that age and one who understood Faraday early, who admits to his own feelings on reading Faraday's records:

'I have heard of mathematicians complaining that Faraday's records of his work are difficult to read and understand, and that they tended to be more like extracts from his rough notes. But that was their own fault, and not Faraday's. For physicists who have come to physics via chemistry, Faraday's writings sound like magnificent, beautiful music.'

What kind of man was Faraday then, to have achieved this, and how did he come to achieve it?

As already mentioned, one might say that with him the opposite is true, almost word for word, of what Goethe himself described as his qualifications for achieving what he did in the field of science. Considering the image one gets of the man as one studies his life and work, one does indeed feel inclined to regard him as the exception to the precept that we all have to learn before we master a skill.

Michael Faraday was born on 22nd September 1791, son of the blacksmith in a village not far from London. He had practically no regular schooling. His mother had promptly removed him from school when his brother Robert had told her that the school-mistress had given him money to buy a cane, as she wanted to punish young Michael for not pronouncing his R's properly (he used to call his brother Wobert, for example). On his way home, Robert, in his fury, had simply thrown the money in the stream. The little that Michael was to learn after this was whatever came to him through life at home and in the village street. When he was twelve, his father apprenticed him to a bookbinder in London, a man who very soon came to hold the boy in benevolent regard. He was one of the French emigrés of whom there were quite a number in London in those days. This turned out to be a significant act of providence, for the social circumstances were such that a number of above-average personalities were regular visitors to his master's house, either as customers in the shop, or as lodgers at his house.

The boy was first on probation for a year, running errands to do with the business, one of his chief tasks being to deliver newspapers, especially on Sundays. He had to be really quick about it then, for through his parents he belonged to a sect founded by a Scot and regular attendance at Sunday worship was very strictly enjoined. As we shall see, this religious affiliation was one of the factors which was to influence the destiny of Faraday. It appears that the boy attracted the attention of those who met him even at that early age. 'A bright-eyed errand boy' was later recalled, 'who slid along the London pavements, with a load of brown curls upon his head and a packet of newspapers under his arm.'

After the probationary year his seven-year apprenticeship began, and 'in view of his faithful services' no premium had to be paid. Now came a time when he avidly read the books he was given to bind. A book on chemistry made tremendous impact and also – when binding the *Encyclopaedia Britannica* – an article on electricity. He immediately started to carry out some very simple chemical experiments, and built himself a primitive electrostatic machine. During the same period, one of his master's lodgers – the boy had to clean his room and polish his boots – noticed the bright youngster and taught him to draw, instructing him also in the theory of perspective.

One day, Faraday saw an announcement in the street of evening lectures on natural science. His great longing to attend these lectures was satisfied by his brother Robert, who gave him the money. At the lectures, Faraday met an educated young Quaker, and a friendship developed which was to continue all his life, something that was to happen on a number of occasions. The letters they wrote to each other have come down to posterity. Faraday, now nineteen years of age, having had no proper schooling at all, wrote a style presenting his thoughts so lucidly and with such warmth of feeling that a later biographer quite rightly speaks of a 'model of letter writing, an art now unfortunately lost'.

The next major event in his life was when one of his master's customers, himself a scientist and Member of the Royal Institution (Faraday was later to become its director for the rest of his life), took him to hear four lectures given by Sir Humphry Davy, already a famous chemist at that time. Hidden behind the clock in the lecture theatre, Faraday listened to these lectures, making notes which he carefully wrote up at home. His apprenticeship was then just coming to an end, and he became a

journeyman with another bookbinder. Again his destiny was to be
influenced by the fact that he was now being treated as badly as
until then he had been treated well. In desperation, he wrote to
Davy, enclosing the notes taken at his lectures, 'as a proof of my
earnestness', asking him to give him employment, wishing '... to
escape from trade, which I thought vicious and selfish, and to
enter into the service of Science, which I imagined made its
pursuers amiable and liberal'.

Davy received him and with a smile warned him not to set
his expectations too high in this respect. He told him that he
was unable to employ him at the moment. It was not long,
however, before an elegant carriage stopped outside the blacksmith's house. A liveried servant descended and asked to speak to
young Mr Faraday. He gave him a note from Davy in which the
latter asked him to come to him. Davy had injured his eye in a
laboratory explosion and was therefore unable to do his own
written work. He now employed Faraday, in the first place to
act as his clerk, but soon began to use him as a laboratory assistant
as well.

At this time Faraday joined an association formed by some
young people who wished to train their ability to think and speak
by giving lectures to each other and holding discussions on scientific subjects. He soon developed the abilities which later were to
make him an outstanding teacher and speaker, arousing enthusiasm in his listeners. Fate then presented the next gift of importance to Faraday, for Davy took him as his servant and laboratory
assistant on an eighteen-month journey through various Continental countries. Wherever he went, Davy visited the leading physicists
and chemists of that time, among them Ampère, Biot, Gay-Lussac
and Volta, and every one of them noticed the young man and
remained in touch with him for the rest of his life. In Geneva,
Davy declined an invitation from a physicist because Faraday had
been invited as well, and he refused to sit at the same table with
his servant. The host did not withdraw his invitation, but had the
young man's meal served separately, in an adjoining room. After
this man's death, Faraday continued in friendship with his son,

who had followed in his father's footsteps. The diary kept by Faraday during these travels is full of the most marvellous and delightful observations on everything that came his way, and the letters he wrote to his mother, his brothers and sisters from all over the place bear witness to his loving nature.

On his return to London, at the age of twenty-four, he became a full-time assistant at the institute. He immediately started to give lectures on a variety of scientific subjects to the association of young people mentioned above. Even at that time, he liked to conclude his wholly objective, factual presentation of a scientific subject with some great fundamental reflections. Deep insight is shown in those addresses, as may be seen from the conclusion of one such lecture, on the subject of oxygen, chlorine, iodine and fluorine.

'It may be observed how great are the alterations made in the opinions of men by the extension of inquiry; and this points out the imperfections of those originally held. Again, by adherents to a favourite theory, many errors have at times been introduced into general science which have required much labour for their removal. These circumstances are the cause of many obstructions in the path of knowledge. Whilst, however, we can thus observe those causes which have at former periods acted in a manner not agreeable to our wishes, let us be careful not to give occasion to future generations to return the charge on us. Man always forms opinions, and he always believes them correct. In pointing out the errors of another he endeavours to substitute for them his own views. At the present day we have our theories and laws, and we believe them to be correct, though they may probably fall, as others have done before them. 'Tis true that, warned by the example of others, we profess to be more reserved in our opinions, and more guarded in our decisions; and yet continual experience shows that our care applies rather to former errors than to those now likely to arise. We avoid those faults which we perceive, but we still fall into others. To guard against these requires a large proportion of mental humility, submission, and independence.

'The philosopher should be a man willing to listen to every

suggestion, but determined to judge for himself. He should not be biassed by appearances; have no favourite hypothesis; be of no school; and in doctrine have no master. He should not be a respecter of persons, but of things. Truth should be his primary object. If to these qualities are added industry, he may indeed hope to walk within the veil of the temple of nature.'

It would be wrong to regard this as an excess of youthful idealism which later in life, as so often happens, rather lost momentum. Faraday himself adhered to the principles we have just quoted all through his life.

The field of electricity and magnetism, where Faraday was to make the great discoveries which have done so much to shape, our present-day life, is also the one which has led mankind directly into the materialism prevalent today. If one considers the history of the human race from the point of view of spiritual science, one has to say to oneself that this materialism is a necessary stage in that history. Man had to come to know matter, to shape it in many and different ways. But materialism as an ideology, the materialistic view of life which has since taken hold of the souls of men, that is another matter. Looking at Faraday, we can see that there was no need for this. It has been mentioned that he belonged to a religious sect. Its members – it existed only for a short time and never had many adherents – rejected any kind of organised religion and consequently also professional clergy. They endeavoured to live together in brotherhood, unanimously deciding who were to be their elders – later in his life, Faraday was an elder for some time, and took this office very seriously – and personal faith was based entirely on the text of the Bible, as understood by the ordinary man. Faraday thus received a religious training which helped him to keep his views of divine and natural things strictly separate. In later life, he accordingly wrote to a lady, in reply to her enquiry:

'You speak of religion, and here you will be sadly disappointed in me ... for in my mind religious conversation is generally in vain. There is no philosophy in my religion. I am of a very small and despised sect of Christians, known, if known at all, as Sandemanians, and our hope is founded on the faith that is in Christ. But though the natural works of God can never by any possibility come in contradiction with the higher things that belong to our future existence, and must with everything concerning Him ever glorify Him, still I do not think it at all necessary to tie the study of the natural sciences and religion together, and, in my intercourse with my fellow creatures, that which is religious and that which is philosophical have ever been two distinct things.'

What Faraday here states to be his attitude does appear to differ very considerably from what Goethe was aiming at, and also from the intention of this book. For Faraday and for the element which he was to bring into the world, however, it was appropriate. It was his attitude to the one sphere which helped him to gain the right attitude to the other. He did not permit rationalistic thoughts to enter into the contents of his faith, and in the same way he also did not permit the latter to enter into his scientific studies and researches. Otherwise his intuitive gifts could not have proved as fruitful as they did. However, the fruits which mankind owes to his genius are not confined to the realm of pure science. His experimental research work has given rise to the electric motors and dynamos we use today, and to the trans-formers which permit us to cover the world with a huge network of mighty electric power. The discoveries which had to be made in order to make such things possible also depended on the particular mental attitude we have been describing. This gave him the con-viction that all the forces of nature have a single common source and, their being thus similar in nature, it must be possible to transform one into the other. When he found that magnetism can be electrically induced, he was immediately convinced that the reverse had to be the case also. Directing his endeavours in this direction, he managed to devise an experiment in which a current-carrying conductor rotated around a magnet, and after ten further years of study he finally discovered electro-magnetic induction.

There is no need here to go into the world-wide acclaim Faraday was soon to receive from all spheres of science in his day, nor of the high and highest honours bestowed on him from all sides. What concerns us above all is his approach to knowledge, and the very special element in his nature on which this was based. As already mentioned, it was given to him, as it was to Goethe, to have and show an inner sense of mathematics, arising from the fact that all their lives they were able to draw on the forces of childhood. Again, let others bear witness of how those around him saw this quality in the man.

One of the things which Faraday really loved were the Christmas lectures he delivered annually before an audience of children. German readers are familiar with these through the translation of the 'Natural History of a Candle'. There is no need here to go into the pleasure to be experienced in reading this, nor into the exemplary educational approach shown in it. Instead, let us hear what was said on the subject by people who attended these and other public lectures which Faraday gave at the Royal Institution.

'He had the art', one such person wrote after his death, in a well-known journal, 'of surrounding science with magic, something which to no small degree was due to the fact that he combined the wisdom of his grey locks with a marvellously youthful spirit.... He could be as boisterously cheerful as a boy, and those who knew him best were aware that he never felt more at home, never seemed so happy, as when he made himself into an old boy, as he used to put it, and delivered his Christmas lectures to a youthful audience.'

A high-ranking lady of that period also wrote: 'He took great delight in talking to them, and easily won their confidence. The vivacity of his manner and of his countenance, and his pleasant laugh, the frankness of his whole bearing, attracted them to him. They felt as if he belonged to them; and indeed he sometimes, in his joyous enthusiasm, appeared like an inspired child....

'His quick sympathies put him so closely in relation with the child that he saw with the boy's new wonder, and looked, and most likely felt for the moment, as if he had never seen the thing before. Quick feelings, quick movement, quick thought, vividness of expression and of perception, belonged to him. He came across you like a flash of light, and he seemed to leave some of his light with you.'

Among the many scientists of that age who came to England to meet Faraday in person was also the son of that physicist in Geneva who had overruled Davy's objections and invited his servant to dinner as well. This visit enabled the son to attend several of the public lectures given by Faraday, and he was later to describe this experience as follows:

'Nothing can give a notion of the charm which he imparted to these improvised lectures, in which he knew how to combine animated, and often eloquent, language with a judgment and art in his experiments which added to the cleverness and elegance of his exposition. He exerted an actual fascination upon his auditors; and when, after having initiated them into the mysteries of science, he terminated his lecture, as he was in the habit of doing, by rising into regions far above matter, space, and time, the emotion which he experienced did not fail to communicate itself to those who listened to him, and their enthusiasm had no longer any bounds.'

The image conveyed by those reports would remain one-sided were we not also to consider the other side of it, Faraday's pain over the shortcomings he perceived in the souls of the men doing scientific research around him. His experiences with these other people meant that he could not retain that innocent faith which had once led him to write to Davy and ask to be allowed to work with him. Thus we hear from a lady who called on him at the Royal Institution at a time when he was already its director. Deeply affected — she writes — by the scientific atmosphere of the place, she said to him: ' "Mr Faraday, you must be very happy in your position and with your pursuits, which elevate you entirely out of the meaner aspects and lower aims of common life." He shook his head, and with that wonderful nobility of countenance which was characteristic, his expression of joyousness changed to one of profound sadness, and he replied: "When I quitted business and took to science as a career, I thought I had left behind me all the petty meannesses and small jealousies which hinder man in his moral progress; but I found myself raised into another sphere only to find poor human nature just the same everywhere — subject to the same weaknesses and the same self-seeking, however exalted the intellect."' And, she continues her story, '...looking at that good and great man, I thought I had never seen a countenance which so impressed me with the characteristic of perfect unworldliness.'

Faraday died shortly before completing his seventy-sixth year, on 26th August 1867. His energies had begun to give out many years before that, as his memory came to be increasingly impaired, the consequence, it was said later, of mercury poisoning. Faraday — and this was not unusual — was in the habit of using small dishes of mercury as contacts that were easily connected and disconnected. But there was one thing he continued to the end of his life — his annual Christmas lectures. He also turned up at his old institute from time to time to hear other scientists speak. On one occasion this happened after an extended interval due to illness, and as we are told by an eye-witness: 'The whole audience rose simultaneously and burst into a spontaneous utterance of welcome, loud and long. ... The eyes no longer flashed with the fire of the soul, but they still radiated kindly thought; and ineffaceable lines of intellectual force and energy were stamped upon his face.'

* * * * *

In view of certain reactions to the first edition of this book, it seemed advisable to include this Appendix. Various spheres of Nature are considered in the book which include some which until now have been exclusively the domain of researches based on the mathematics of physics. Only one of the chapters is concerned specifically with mathematics, this being a particular aspect of geometry. Apart from this, the investigations are concerned with purely qualitative aspects. This does not mean, however, that they are devoid of mathematics, in the sense referred to in this Appendix. It has certainly been the endeavour of the author to conduct them in the spirit demanded and acted upon by Goethe, that 'even if we are not doing calculations, we should proceed always as if we were accountable to the strictest of geometricians.'

Appendix IV

NEWTON'S RE-INTERPRETATION OF KEPLER'S THIRD LAW

Goethe's prose aphorisms (*Sprüche in Prosa*, also known as *Maximen und Reflexionen*), contain the following statement: 'As a mathematician, Newton is held in such high regard that the clumsiest of errors, the view that light − clear, pure and eternally unclouded − is a composite of a number of dark lights, has persisted to this day.' If Goethe had decided to make a statement on Newton's law of gravitation (the reader may recall the words of Heisenberg quoted earlier in this book) which according to Newton was responsible for the movement of the planets around the sun, he might have used almost the same words, more or less as follows: 'As a mathematician, Newton is held in such high regard that the clumsiest of errors, the view that the orbits set for the planets by the spirit are a composite of two linear motions alien to the spirit, has persisted to this day.'

Newton was by nature primarily an analytical mathematician. His reasoning was therefore based on purely kinematic concepts. He did not think in terms of real bodies moving in real orbits, but in terms of points moving along imaginary lines − or rather along lines of points − changing location from point to point. A mind thinking in this fashion must also have had the inclination to reduce complicated mathematical issues to simpler mathematical formulations, and in this particular case, therefore, to see curvilinear orbits as resulting from simple linear motions.

Newton's achievement, and none will deny this, was to show that a point moving at uniform velocity in a circular orbit would have the same motion if it were to move forwards in a straight line at the same velocity, and at the same time also moved at right angles to this at a constant rate of acceleration. The first motion would then be tangential to the orbit, the second centripetal and

MAN OR MATTER

in the direction of the centre. On its own, the first would take the point into infinite space, whilst the latter would cause it to move with increasing velocity along a radius towards the centre. Together, the two combine to give a circular motion around the centre. If the point describes a circle with the radius r, and requires the time t to complete one circle, then, as Newton* has shown, the centripetal acceleration of the imagined motion would be

$$a = \frac{4\pi^2 r}{t^2}$$

As one would expect, considering Newton's laws of mechanics, it was a matter of course for him to consider only *external* forces as the causative factors in motion and changes of motion. Experience has shown that for these forces, and only these (this has been discussed in detail in earlier pages), the resulting acceleration (a) is proportional to the force applied (P) and inversely proportional to the mass of the moving body (m). Thus,

$$a = \frac{P}{m}$$

or

$$P = ma$$

This relationship may be used purely algebraically to transform the above equation for centripetal *acceleration* into one expressing the corresponding centripetal *force*, simply by multiplying with the factor m. Thus one gets

$$P = ma = 4\pi^2 m \, \frac{r}{t^2}$$

* Newton's method of arriving at the formula may be found in elementary physics textbooks. There is no need, therefore, to describe it here.

This is the formula for Newton's centripetal force through which
the planets are 'attracted' by the sun, 'falling' towards it and being
'prevented' from doing so only because they simultaneously also
possess a constant linear velocity which is at right angles to it.

Note what has happened. Until the factor m made its appearance, the contents of all thought processes were wholly kinematic
and rightly so, as one was dealing with the assumed motions of
imaginary points along imaginary lines. The moment the factor
m was introduced we moved into another field, the sphere of
dynamics. And it is incorrect to make the uncritical assumption
that the method of reasoning used in kinematics continues to be
valid. It has been shown in the earlier part of this book that the
relation $F = ma$ does not apply to all forces. At the same time it
is never possible to determine the nature of a particular operant
force by mere onlooker observation or through logical deduction.
It therefore does not apply — though for the onlooker approach
it is a matter of course, and so long as one remains entirely within
the sphere of pure kinematics there is some justification for it
— that if something can be divided into two parts one may consider it to be made up of those two parts, in the present case a
curvilinear motion as composed of two linear motions. Onlooker
consciousness can do no other but think from parts to wholes.
Hence the resolution of the orbital curve into a sum of points,
something which it certainly is not in reality. Newton had to use
this type of operation so that with the aid of differential analysis
followed by integration he was able to arrive at his formula for
acceleration. The unreality of the whole complex of ideas becomes
strikingly obvious if one considers it from the *genetic* point of
view. For if it were the case that the movement of a planet is
due in part to a constant force exerted by the sun causing it to
fall towards it, and in part also to a uniform linear tangential
motion of the planet itself, one really would have to ask oneself:
If the latter, being uniform, continues unchanged, according to
Newton, without any force being applied, there must nevertheless
have been a point at which it started, and that did require the
application of force. How, then, was each of the planets given

that 'original push'? This question is inescapable when the construct of Newton's ideas is examined in the light of reality related
logic applied without preconception.

Let us consider the purely mathematical process by which
Kepler's third law was — with the aid of Newton's equation for
the centripetal force — converted to Newton's law of gravitation,
for this is supposed to show that Kepler's law already contains
within it Newton's concept of a universe kept in motion purely
through the effects of gravitation.

Expressed in mathematical symbols, Kepler's law reads:

$$\frac{r_1^3}{r_2^3} = \frac{t_1^2}{t_2^2}$$

(See p. 445)

Re-arranging, it may also be written as follows:

$$\frac{r_1^3}{t_1^2} = \frac{r_2^3}{t_2^2}$$

Instead of having on one side the space factors of two different
planets and on the other the time factors of those planets, we now
have the space and time factors for the two planets on opposite
sides of the equation. In this form the equation may also be put in
very general terms:

$$\frac{r^3}{t^2} = c \text{ (constant)} \tag{1}$$

It then expresses something that applies equally to every member
of our planetary system, namely that the ratio of the space enclosed by a planetary orbit to the square of its period is the same
for all planets. The constant c is therefore a definite structural
element in this system.

Up to this point, algebraic transformation of the original

equation has not touched upon its inherent significance. On the contrary, it has brought out an ideal content in it — the existence of the cosmic constant c — which was previously less apparent. The same cannot be said of the steps one has to take to get from Kepler's formula to that of Newton.

For a mind thinking entirely in terms of mathematics (which Newton's was), no objection can be raised to the following mathematical operation. On the left side of the equation, the distance of the planet from the sun, at present shown in cubic form, needs to be shown in linear form. This may be achieved by dividing both sides of equation (1) by r^2:

$$\frac{r}{t^2} = c\,\frac{1}{r^2} \tag{2}$$

All it now needs is to expand the equation with the factor $4\pi^2 m$, and the left side becomes the term used for Newton's centripetal force:

$$P = 4\pi^2 m\,\frac{r}{t^2} = 4\pi^2 c\,\frac{m}{r^2} \tag{3}$$

If the constant product $4\pi^2 c$ on the right is then made a new constant f, this actually gives the formula for Newton's law of mass attraction:

$$P = f\,\frac{m}{r^2}$$

From certain observations in a particular area of the world of phenomena, where large masses exert a pure mass action on smaller ones, it has been deduced that this law was of more general validity. This is the result of calculations combining Newton's formula for the supposed tendency of planets to accelerate as they theoretically move in the direction of the sun, or their mutual attraction, with Kepler's law, strictly in accordance with observation, concerning the movement of the planets in relation to their distance from the sun. It was deemed to provide sufficient proof that Newton's view of the universe was the right one, and led to this view being generally accepted and dominating men's thinking from that time. But how appropriate is the method shown above for arriving at the equation for the law of gravitation?

In terms of pure mathematical logic, there is nothing improper in converting the formulation of Kepler's equation (1) into equation (2). If the distances and times relating to a specific planet are used with this equation, it will of course be satisfied just as much as the preceding one. This is all that is needed to meet the demands of mathematical logic. But not a logic relating to reality. For what point is there in an equation which in this form says, in relation to the universe that reveals itself to our physical senses in space and time, that 'the ratio of the mean distance of a planet from the sun and the square of its period is inversely proportional to the area of its orbit'?

Again, mathematically speaking there can be no objection to an algebraic treatment of the equation which results in giving it the form of equation (3). The interpretation given to this equation does however assume that the formula $F = ma$ is applicable, i.e. that the forces exerted upon each other by the heavenly bodies are of this type of *external* nature. It is not surprising, then, that the result matches the presupposition. Once again we have the proof of a foregone conclusion, something our investigations in this book have uncovered on a number of occasions.

In this way Kepler's third law, the outcome of pure observation and his profoundly reality-based intuition, has been put through a number of algebraic operations — every one of them completely 'correct' — and become something which in terms of reality is not 'true'. To recognise the fact that something which has been correctly reasoned nevertheless need not necessarily be true, i.e. in accord with reality, is of fundamental importance for the progressive enlightenment which is the intention of this book.

NOTES

INTRODUCTORY

1   The speaker was the late Dr. Elizabeth Vreede, for some years leader of the Mathematical-Astronomical Section at the Goetheanum, Dornach, Switzerland.

2   The activities mentioned above do not exhaust the practical possibilities of spiritual science. At that time (1921) Rudolf Steiner had not yet given his indications for the treatment of children needing special care of soul and body, or for the renewal of the art of acting, or for the conquest of materialistic methods in agricultural practice. Nor did there yet exist the movement for religious renewal which Dr. Friedrich Rittelmeyer later founded, with the help and advice of Rudolf Steiner.

CHAPTER I

1   *Zur Geschichte der physikalischen Naturerklärung*, W. Heisenberg, English ed. 'Philosophic Problems of Nuclear Science', (eight lectures) trans. F.C. Haymer, Faber, 1952.

2   More of this in Chapter IV.

3   See also Eddington's more elaborate description of this fact in his *New Pathways in Science*. The above statement, like others of Eddington's, has been contested from the side of professional philosophy as logically untenable. Our own further discussion will show that it accords with the facts.

4   The Greek word *kinēma* means motion. 'Kinematics' is the science of motion where motion is considered without reference to force or mass.

5   Philipp Frank, *Modern Science and its Philosophy*.

CHAPTER II

1   First published in 1917, after thirty years of research, in his book *Von Seelenrätseln* ('Riddles of the Soul').

CHAPTER III

1   In the light of Goethe's method it will become clear that this observation of Hooke's calls for quite another interpretation than his own.

2   In his book, *Science and the Human Temperament* (Dublin, 1935).

CHAPTER IV

1   E. du Bois-Raymond, *Investigations into Animal Electricity* (1884). Galvani published his discovery when the French Revolution had reached its zenith and Napoleon was climbing to power.

2 The above account follows A.J. von Oettingen's edition of Galvani's monograph, *De viribus electricitatis in motu musculari*.

3 For what follows see *The Life of Sir William Crookes*, by E.E. Fournier D'Albe (London, 1923).

4 This rendering attempts to do justice to the Greek words in the sense of Paul's teaching. For instance, the words 'archai' and 'exusiai' are names of orders of cosmic beings in correspondence with the nomenclature of the doctrine concerning the heavenly hierarchies. At the end of this book the reader will find a brief outline of how modern spiritual science speaks about this subject for the understanding of present-day man.

CHAPTER V

1 *Critique of Judgment*, II, 11, 27. Goethe chose the title of his essay so as to refute Kant by its very wording. Kant, through his inquiry into man's *Urteilskraft*, arrived at the conclusion that man is denied the power of *Anschauung* (intuition). Against this, Goethe puts his *Anschauende Urteilskraft*.

2 *Der Alte vom Königsberge* — a play upon words with the name of Kant's native town, Königsberg.

3 It is naturally to be expected that new light will also be thrown on the various realms of knowledge as such dealt with in these pages.

4 Delphinium, in particular, has the peculiarity (which it shares with a number of other species) that its calyx appears in the guise of a flower, whilst the actual flower is quite inconspicuous.

5 Goethe also describes a proliferated pink.

6 The terms 'primeval' or 'primordial' sometimes suggested for rendering the prefix *ur* are unsuitable in a case like this. 'Primeval plant', for instance, used by some translators of Goethe, raises the misunderstanding — to which Goethe's concept has anyhow been subject from the side of scientific botany — that by his *ur-plant* he had in mind some primitive, prehistoric plant, the hypothetical ancestor in the Darwinian sense of the present-day plant kingdom.

7 The following observation is not one made by Goethe himself. It is presented here by the author as an example of the *heuristic* value of Goethe's method of pictorial-dynamic contemplation of the sense-world.

8 *Entdeckung eines trefflichen Vorarbeiters.*

9 *'Die Vernunft ist auf das Werdende angewiesen, der Verstand auf das Gewordene.'*

10 *Der Versuch als Vermittler zwischen Subjekt und Objekt.*

11 By Ernst Stiedenroth.

12 *Exakte sinnliche Phantasie.*

CHAPTER VI

1 These words should be weighed with the fact in mind that they were written at the time when Crookes was intent on finding the unknown land of the spirit by means of just such 'a mere force of junction'.

2 Goethe's *Dunstkreis* — meaning the humidity contained in the air, and as such, spherically surrounding the earth. I had to make up the word 'hygrosphere' (after hygrometer, etc.) to keep clear the distinction from both atmosphere and hydrosphere. Except for this term, the above follows Oxenford's translation (who, following the dictionaries, has rendered Goethe's term inadequately by 'atmosphere').

3 Stratus means layer, cumulus — heap, cirrus — curl.

4 There exists no adequate translation of these verses.

5 Genesis ii, 19, 20.

6 A fact which Howard did not mention, and which presumably remained unknown to Goethe, was the work he had done as chairman of a relief committee for the parts of Germany devastated by the Napoleonic wars. For this work Howard received a series of public honours.

7 We may here recall Eddington's statement concerning the restriction of scientific observation to 'non-stereoscopic vision'.

CHAPTER VII

1 The present writer's interest in Reid was first aroused by a remark of Rudolf Steiner, in his book *A Theory of Knowledge according to Goethe's World Conception*.

2 This observation of Reid's shows that the origin of language is very different from what the evolutionists since Darwin have imagined it to be.

3 No exact equivalents exist in English for these two philosophic terms. They refer to the two trends in philosophy of which one is usually denoted as empiricism, the other as idealism.

4 An example of this is Reid's commentary on existing theories about sight as a mere activity of the optic nerve. (*Inq*, VI, 19.)

5 See *Inq.*, 13. This is precisely what Kant had declared to be outside human possibility.

6 *St Augustine's Confessions*, translation and introduction, R.S.P. Collin, Penguin Classics 1970.

7 As we have seen, the word had better luck with Goethe.

8 Wordsworth, with all his limitations, had a real affinity with Goethe in his view of nature. Mr Norman Lacey gives some indication of this in his book, *Wordsworth's View of Nature and its Ethical Consequences*, CUP, 1948.

9 The difference in spelling between the prose and poetry excerpts arises

MAN OR MATTER

from the fact that whereas we can draw on Miss Wade's new edition of the poems for Traherne's original spelling, we have as yet only Dobell's edition of the *Centuries*, in which the spelling is modernised. See: *Poetical Works of Thomas Traherne*, ed. G.I. Wade, Princeton University Press, 1944.

10 *Thomas Traherne: Poems of Felicity*, ed. H.I. Bell, OUP, 1910.

11 In his *Philosophy of Spiritual Activity* (Philosophy of Freedom), published two years before Traherne was discovered, Rudolf Steiner, at approximately the same age as Traherne was when he wrote this phrase, used the very same picture for the nature of thought by saying: 'What right have you to declare the world to be complete without thinking? Does not the world produce thinking in man's head with the same necessity as it produces the blossom on a plant?' See *Philosophy of Freedom*, translation Michael Wilson, Rudolf Steiner Press, 1974.

12 See Appendix I.

13 *The Autobiography of J.W. von Goethe*, translation John Oxenford, 2 vols., University of Chicago Press, 1975.

CHAPTER VIII

1 Albert Einstein, *Geometry and Experience: An Essay*, Berlin, 1921, the time when the present author first met Rudolf Steiner and his work.

2 In a later context light will be thrown from yet another angle on the historical significance of these observations.

CHAPTER IX

1 For Van Helmont, owing to the Flemish pronunciation of the letter G, the two words sounded more alike than their spelling suggests. See: J. Baptist van Helmont, *Ortus Medicinae*, Apud L. Elzevivium, Amsterdam, 1648.

2 John Ruskin, *The Storm Cloud of the Nineteenth Century*, G. Allen, Orpington, 1884.

3 *Conversations of Goethe with Eckermann*, (abridged from the translation of John Oxenford), introduction Havelock Ellis, J.M. Dent & Sons, 1971.

4 For a vivid description of the interplay of both types of force in nature, see E. Carpenter's account of his experience of a tree in his *Pagan and Christian Creeds*, George Allen & Unwin, London, 1920.

CHAPTER X

1 Published by Rudolf Steiner Press, London. See also other writings by the same author and those of the Swiss mathematician, Prof. L. Locher-

Ernst, from whom the expression 'polar-Euclidean' has here been taken over.

2 See in this respect, *The Plant between Sun and Earth*, by George Adams and Olive Whicher, published by Rudolf Steiner Press, London, 1980.

3 Readers who are acquainted with Richard Wagner's *Parsifal* may be reminded of young Parsifal's remark and the reply of his companion, Gurnemanz, while the latter is guiding him through the forest towards the castle of the Holy Grail. Parsifal, wondering at the transforming of the surrounding conditions while they walk, says:

'My steps are few, yet seem to take me far.'

To which Gurnemanz replies:

'You see, my son, how time here turns to space.'

In these words Wagner witnessed the change in the apprehension of space and time which is undergone by a soul embarking on the road to supersensible experience. Note the coincidence with the way in which Traherne describes the same thing from his early memory. See R. Wagner, *Parsifal: The Sacred Festival-drama of Parsifal . . . the Argument, the Musical Drama and the Mystery*, libretto translated by Amhurst Webber, edited by Charles T. Gatty, Boosey & Co., London & New York, 1914, 8 vols.

CHAPTER XI

1 Ernst Haeckel, *Art Forms of Nature*, Dover Publications, New York, 1944.

2 Roger Bacon in the thirteenth, and Berthold Schwartz in the fourteenth century, are reputed to have carried out experiments by mixing physical salt (in the form of the chemically labile saltpetre) with physical sulphur and — after some initial attempts with various metals — with charcoal, and then exposing the mixture to the heat of physical fire. The outcome of this purely materialistic interpretation of the three alchemical concepts was not the acquisition of wisdom, or, as Schwartz certainly had hoped, of gold, but of . . . gunpowder!

3 For particulars of the lemniscate as the building plan of the middle part of man's skeleton, see K. König, M.D., *Beiträge zu einer Anatomie des menschlichen Knochenskeletts* in the periodical *Natura* (Dornach, 1930-1). Some projective-geometrical considerations concerning the lemniscate are to be found in the previously mentioned writings of G. Adams and L. Locher-Ernst.

CHAPTER XII

1 See Chapter IV. The other title of the paper, 'Radiant Matter', will gain significance for us in the next chapter. See: William Crookes, *Fourth*

State of Matter: A Course of Six Lectures on the Various Forces of Matter and their Relation to Each Other, edited W. Crookes, 1860; and (same author) *Radiant Matter: A Lecture Delivered to the British Association for the Advancement of Science, August 22nd, 1879*, E J. Davy, London, 1879.

2   John Tyndall, *Heat: A Mode of Motion*, Longmans, Green & Co., London, 1890.

3   We shall hear more about this later on.

4   Since this book was first written, this picture of the earth as seen from space has been dramatically confirmed.

5   Note that in both cases the process of *spreading* one substance within another plays an essential part.

6   See L. Kolisko, *Wirksamkeit kleinster Entitäten* ('Effects of Smallest Entities'), Stuttgart, 1922, an account of a series of experiments undertaken by the author at the Biological Institute of the Goetheanum following suggestions by Rudolf Steiner. Her aim was to examine the behaviour of matter on the way to and beyond the boundary of its ponderable existence.

7   The following is based on a discourse given by A.F.P. Bowden, F.R.S., at the 1954 meeting of the British Association for Advancement of Science at Oxford. (Published in the British Association Journal, *The Advancement of Science*, Vol. XII, No. 45.)

8   The reader is asked to imagine himself into the above process in order to gain a true experience of the character of the alteration we have described. Otherwise he may be misled by his accustomed quantitative thinking into concluding that, as a result of the quantitative increase of the superficial area, more levity is becoming bound to the total mass than before.

9   *Foliar Application of Plant Nutrients to Vegetable Crops*, by Jackson P. Rester, Reprint SS-11-54, distributed by the American Potash Institute, Washington D.C.

10 Report from the Tata Institute of Fundamental Research, Bombay, in *Nature* (London), 29th December 1956.

11 See 'Composition of the Ash of Spanish Moss', by E.T. Werry and E. Buchanan, Bureau of Chemistry, US Department of Agriculture, from *Ecology*, Vol. VII, No. 3, July 1926.

12 This throws light also on the problem of the use of chemicals as artificial fertilisers.

13 This is done in the so-called Bio-Dynamic method of farming and gardening, according to Rudolf Steiner's indications.

14 Since the original printing of this book, meteorological research has come to recognise in a certain high stratum of the atmosphere a phenomenon which contradicts all gravity concepts. In the so-called zero stratum of

the atmosphere there is a motion of the air from areas of lower to those of higher pressure. Up there the air, in fact, flows against the pressure gradient, as it were up-hill. In our mode of conception we may take this as a character in nature's script, telling us that levity-effects prevail over the gravity field in the outer reaches of the earth's organism. See *Archiv für Meteorologie, Geophysik und Bioklimatologie*, Serie A, B.6, S.334.339, 1954.

15 This is genuine pragmatism in the sense of the philosopher William James, resulting inevitably from man's spectator-relationship to the world.

16 For this and the following quotations see, *Faraday, Life and Letters*, by Dr. Bence-Jones.

17 We shall come back in the last part of this book to Faraday's way of thus conceiving numerical relationships as realities in themselves.

18 We thankfully record the fact that the Goethean way, consistently pursued, has led us quite independently — to the author's surprise, he must confess — into the neighbourhood of Faraday's bold conceptions, thus enabling us to rescue from oblivion what scientific thinking in the past failed to heed.

CHAPTER XIII

1 See footnote p. 247.

2 In expressing the above antithesis by the terms 'discovery' and 'manufacture' we follow the formulation used most aptly by Eddington when discussing a relevant optical problem. In so doing he raised a general question that concerns the present-day experimentalist, including even the researcher in the sphere of nuclear physics. (See chapter entitled 'Discovery or Manufacture?', in Sir Arthur Stanley Eddington, *The Philosophy of Physical Science*, Tarner Lectures, CUP, 1949.

3 Note that the series starts on the left with graphite, i.e. with carbon. This substance appears here as a metal among metals, and indeed as the most 'noble' of all. Electricity in this way reveals a secret of carbon well known to the medieval alchemist and still known in our day to people in the Orient.

4 People with some sensitivity for such things clearly feel that the quality of electrically generated heat differs from that set free by combustion. Experiments of general validity showing the effects of the two kinds of heat, e.g. on living organisms, are still lacking.

5 J.H. Gladstone, *Michael Faraday*, Macmillan & Co., London, 1873.

CHAPTER XIV

1 'To see is my dower, to look my employ.' Words of the Tower Watcher in *Faust*, II, 5, through which Goethe echoes his own relation to the world.

2 The last chapter but two in the edition of 1924.

3 For the drastic and as such very enlightening way in which Eddington presents the problem, the reader is referred to Eddington's own description.

4 *Konfession des Verfassers.*

5 Colour as *quality* being no essential factor in the scientific explanation of the spectrum.

6 Isaac Newton, *Optics*, Dover Publications.

7 *Contributions to Optics.*

8 *Outline of a Theory of Colour.*

9 See Rudolf Steiner's edition of Goethe's *Farbenlehre*, under *Paralipomena zur Chromatik*, No. 27.

10 This is not to be confused with the meaning of 'purple' in modern English today.

11 This follows from the application of Fourier's Theorem, according to which every vibration of any kind is divisible into a sum of periodic partial vibrations, and therefore is regarded as compounded of these.

CHAPTER XV

1 J.W. von Goethe, *Farbenlehre*. See *Theory of Colour*, translation, Eastlake, MIT Press, Mass., USA, 1970.

2 As regards the principle underlying the line of consideration followed here, see the remark made in Chapter V in connection with Goethe's study of the 'proliferated rose' (p. 88).

3 *Inquiry*, VI, 1. The italics are Reid's.

4 Presumably Kant and his school. Schopenhauer was definitely of this opinion.

5 John Ruskin, *Modern Painters*, 6 volumes, G. Allen, Orpington, 1898.

CHAPTER XVI

1 It will be well to remember here the discussion of our experience of temperature through the sense of warmth in Chapter V.

2 Along these lines the true solution of the problem of the so-called coloured shadows will be found. Goethe studied this without finding, however, a satisfactory answer.

3 We point here to a conception of the mirror phenomenon which will have to be developed by future research. This applies also to the so-called polarisation of light as an effect of reflection.

CHAPTER XVII

1 Compare with this our account in Chapter XII of the rise of the atomistic-kinematic interpretation of heat.

2　The following critical study leaves, of course, completely untouched our recognition of the devotion which guided the respective observers in their work, and of the ingenuity with which some of their observations were devised and carried out.

3　Once this is realised there can be no doubt that with the aid of an adequate mathematical calculus (which would have to be established on a realistic understanding of the respective properties of the fields of force coming into play), it will become possible to derive by calculation the speed of the establishment of light within physical space from the gravitational constant of the earth.

4　The change in our conception of number which this entails will be shown at a later stage of our discussions (Chapter XIX).

CHAPTER XVIII

1　See also, in this respect, Rudolf Steiner's footnote to Goethe's criticism of Nuguet's theory of the spectrum, in his edition of the historical part of Goethe's *Farbenlehre* (Vol. IV, p. 248, in Kürschner's edition).

2　It is obvious that the reader who wishes to appreciate fully the significance of the observations described in this and the following paragraphs, must carry out these observations for himself. The above descriptions should be accompanied, while being read, with a few simple line-drawings.

3　The difference in character of the various parts of the spectrum, as described above, comes out particularly impressively if for capturing the colour phenomenon one uses, instead of a flat white surface, a clear crystal of not too small size, or else a cluster of crystals — moving it slowly along the coloured band from one end to the other. (I am indebted to F. Julius, teacher of natural science at the Free School in The Hague, for this suggestion.)

4　In the early twenties of this century a special institution existed in Stuttgart for experimental research where the above was undertaken, resulting in a first slight effect pointing in this direction. After a few weeks of work, however, this institution became a victim of the general economic decline.

CHAPTER XIX

1　*Aithō* in Greek — with *aither* as the noun — means: to burn, to blaze, to shine. The Greeks thus designated the realm above the physical air, the first unpolluted by physical matter and as such part of the 'heavens'.

2　See *Space and the Light of Creation*, by G. Adams (publ. by the author, 1933), where this 'weaving' is shown with the help of projective geometry.

3   Translation by J. Darrell.

4   We may recall here also the passage from Ruskin's *The Queen of the Air*, quoted earlier (p. 111).

5   *Kalevala*, translation W.F. Kirby, Everyman Library, J.M. Dent & Sons, London, 1956.

6   By attending Chladni's lectures on his discovery in Paris the French physicist Savart became acquainted with this phenomenon and devoted himself to its study. Chladni and Savart together published a great number of these figures.

7   In the present context we are not yet taking account of the life ether, indispensable for the coming about of finite forms in nature.

8   Alexis Carrel, *Man the Unknown*, Burns and Oates, London, 1961.

9   With this example we touch upon the wide field of catalytic effects, both organic and inorganic, which are all due to particular actions of the chemical ether.

10 Understanding the attributes of the chemical ether enables us to see in their right perspective Rudolf Steiner's suggestions to farmers for the preparation of the soil and for keeping healthy the crops growing on it. Attempts have been made to dismiss these suggestions by calling them 'mysticism' and 'medieval magic'. Both terms are titles of honour if we understand by the one the form of insight into the supersensible realm of nature acquired by the higher mode of reading, and by the other a faculty of nature herself, whose magic wand is the chemical or sound ether.

11 See Eddington's humorous and at the same time serious treatment of this problem in his *Philosophy of Physical Science*.

12 We remember Ruskin's utterance, quoted in Chapter XII, that he would 'like better in order of thought to consider motion as a mode of heat than heat as a mode of motion'.

13 See *Scientific Autobiography and Other Papers, with Memorial Address on Max Planck*, by Max von Lane, translation F. Gaynor, Williams & Norgate, London, 1950.

14 Of the difference between external and internal ether-action more will be said in the concluding chapter.

15 To avoid misunderstandings, it should be emphasised that spiritual imagination is not attained by any exercise involving directly the sense of sight and its organ, the eye, but by purely mental exercises designed to increase the 'seeing' faculty of the mind. For detailed information, see Rudolf Steiner's *Knowledge of the Higher Worlds: How is it Achieved?*, publ. Rudolf Steiner Press, London.

CHAPTER XX

1   We must here distinguish sensation from feeling proper, in which sen-

sation and motion merge in mercurial balance.

2 Note how for Ruskin the gulf which for the onlooker-consciousness lies between subject and object is bridged here — as it was for Goethe in his representation of the physic-moral effect of colour.

3 Max Planck, *Introduction to Theoretical Physics*, translation, Henry L. Brose, 5 volumes, Macmillan & Co, London, 1932.

4 Knowledge of this biological rhythm is still preserved among native peoples today and leads them to take account of the phases of the moon in their treatment of plants. A cosmic nature wisdom of this kind has been reopened for us in modern form by Rudolf Steiner, and has since found widespread practical application in agriculture. See L. Kolisko, *The Moon and Plant Growth*, Kolisko Archive Publications, Bournemouth, 1978.

5 See L. Kolisko, *Working of the Stars in Earthly Substances*, and other publications by the same author.

6 *De motu animalium* and *Theoria medicorum planetarum ex causis physicis deducta.*

7 The close connection between the ear and the motor system of the body is shown in another way by the fact that part of the ear serves as an organ for the sense of balance.

8 The muscle tone can be made audible by the following means. In a room guarded against noise, press the thumbs lightly upon the ears and tense the muscles of the hand and arms — say by pressure of the fingers against the palms or by contracting the muscle of the upper arms. If this is done repeatedly, the muscle tone will be heard after some practice with increasing distinctness. It is easily distinguished from the sound of the circulating blood as it is much higher. (As an example: the author's muscular pitch, not a particularly high one, has a frequency of approx. 630 per sec., which puts it between Treble D sharp and E.)

9 For the particular reasons by which Goethe justifies his assertion, see his essay *Leben und Verdienste des Doktor Joachim Jungius.*

10 In the first edition of this book the above was followed by a criticism of the conceptual procedure through which it has been thought possible to prove the identity of Kepler's and Newton's formulae. It has, however, been seen in the meantime that within the framework of this book it is not possible to go far enough into the problems involved to give sufficient weight to this criticism. As it is not essential for our further expositions, this particular passage has been dropped from the present edition.

11 J. Kepler, *Harmonices Mundi*, Libri V, Lincii Austriae, 1619.

12 The natural question, why Kepler himself did not take this step, will be answered later on.

PROSPECT

1 J.H. Lupton, *Two Treatises on the Hierarchies of Dionysius*, London, 1869.

2 Rudolf Steiner, *Christianity as Mystical Fact*, Rudolf Steiner Press, London, 1972.

3 This received public recognition in one instance in the American periodical *Time*. See the letter to the editor under the heading, *New Thoughts on Old Scrolls*, in the issue of 5th March 1956.

4 Rudolf Steiner, *Occult Science – An Outline*, Rudolf Steiner Press, London, 1970.

5 One may recall our endeavours to understand physical matter as cosmic will that has become old.

6 Called 'Manifesters' in Chapter IV, in our translation of the words of Paul. In the Old Testament they bear the name of Elohim. One of them, called Yahveh in the Bible, undertook the leadership of the Hebrew people, as a Divinity working at the same time in nature and in human history.

7 Rudolf Steiner, *Mission of Individual Folk-Souls*, Rudolf Steiner Press, London, 1970.

8 Regarding the interchange of the names 'Mercury' and 'Venus', see note on page 425.

APPENDIX II

1 See Chapter VIII.

2 In his work, *On the Heavens*, Aristotle distinguishes explicitly between the properties 'absolutely light' and 'relatively light' (also called 'lighter' by him). While defining the latter as pertaining to a body subject to gravity but with a lesser specific gravity than its surroundings, he reserves the former for bodies that are not subject to gravity at all. In Chapter XXI we came in our own way to speak of bodies of this latter kind as 'ether-bodies'.

3 A survival of this is to be seen in the various continental languages which still use the reflexive form of the verb where English resorts to the intransitive; in German, for example, 'the body moves' would become '*der Körper bewegt sich*'.

APPENDIX III

1 The author first came to see this, to his satisfaction, through the way in which Rudolf Steiner presented these matters, in the lectures referred to in the Introduction.

2 Mentioned in footnote 1, Chapter I.

3 Taken mainly from *Life and Letters of Michael Faraday*, by Bence-Jones, and *Michael Faraday, his Life and Work*, by S.P. Thompson. A new edition of the German translation of the latter was published by Dr Martin Sändig in Wiesbaden in 1965.

INDEX

Aberdeen, 125
aberration, 362
abnormal (pathological) conditions,
    90, 328
Accademia del Cimento, 191, 357
acceleration, 162, 177
acoustics, 433
Adam, 122, 148
Adams, 202, 525, 528
adaptation, biological, 98, 140
    – optical, 329
addition, 403
adult, 26, 29, 132-3, 156
afferent, 30
after-images, 328, 372, 412
aged material, 186
agnosticism, 76
Ahriman, 68, 472
air, 179, 230, 410
alchemy, 242-4, 265, 296, 417, 487
alertness, 176-7, 188
alga, 91, 92, 392
all-embracing periphery, 266
    – plane, 213
    – quantity, 402
all-relating point, 213
Alpine regions, 88
amber, 284, 287
amoeba, 240
Ampère, 295, 508
amplitude, 36
anastomosis, 95, 393
Andersen, *see* child
animal, 113, 195, 235, 245-6, 272,
    302, 421, 450
animism, 26

anode, 303-4, 346
anomaly of water, 239, 262
Anschauen, 77
anthroposophical movement, 11, 12,
    14, 15, 140, 417
anti-gravity, 190, 384, 391
anti-matter, 286
Aphrodite, 427
Apocalypse, 460
apostasy, 148
apparent depth, 367
appearance, 86, 92, 222
apple, 191, 401
Arabs, 403
archetype, 74, 77, 88, 179, 186
archetypal plant, 90
Aristotle, 138, 180, 489 *et seq.*
arm, rising, 176, 281, 286
art, 9, 137
arthropods, 241
ash, 238, 297
assimilation, 268, 270, 428
astral, 422 *et seq.*
atma, 184
atom, 22, 254, 280-1
atomic bomb, 62
    – fission (fusion), 408
    – energy, 56
    – nucleus, 268
atomism, 35
attraction, 285, 297
Augustine, St, 139, 140, 149, 150,
    459
aurum, 243
auxiliary concepts, 22, 161, 173, 279
avalanche, 197

bacilli, 392
Bacon, Francis, 123-4, 248, 278, 441
Bacon, Roger, 525
balance, 24, 47, 194
Bamm, 69
Becquerel, 61
begonia, 87
being, 86
beingness, 458
Berzelius, 277
Berkeley, 128, 154 et seq.
Bernese Alps, 274
Bible (biblical), 65, 68-70, 122, 183, 190, 193, 276, 380, 510
biodynamics, 242, 526
birch, 241
bird, 241, 246
Blake, 389
blood, 34, 109, 428
body (etheric, astral), 450
bone, 186, 230, 241, 439
Book of Nature, 108, then passim
border of nature, 60, 247, 275
borderland, 58
Borelli, 432
boundary, see border
—, optical, 318
Bowden, 526
Bradley, 359 et seq.
Brahma, 184
brain, 29 et seq.
breath, breathing, 34, 184-6, 235
Britain, 110
British Association, 58, 526
Buchanan, 526
Buddha, 465
Büttner, 313
butterfly, 85

cactus, 241
calcite, 290
calcium, 240, 241
calyx, 82-5

camera, see pinhole
Campbell-Fraser, 126
Canizzaro, 277
capacitance, 300
carbohydrates, 235
carbon, 179, 221, 222, 234 et seq, 244, 264, 276, 527
carnivorous animals, 246
Carpenter, 514
Carrel, 21, 398
Cassinian curves, 246
catalysis, 530
caterpillar, 85
cathode rays, 56, 299, 346
causation, magical, 186-7
—, mechanical, 174-5
cause and effect, 174
cellular structure, 38
chain reaction, 304
chalk, 240, 242
Chaos, 43, 45, 179, 183-4, 238, 247. 272, 391, 427
chaoticizing ether, 392
chemical ether, 390, 395 et seq.
chemical fertilizer, 526
chemistry, 219, 398
child, in Galileo, 169
—, forces at work in, 496
—, Hans Andersen's, 31, 162, 322
—, nature of, 26-7, 132-3, 334-5
—, to become, 135, 149-50, 157-8, 168-9, 170. 217
childhood, 109, 124, 135, 154. 156, 215, 415
Chladni, 395 et seq.
choroid, 329, 330
chronometer, 36
cirrus, see clouds
clay, 242
climatic conditions, 98
clouds, 114-23, 158, 238, 427, 499
coagulation, 269
coherence, cohesion, 253, 254, 266, 307

co-images, 413
cold, 105, 181, 191, 227 *et seq*, 249, 253, 346
Colet, 460, 463, 464
colour theory, *passim*
colour-blindness, 21, 25, 36 *passim*
colour-circle, 385
coloured shadows, 528
Columbia University, 423
combustion, 218, 219, 221-3, 291, 297
Commenius, 482
common sense, 125, 126, 130, 140, 165
condenser, 300
conductance, 300
conductor, 295
conifers, 92
conscience, historical, 489
consciousness, *passim*
consumption, consumer, 47, 301
contemplation, 77: —, higher, 337
Contra Levitatem, 116, then *passim*
contraction, (contractedness), 86, 102, 117, 121, 182, 364
contrast colours, 331, 333
convolvulus, 94
Copernicus, 422
corolla, 82
corrosion, 291
cosmic consciousness, 154
cosmosophy, 389
countenance, of sky, 114
counter-space, 202 *et seq.*
cow, 246
crab, 241
Critique of Judgment, 73
Crookes, 50, 56-61, 247, 299, 303, 403, 523
cryptograms, 92
crystallisation, 232-4, 410
cumulus, *see* clouds
Cunaeus, 49

Curie, 61
current (electric), 295
cuttings, 87

Dalton, 36, 277 *et seq*, 307, 404
dancing, 438
dark, 32
— and light, 317, 344
darkness, 68, 344, 372 *et seq.*
Darrell, 524
Darwin, 98, 113, 517
David, 68
Davy, 220, 250, 267, 507 *et seq.*
Dead Sea scrolls, 465
death, 28
—, pole of, 33, 192
deception, optical, 39, 128
deficiency, 270 *et seq.*
delphinium, 79, 81, 84
density, 182, 254, 286, 293, 297
—, optical, 316, 319, 343
—, negative, 347
Descartes, 38, 40, 128
Devil, 20, 67
diagnosis, 25
diamond, 236
diaphragm, 29
diastole (*see also* expansion), 212, 331
dicotyledons, 92
diffraction, *see* light
dilution, 261
Dionysius the Areopagite, 461 *et seq.*
disappearance of energy, 252, 296
discontinuity, 97, 98
discovery, 284, 322, 406
displacement, optical, 368
division, 403
Dobell, 145, 154, 155
doing, 66, 82, 102, 104, 472
doubling flowers, 82
doubt, 38

dream, dreaming, 33, 34, 327, 331, 332, 412, 471
dry, 181, 227 et seq, 267, 286, 303, 406
Du Bois-Raymond, 521
Dufais, 49
Dunstkreis, 523
dynamics, 33, 46, 62, 111, 161, 165, 198, 199, 224, 227, 259, 369, 419
dynamo, 294

eagle, 246
ear, 350, 438
earth, picture of, 526
earthquake sky, 195
ebonite, 288
ecstasy, 439
Eckermann, 119, 195, 309
Eddington, 20-1, 62, 105, 322, 338, 406, 517, 523, 527, 528, 530
ego, 449
Egypt, 448
Einstein, 11, 12, 63, 203-4, 215, 359, 524
elasticity, 167
electricity, electrical, 15, 31, 42, 46 et seq, 73, 275, 282 et seq, 404, 409, 500 et seq.
electro-magnetic theory, 54, 503
electro-magnetism, 292, 295, 503, 511
electron, 62
element, chemical, 220, 269
elements, four, 180, 229-30, 242, 436
embryonic condition (development) 26, 101, 186, 215
Empedocles, 180
energy, 22, then passim
ἓν καὶ πᾶν, 402
enzyme action, 272
epileptic, 31
equilibrium, 166, 439

equipotential, 296
essential oil, 265
ether, hypothetical, 433
— real, 390 et seq.
Euclid (Euclidian), 202, 204, 206 et seq, 214, 215, 490
eurythmy, 14
evaporation, 257
evolution, 10, 11, 25, 26, 186, 187
exact sensorial fantasy, 94, 109, 135, 159
exclusion, method of, 31
exhaling, 119, 235, 331
experiment, 107-8, 500
explanation, 120, 334, 342
eye (of body, spirit), 102, 241, 259, 347

faith, 76, 130
fall, free, 160 et seq, 170, 489 et seq.
—, original, 65, 69, 139
Fango, 194, 197, 231
fantasy, 33, 109 (see also exact sensorial fantasy)
Faraday, 54, 197, 198, 277 et seq, 285, 292, 299, 300, 404, 495, 527
fatigue, 332
Faust, 66-70, 393, 443, 485, 527
feeling, 34, 420
female, 95-7
fertilisation, 82, 86, 93
fertiliser, 526
Ficina, 463
field-concept, 199, 253, 285
field-gradient, (opt.), 374
field, gravitational, 253
—, thermal, 298
field of force, 55, 197-200, 501
fire, 179, 188, 218, 228, 230
—, making of, 267, 391
— rites, 188-9
fish, electric, 302-3

Fizeau, 358, 365
flames, frozen, 234
flash, 359
flint, 240, 242, 264
flood, 69, 380
Florentine Academy, see Accademia
flower, 82 et seq, 230
flowing of metals, 255
floraminifera, 240
force, experienced, 165-6, 457
—, form against, 111, 115, 271
—, lack of concept, 22-3, 62, 161
—, lines of, 501, 503
—, parallelogram, 41, 160, 163 et seq.
foregone conclusion, 358, 362
form, 103, 111, 174, 271, 390, 397, 428, 458
Fortlage, 28
Foucault, 358, 365
Fournier-d'Albe, 516
Frank, 22
Franklin, 50, 51, 275
French Revolution, 521
friction, 220, 261, 267, 286, 406
frictional electricity, 286
fumarole, 331
function (-al), 9, 30, 33, 224, 231, 238, 241, 242, 271
—, (flux), 272
fur, 289

Galileo, 36, 41, 105, 106, 160 et seq, 168 et seq, 215, 357, 489 et seq, 497
Galvani, galvanism, 49, 51 et seq, 56, 73, 89, 291, 302, 314
gas, 178, 184
gaseous state, 191, 258, 262
gaze, active, 342
Genesis, 70, 523
geometry, 514
—, Euclidean, see Euclid
— and experience, 161

—, experienced, 169
—, projective, 12, 205 et seq.
gesture, 240, 241
Gladstone, 277, 300
glands, 427
Glasgow, 125
glass, 242, 288, 304
gloxinia, 87
glue, 228
God, 139, 141, 146, 150, 153
Goethe, passim
Goliath, 69
Grand Duke of Weimar, 121
graphite, 236, 292
gravity, gravitation, 183, then passim
Greece, 64
ground plan, 81
group soul, 451
group velocity, 360
growth principles, 94
Guericke, 49

Haeckel, 240
hail, 275, 437
hair, 288, 289
hearing, 350, 433
heat, 105, 182, 218, 222
—, (mech. theory), 248
—, (mech. equivalent), 250
—, (free, latent), 256, 274, 297
heat mantle, 274
heightening, see Steigerung
Heisenberg, 19, 20, 21, 48, 66, 107, 310, 433, 497
heliocentric, 442
Helmholtz, 435, 504, 505
Herder, 90
heredity, see inheritance
Hermes, 427
— (Trismegistos), 485
Hertz, 55, 405
hierarchies, 460 et seq, 522
high frequency, 8, 15

Homer, 29
homoeopathy, 260
Hooke, 38 *et seq*, 44, 63, 103, 104, 160, 248, 278
Hopton, 487, 488
horsetail, 92
horticulture, 241
Howard, 110, 113-8, 121-3, 253, 273, 458, 499
Hume, 40, 44, 63, 75, 126, 127, 130, 165
hydrogen, 235, 238-9, 342
hydrodynamics, 295
hygrosphere, 119
'I', 449 *et seq.*
ice, 237, 255, 265-6
Idea, 100, 102, 122, 142, 153 *et seq*, 186, 223, 239, 460, 495, 500
ideas system, 143
illusion, 55, 104, 166, 222, 275, 366
image, 355, 368, 372, 373, 394
imagination, 33, 432
—, spiritual, 413 *et seq*, 432, 454, 471
imponderable, 268, 273, 380
impressed force, 23
impressed peculiarity, 360
inclined plane, 162
indeterminacy, 41 *et seq*, 63, 279
induction, 294
inertia, inertness, 176-7, 190
infinite, infinity, 204 *et seq*, 306
inflammability, 267
infra-red, 383, 404
inhaling, 119, 235, 331
inheritance (heredity), 98, 140, 141
insects, 241
inspiration (spiritual), 432 *et seq*, 454, 471
intellect (-ual), 65, 73, 74, 104, 133
intelligence, intelligent, 48, 111, 131
interval, 447
Intuition, 113, 148, 471, 502, 505

intuitive force, 193
— judgment, 73, 98-99
— knowledge, 76, 134, 169
— participation, 166
— relationship, 255
invariants, 407
involution, 451
iris, 380
Italy, 88, 312, 317

James, 527
Janus, 391
Java, 250
Jeans, 161
Jehovah, 184, 193
Jena, 93, 99, 313
John, St., 150, 459, 460, 485
Jones, 527, 532
Joule, 250, 277
jump, 375, 407
Jungius, 441
Jupiter, 359 *et seq*, 425 *et seq*, 446 *et seq*, 470

Kalevala, 395
Kant, 40, 73-6, 98, 100, 104, 125, 126, 141, 497, 528
Kaufmann, *see* Adams
Kepler, 422, 441 *et seq*, 447, 515 *et seq.*
Kincardine, 125
kinematic (kinetic), 21, 161, 165, 493
Kleist, 49
knowing, 66, 102

Lacey, 517
language, 131 *et seq*, 148
larynx, 350, 438, 452
Lavoisier, 219, 238, 276
law (natural), 41, 42, 44, 136, 161, 500
— of gravitation, 20

— of pendulum, 36
leaf, 85, 91, 245
leap, 86
leather, 288
Leibniz, 63
left-eyed vision, 352, 373
lemniscate, 246
lens, 241
level, 106
levity, 190, then *passim*
Leyden jar (phial), 49, 53, 54, 296
life, *passim*
life-pole, 227
light and dark, 68, 317, 350, 364, 372, 373
light diffraction, 311, 373
— impulse, 365, 374
— inner, 70, 329, 335, 369, 377, 412
— ray, 353 *et seq*, 365, 369
— refraction, 353 *et seq*, 365-9
— velocity, 353 *et seq*,
— visibility, 42, 338, 354
lightness, 343 *et seq*.
lightning, 190, 193, 274, 275, 428
limestone, 242
line, straight, 39, 103, 205
linear, 245
Linnaeus, 118-9
lion, 246
liquefaction, 256-7
liquid state, 227, 257, 262
Lizetti, 168
Locher-Ernst, 524
Locke, 128, 139, 142, 248
Lorenzo, 441
Lucifer, 65, 68, 70, 472
lung, 235
Lupton, 532

Mach, 22, 161
magic (-al), 175-6, 186, 200, 399, 408, 452

magnetism, 54-5, 292 *et seq*, 383, 404, 409, 500
male, 95-7
Malebranche, 128
mallow, 79, 84
man, threefold, 34, then *passim*
manufacture, 284, 322, 406-7
Marconi, 55
mare's tail, 241
Mars, 425 *et seq*, 470
mass, 177
— centre, 253, 262, 266, 280
master-eye, 348
mathematics, 8, 12, 43, 170, 495
Matthew, St., 68, 149
Maxwell, 54, 55-6, 61, 299, 503
Mayer, 250 *et seq*, 404, 505
mechanics (mechanical), 20, 174, 175, 186
— (equivalent of heat), 250
mechanism, 103
mechanistic, 174, 248, 429, 505
medieval, 242
medical, 241
Medici, 463
melody, 447
memory, 33, 34, 109, 143, 145, 156, 301
meniscus, 228
mental, 227
— images, 33
Mephistopheles, 66 *et seq*, 443
mercaptane, 265
Mercury, planet, 424 *et seq*, 470
mercury, alchemical, 243 *et seq*, 291, 296, 424
Messina, 196
metabolism, 29 *et seq*, 85, 230, 231, 243, 272, 420, 502
metals, 233, 255, 263, 291
metamorphosis, general, 79 *et seq*, 109, 175, 262, 415, 438
—, geometrical, 163

metamorphosis, irregular, 87
— of energy, 252
— of heat, 256
— of levity, 384
meteorology, 110, 116, 192, 196, 235
Michelson-Morley, 358
micrographia, 39
microscope, 38, 39, 45, 101, 103
miracle, 188
Mirandola, 463
mirror, 345
moist, 181, 227 *et seq*, 286, 303
molecule, 223, 254, 277
momentum, 493
morphology, 78
Moses, 190, 193
motion, movement, 31, 162, 175, 421, 441
motor nerves, 30
motor system, 440
muscles, 29, 175
muscle tone, 439, 531
muscular system, 175, 302, 438
music, 34, 444 *et seq.*
Musschenbroek, 49
musk, 265
Mysteries, 460 *et seq.*

Nature, 89, then *passim*
negative form, 81
— resistance, 343
— spectrum, 320
— space, 382
needfire, 189
Neoplatonism, 462
nervous system, 26 *et seq*, 85, 109, 187, 230, 231, 243, 302, 420, 501
Newton (-ian), 20, then *passim*
Nicodemus, 150
nimbus, *see* clouds
node, 87
nominalism, 401

non-physical, 201
note, 447
nuclear physics research. 267, 280
Nuguet, 523
number, 400 *et seq.*
nutrition (plant), 268, 270, 301

oak, 241
Object and Idea, 103, 160
Oersted, 54
Oettingen, 522
old, 249, 272
Old Testament, 55
one, 403
one-eyed, colour-blind, 36, then *passim*
onlooker (spectator), 38, then *passim*
ontological concepts, 173
Open Sesame, 136
Oppenheimer, 64
Orestes, 64
organism, 103, then *passim*
Orpheus, 395
oscillating circuit, 300, 301, 429
Ostwald, 220, 224
overcoming, 12, then *passim*
Oxenford, 523, 524
Oxford, 464, 481
oxidisation, 222, 235, 398
oxygen, 218, 222, 223, 235 *et seq*, 276

Padua, 90
Palermo, 90
Palestine, 465
parallelogram, theorems of, 41, 163 *et seq*, 177
Paradise, 65
Parsifal, 525
parts, 99, 283
pattern, 81
Paul, St., 68, 70, 459, 460-1, 472, 474, 485

peach-blossom, 321, 385
Pelagius, 140-1
perception, 32-3, 46, 134, 500
pericarp, 402
peripheral, 202, 254
periphery, cosmic, 254, 279
Peter, St., 459
Philistines, 69
philosophy, 11
phlogiston, 219, 267
phosphorus, 221, 224, 225, 230 *et seq*, 280
photosynthesis, 268
phrenes, 29
physiology, 11
physics, 8, 15, 54, 66, 256
pictorial-dynamic, 111
piezo-electricity, 290
pinhole-camera, 355
pink, proliferated, 88
Pisa, 36, 161, 489
pith-ball, 285
pitch, 434
Planck, 406, 423
plane at infinity, 206, 213
planetary condition, 256
planets, 431
Plato, 138, 142, 157, 461, 485, 489
Pliny, 49
Plotinus, 461 *et seq*, 485
plurality, 402
pneuma, 184
point, 39, 198, 199
— and line, 39, 45, 103
— and plane, 244
— at infinity, 204-6
pointer-instrument, 167
pointer-reading, 105 *et seq*.
polar-Euclidean space, 214, 525
polarity (primary, secondary), 226, then *passim*
polarisation, 528
pollination, 93 *et seq*.

ponderable, 248, 268, 273, 380
post-images, 413, *see also* after-images
potato, 392
potential, gravitational, 200
potentisation, 260, 269
Poynting's vector, 299
precious stones, 234
predestination, 138-9
pre-established harmony, 63
preformation theory, 101
pre-images, 413
pre-natal, 141, 143
preservation of species, 113
pressure, 254, 255, 265
— gradient, 527
Principia, 41, 177
prism, 313, 318 *et seq*, 355, 373-4
Proclus, 461
projective geometry, *see* geometry
psyche, 30-1
psychology, 11, 28, 109
psychical research, 57
pulse, 37
Purkinje, 351
purple, 321
pyro-electricity, 290
Pythagoras, 443

quantity of motion, 493
quantum theory, 174, 279, 406
quartz, 290
quick, 493
quicksilver, 228

radioactivity, 277, 308
radiolaria, 240
radio-waves, 360
radium, 220
radius and sphere, 207, 346, 380
Raphael, 347
rain, 116, 238, 275, 428
rainbow, 332, 337, 379, 380-1
Ranunculus, 393

ray, *see* light
Rayleigh, 284, 311
reason, 44-5, 73, 148, 153
reduction, 221, 234, 398-9
refraction, *see* light
Reid, 125 *et seq*, 149, 155, 156, 165,
    217, 335, 341, 354, 413, 458
relativity theory, 11, 174, 203
religion, 9, 510-11
renunciation, 85
resin, 288, 304
resistance (electrical), 293, 300
Rester, 526
retina, 328, 341, 342
rhythm, rhythmic system, 31, 34, 86,
    243, 301, 420, 502
rhopē, 491
rickets, 231
right-eyed vision, 350 *et seq*, 373
Rittelmeyer, 521
Ritter, 289
rock crystal, 233
Roemer, 359 *et seq.*
Röntgen, 61
root, 230
rose, 83, 91, 92
—, proliferated, 88
Royal Institution, 58, 507, 512, 513
Rumford, 220, 250, 267
ruminants, 246
Ruskin, 110 *et seq*, 175, 191-2, 200,
    249, 271, 335, 336, 337, 338,
    354, 381, 426, 530, 531

saline, 244, then *passim*
salt, (*see also* alchemy), 27, 243 *et
    seq*, 286, 296, 302, 349, 420
Saturn, 425 *et seq*, 470
Satan, 68
Savart, 530
scepticism, 41, 45
Schelver, 93
Schiller, 98 *et seq*, 314, 504

Schopenhauer, 522
Schrödinger, 43, 45
seed, 83, 87
seismic activity (processes), 192, 195,
    391
self, 30, 32, 41
self-deception, 107
—-knowledge, 10
—-restriction, 20
sensation, 134, 302, 421
Sensualismus, 136
senses, general, 131, 134, 138, 501
sense of balance, 531
— of hearing, 350, 433
— of movement, 32
— of smell, 35, 264
—, seeing, *passim*
— of warmth, 105, 248, 528
sensory nerves, 30
sepal, 83
sexuality (dogma), 93
Shakespeare, 118
shellfish, 241
sidalcea, 79
sight, 35, 102
signal velocity, 360
silicon, 240, 241, 288
Sinai, 190, 193, 276
skeleton, 175
sleep, 28, 30, 32, 34, 231, 329, 471
smell, 35, 264
Smith, 125
Snell's Law, 370
snow (formation), 232, 235, 346, 428
society, 9
Society for Psychical Research, 57
solar, 380
Solfatara, 194 *et seq*, 212, 231, 232,
    245
solid state, 228, 410
soul, 26, 27, 28, 34, 69, 138, 226,
    245, 496 *et seq.*
— and matter, 265

sound ether, 395
space systems, 204
space-time continuum, 203
Spanish moss, see Tillandsia
spatial vision, 35
specific gravity, 259
spectator, see onlooker
spectroscope, 380
spectrum, spectral, 284, 320 *et seq*, 373 *et seq.*
speech, 131 *et seq*, 148, 451 *et seq.*
sphere, see radius
spherical, 246
Spinoza, 63, 118
spiral tendency, 94, 95
spiritual, anastomosis, 95, 96, 270
  – eye, 102
  – ladder, 85, 259, 274
  – science, *passim*
spiritism, 57 *et seq.*
Spiritualismus, 136
Spiritus, 184
spring balance, 167
Stahl, 219
starch, 235, 245, 268
static, 9, 33
steam engine, 47
Steigerung, 85, 112
Stein, Frau von (Mme de), 196
Steiner, *passim*
Stewart, 136
Stiedenroth, 522
storage (electrical), 301
Strachan, 125
stratus, see clouds
structure, 281
Stuttgart, 11, 12, 14
suction, 197 *et seq*, 285, 294
sugar, 236, 268
suicide, intellectual, 41
sulphur, 221, 224, 225, 230 *et seq*, 243 *et seq*, 264, 280, 286, 296, 302, 349, 420

sulphurous, 244, then *passim*
sun, *passim*
sun-disk, 378
synthesis, 13, 504
systole (*see also* contraction), 212, 331
Switzerland, 88

tabula rasa, 139
Tata Institute, 526
telepathy, 60
terrestrial, 380
terminology, 118
Thales, 284
theory, 124
thermal expansion, 254
thermometer, thermoscope, 105, 106
thing in itself, 104
third force, 409
thinking, thought, 38, 39, 46, 104, 153, 169, 186, 451, 501
Thomson, 61
thunder, 190, 193
thunderstorms, 31, 273 *et seq*, 437
tides, 429
Tillandsia, 269
time, 148, 203
tissue, 393
tone colour, 434
trace elements, 270
tragedy, 64
Traherne, 125, 143, 144 *et seq*, 216, 223, 414, 459, 479 *et seq.*
trance, 471
trans-audient, 436
transformer, 511
transparency, transparent, 233, 436
transverse impulse, 374
tree, 91
  – formation, 92, 200, 241
Tree of Knowledge, 65, 128
triangle, 164
Trübe, 317, 318, 376

Turner, 336
tunnel, 364
Tycho Brahe, 442
Tyndall, 249
type, 77, 93, 97, 101, 224, 271

ultra-realm, 172
—region, 174
—violet, 42, 289, 383, 404
unity, 402
universalia, 123
un-logic, 358
uphill (flow of air), 527
Ur-deeds, 452
—-force, 252
—-image, 413
—-matter, 224
—-phenomenon, 123, 124, 136, 170, 177, 221, 233, 246, 316
—-plant, 90, 91-3, 100, 224, 406
—-representative, 229

vacuum, 212, 303, 308, 403
Valhalla, 380
Van Helmont, 178-180, 183-7, 273, 441
vantage point, 11
vapour, 116, 179, 183-4, 237
velocity of light, see light
Venus, 425 et seq, 470
vertical tendency, 94
Vesta, 188
vine, 96
vision (outer, inner), 327
visibility, see light
volcanism, 190 et seq, 197, 199, 231, 234, 244, 257, 276, 346
volition (-al), 29, 30, 168, 175, 227, 302, 342
Volta, 53-4, 291, 295, 296, 302, 508
vowels, 435
Vreede, 515

Wade, 145, 154

Wagner, 519
waking, 30, 451
Waldorf School, 14
Walsh, 50, 51, 302
warm, 181, 227 et seq, 346
warmth ether, 390, 391-2
water, 119, 179, 227-30, 237-8, 239
— circuit, 262
— power, 47
wavelength, 42
wave velocity, 360
weaving-ether, 394
Wegener, 257
weight, 182-3, 190, 219-20
Weimar, 90, 96, 99
Werry, 526
Whicher, 525
white light, 284
white and black, 339
Whitehead, 20, 203
whole, 99
will, 26, 31, 32, 48, 130, 133, 177, 230, 302, 469, 502, 526
wireless, 55
withdrawal, 85
Wolff, 100-2, 104, 258, 441
wood, 311
wool, 288
word-ether, 411
Wordsworth, 125,143, 158, 419, 443

x-rays, 42, 61

Yahveh, 532
yoga, 29, 185
young, youthful condition, 186, 249, 271, 272

Zarathustra, 465
zero, 106, 286, 364, 403
Zeus, 190
zinc, 269